Probability Theory in Finance

A Mathematical Guide to the Black-Scholes Formula

Seán Dineen

Graduate Studies
in Mathematics

Volume 70

American Mathematical Society

2000 *Mathematics Subject Classification.* Primary 60-01, 91Bxx.

For additional information and updates on this book, visit
www.ams.org/bookpages/gsm-70

Library of Congress Cataloging-in-Publication Data

Dineen, Seán, 1944–
    Probability theory in finance : a mathematical guide to the Black-Scholes formula / Seán
Dineen.
        p. cm. (Graduate studies in mathematics ; v. 70)
    Includes bibliographical references and index.
    ISBN 0-8218-3951-9 (alk. paper)
    1. Business mathematics. I. Title. II. Series.

HF5691.D57   2005
332′.01′519—dc22

2005053572

Dedicated to the memory of
LEOPOLDO NACHBIN (1922–1993)
Teacher and Friend

Contents

Preface

To doubt all or believe all are two equally convenient solutions, in that both dispense with thinking.

Henri Poincaré, 1854-1912

Mathematics occupies a unique place in modern society and education. It cannot be ignored and almost everyone has an opinion on its place and relevance. This has led to problems and questions that will never be solved or answered in a definitive fashion. At third level we have the perennial debate on the mathematics that is suitable for non-mathematics majors and the degree of abstraction with which it should be delivered. We mathematicians are still trusted with this task and our response has varied. Some institutions offer generic mathematics courses to all and sundry, and faculties, such as engineering and business, respond by directing their students to the courses they consider appropriate. In other institutions departments design specific courses for students who are not majoring in mathematics. The response of many departments lies somewhere in between. This can lead to tension between the professional mathematicians' attitude to mathematics and the client faculties' expectations. In the first case non-mathematics majors may find themselves obliged to accept without explanation an approach that is, in their experience, excessively abstract. In the second, a recipe-driven approach often produces students with skills they have difficulty using outside a limited number of well-defined settings. Some students, however, do arrive, by sheer endurance, at an intuitive feeling for mathematics. Clearly both extremes are unsatisfactory and it is natural to ask if an alternative approach is possible.

It is, and the difficulties to be overcome are not mathematical. The understanding of mathematics that we mathematicians have grown to appreciate and accept, often slowly and unconsciously, is not always shared by non-mathematicians, be they students or colleagues, and the benefits of abstract mathematics are not always obvious to academics from other disciplines. This is not their fault. They have, for the most part, been conditioned to think differently. They accept that mathematics is useful and for this reason are willing to submit their students to our courses. We can—and it is in our own hands, since we teach the courses—show that it is possible to *combine* abstract mathematics and good technical skills. It is not easy, it is labor intensive, and the benefits are usually not apparent in the short term. It requires patience and some unconditional support that we need to earn from our students and colleagues.

Although this book is appearing as a graduate text in mathematics, it is based on a one-semester undergraduate course given to economics and finance students at University College Dublin. It is the result of an opportunity given to the author to follow an alternative approach by mixing the abstract and the practical. We feel that all students benefited, but some were not convinced that this was indeed the case.

The students had the usual mathematical background, an acquaintance with the *techniques* of one variable differential and integral calculus and linear algebra. The aim of the course was to provide a mathematical foundation for further studies in financial mathematics, a discipline that has made enormous advances in the last twenty-five years and has been the surprise catalyst in the introduction of certain high-level mathematics courses for non-mathematics majors at universities in recent years. Even though the eventual applications are concrete the mathematics involved is quite abstract, and as a result business students, who specialize in finance, are today exposed to more demanding mathematics than their fellow students in engineering and science. The students' motivation, background, aspirations and future plans were the constraints under which we operated, and these determined the balance between the choice of topics, the degree of abstraction and pace of the presentation.

In view of its overall importance there was no difficulty in choosing the *Black-Scholes formula* for pricing a call option as our ultimate goal. This provided a focus for the students' motivation. As the students were *not* mathematics majors but the majority would have one or two further years of mathematically oriented courses, it seemed appropriate to aim for an understanding that would strengthen their overall mathematical background. This meant it was necessary to initiate the students into what has unfortunately become for many an alien and mysterious subject, *modern abstract mathematics*. For this approach to take root the security associated with recipe-driven and technique-oriented mathematics has to be replaced by a more mature and intrinsic confidence which accepts a degree of intellectual uncertainty as part of the thinking process. Even with highly motivated students, this requires a gradual introduction to mathematical abstraction, and at the same time it is necessary to remain, for reasons of motivation, in contact with the financial situation.

Probability theory, Lebesgue integration and the Itô calculus are the main ingredients in the *Black-Scholes formula*, and these rely on set theory, analysis and an axiomatic approach to mathematics. We take, on the financial side, a first principles approach and include only the minimum necessary to justify the introduction of mathematical concepts and place in context mathematical developments. We move slowly initially and provide elementary examples at an early stage. Hopefully, this makes the apparently more difficult mathematics in later chapters more intuitive and obvious. This cultural change explains why we felt it necessary on occasion to digress into non-technical, and even psychological, matters and why we attempted to present mathematics as a living culture with a history and a future. In particular, we tried to explain the importance of properly understanding questions and recognizing situations which required justification. This helped motivate, and place in perspective, the need for clear definitions and proofs. For example, in considering the concept of a convergent sequence of real numbers, on which all stochastic notions of convergence and all theories of integration rely, we begin by assuming an intuitive concept of limit in Chapter 1; in Chapter 3 we define the limit of a bounded increasing sequence of real numbers; in Chapter 4 we define the limit of a sequence of real numbers; in Chapter 6 we use upper and lower limits to characterize limits; in Chapter 9 we use Doob's upcrossing approach to limits; and in Chapter 11 we employ subsequences to obtain an equivalent definition of limit. In all cases the different ways of considering limits of sequences of real numbers are used as an introduction to similar but more advanced concepts in probability theory.

The introduction of peripheral material, the emphasis on simple examples, the repetition of basic principles, and attention to the students' motivation all take time. The real benefits only become apparent later, both to the students and their non-mathematical academic advisors, when they, the students, proceed to mix with other students in mathematically demanding courses.

The main mathematical topics covered in this book, for which we assume no background, are all essentially within probability theory. These are *measure theory, expected values, conditional expectation, martingales, stochastic processes, Wiener processes* and the *Itô integral*. We do not claim to give a fully comprehensive treatment, and we presented, even though otherwise tempted, certain results without proof. Readers who have worked their way through this book should be quite capable of following the standard proofs in the literature of The

Central Limit Theorem, The Radon-Nikodým Theorem, etc., and we hope they will be motivated to do so. Our self-imposed attempt at self-sufficiency sometimes led to awkward proofs. Although probability theory was the initial focus for our studies, we found as we progressed that more and more analysis was required. Having introduced sequences and continuous functions and proved a number of their basic properties, it did not require much effort to complete the process and present with complete proofs the fundamental properties of continuous and convex functions in Sections 7.2 and 7.6 respectively.

Different groups may benefit from reading this book. Students of financial mathematics at an early, but not too early, stage in their studies could follow, as our students did, Chapters 1-5; Sections 6.1, 6.2, 6.3 and 7.3; the statements of the main results in Sections 6.3, 6.4, and 7.5; and Chapters 8-10. Students of mathematics and statistics interested in analysis and probability theory could follow Chapters 3-7 with the option of two additional topics: the combination of Section 8.2, Chapter 9 and Section 10.3 forming one topic and Chapter 11 the other. Students of mathematics could follow Chapters 3-6 as an introduction to measure theory, while Chapter 11 is, modulo a modest background in probability theory, a self-contained introduction to stochastic integration and the Itô integral. Finally anyone beginning their university studies in mathematics or merely interested in modern mathematics, from a philosophical or aesthetic point of view, will find Chapters 1-5 accessible, challenging and rewarding.

The exercises played an important role in the course, on which we based this book. Some are easy, others difficult; many are included to clarify simple points; some introduce new ideas and techniques; a few contain deep results; and there is a high probability that some of our solutions are incorrect. However, *an hour or two attempting a problem is never a waste of time*, and *to make sure that this happened* these exercises were the focus of our small-group weekly workshops. This is a secret that we mathematicians all too often keep to ourselves. Mathematics is an active discipline, progress *cannot* be achieved by passive participation, and with sustained active participation progress *will* be achieved.

It is pleasure to see this book, written for undergraduate non-mathematics majors, appearing in a series devoted to graduate studies in mathematics. I greatly appreciate the support and encouragement that I received from the editorial staff of the *American Mathematical Society*. In particular, I would like to thank Sergei Gelfand, for being so positive and helpful, and Deborah Smith, for her suggestions and impressive proof-reading.

Dan Golden, from the Department of Banking and Finance at University College Dublin was the main inspiration behind this book. He set up the degree programme in economics and finance, and his constant advice, insight and encouragement were an enormous help over the last five years. It is a pleasure to thank Shane Whelan for numerous conversations on all matters connected with this book, Maciej Klimek for his interesting and constructive suggestions, Michael Mackey for his mathematical insight and excellent diagrams, Milne Anderson for encouragement and perspective over many years and Chris Boyd for his suggestions. Maria Meehan, Louis Murray, Cora Stack, Silvia Lassalle and David Horan helped more than they think. I would especially like to thank the students of economics and finance at University College Dublin, who were subjected to many pre-book versions of this material and who, by their questions and answers, left a lasting impression on the final shape of this book. Finally I would like to thank Carol, Deirdre, and Stephen for displaying great patience while the endless revisions of this book were taking place.

Seán Dineen
Department of Mathematics,
University College Dublin,
Belfield, Dublin 4,
Ireland.
Sean.Dineen@ucd.ie

Chapter 1

Money and Markets

*There are very few things which we know, which
are not capable of being reduc'd to a Mathematical
Reasoning: and when they cannot, it's a sign our
knowledge of them is very small and confus'd; and
where a mathematical reasoning can be had, it's as
great a folly to make use of any other, as to grope
for a thing in the dark, when you have a candle
standing by you.*

John Arbuthnot, 1692,
Preface, Of the Laws of Chance

Summary

We give an extremely basic introduction to the financial markets and use some simple mathematics to examine interest rates.

1.1. Introduction

In this book we lay the mathematical foundations necessary to model certain transactions in the world of finance. Our goal is to provide a complete self-contained mathematical background to the Black-Scholes formula for pricing a call option. This involves two cultures, mathematics and finance, each having its own internal intuitions, concepts, rules and language. In finance, we confine ourselves to the minimal background necessary to achieve our purpose. This involves concepts such as interest rates, present worth or value, discounted value, hedging, risk, bonds, stocks, shares, options, expected return and arbitrage. In the first two chapters we explore these concepts and begin the process of interpreting them mathematically. To illustrate certain points we use examples, artificial from a finance perspective, but as we progress we make them more realistic.

We suppose the reader has some acquaintance with the techniques of one variable differential and integral calculus. All other mathematics required, for example, set theory, integration theory and probability theory, are developed *ab initio* as we proceed. History shows that intuition generally precedes rigor in mathematics, and, guided by this principle, we adopt an intuitive approach in the first two chapters. Afterwards we introduce the necessary rigorous mathematical definitions and provide proofs. The mathematical examples given are often elementary and are provided to improve our *understanding* of basic concepts. Complicated mathematical formulae and equations often turn out to be nothing more than clever combinations of simple well-known mathematical facts.

1.2. Money

In ancient times trade was conducted by exchanging goods, a system known as *bartering*. To simplify this process a fixed amount of a single commodity, often silver or gold, was chosen as a *unit of value* and goods were valued in units of this standard. We call this standard *money*.[1] Silver and gold are maintenance free and easily divided and thus suitable choices. Life would have been more complicated if the unit chosen had been a live chicken. Money's original role as a *medium of exchange* led to the separation of the acts of buying and selling, and it assumed a further role as a *store of value* as people realized its potential to be used *when* it suited them. Thus began the relationship between *money* and *time*.

When prices are stable, those with money feel financially secure. However, prices do change depending on *supply* and *demand*. The *rate of change over time* in the price of a commodity or a number of commodities is called *inflation*. If product A cost \$10 this time last year while today it costs \$12, then the percentage increase in price over the year is $\frac{12-10}{10} \times 100\% = 20\%$ and product A has a 20% annual rate of inflation. The inflation rate for a country is obtained by taking the weighted average of a basket of goods in the overall economy. If we call the *real*, in contrast to the *nominal*, value of money what it is capable of buying, then the presence of inflation means that the real value of money is a *function of time*.

---

[1]Similar to the way we have developed standard units of measurement for distance, temperature, land, etc.

Inflation is a problem for those with money. In its absence they can estimate their financial obligations and requirements. The presence of inflation reduces their financial security and forces them to confront an intrinsic problem: *how to maintain the future real value of money?* Money securely locked away is safe but may be losing value. On the other hand there are others who need money to buy houses, to set up businesses, etc. To cater to these needs, renting money became a business, and successful moneylenders prospered and became respectable bankers. Those with money and no immediate need of it rented it to the bank, and those who needed money rented it from the bank. The price of renting money is called *interest*.[2] Money deposited in a savings account grows at the prevailing rate of interest,[3] and as most deposits are insured and often guaranteed by governments, they are, for all practical purposes, a risk-free way of maintaining *some growth*. Any other way, such as investing in a business venture, involves *risk*. Interest rates and inflation rates are distinct processes, one increasing the nominal value of money, the other reducing its real value. However, it is often observed in economies that interest rates tend to be slightly higher than inflation rates. It seems savers generally demand a positive real interest rate and borrowers generally are willing to pay it. We can also identify two groups with different approaches to the management of money. *Hedgers* are those who wish to eliminate risk as much as possible, while *speculators* are willing to take risks in the expectation of higher profits.

1.3. Interest Rates

We now discuss interest rates and at the same time review some important results from one variable calculus. Interest rates are presented in various forms: simple interest, compound interest, continuously compounded interest, effective rate of interest, etc., with charges usually given as annual percentage rates, say $5\%, 10\%$. Since all involve the same basic concept they are comparable. We show how to compare them and having done so, settle on one and use it more or less exclusively afterwards. We let t denote the time variable, $t = 0$ will denote the present, while $t = 10$ will be 10 units of time, usually measured in years, into the future. Interest rates vary with time, but initially we assume they are constant.

---

[2]Nowadays we think of interest in this way, but essentially interest is the price of renting any object or service. Interest has been around for over *five thousand years* and for two thousand years before coins were introduced. Early Irish law, *The Brehon Law*, operated from around 200 BC to 1600 AD and relied heavily on the use of pledges to ensure that legal obligations were carried out. A *pledge* was an object of value delivered into the custody of another for a fixed period. A person who gave a pledge on behalf of another was entitled to *interest* while the pledged object was out of his possession. For example, if a lord supplied a goblet as a pledge, he was entitled to receive interest of 2 ounces of silver every three days until nine days were up and afterwards the rate of interest increased.

[3]The method of setting bank interest rates is complicated and involves central banks, governments, supply and demand, etc.

We begin with the simplest case, simple interest. Ten percent *simple interest* on a loan of $1,000 for five years means that 10% of the amount borrowed, the *principal*, is charged for each year of the loan. Thus the interest charged is $\$\frac{10}{100} \times 5 \times 1,000 = \$500$. The general formula for calculating simple interest is straightforward: if an amount A is borrowed or saved for T years at a rate[4] r of simple interest, then the repayment due at time T is

$$A + ArT = A(1 + rT).$$

Simple interest is rarely used by banks, and it is easy to see why. If $1,000 is deposited for 2 years at a rate of 10% simple interest, then the amount accumulated at the end of two years, the maturity date, would be $1,200. If, however, at the end of year one the amount accumulated at that time, $1,100, is withdrawn and immediately deposited for a further year at the same rate of simple interest, then, at maturity, the amount accumulated would be $1,210, a gain of $10 on the previous amount. If simple interest was the norm, people would be in and out of banks regularly withdrawing and immediately re-depositing their savings. For this reason a different method of calculating interest is normally used. This is called *compound interest*[5] and is based on applying simple interest over regular preassigned periods of the savings or loan to the amount accumulated at the beginning of each period. If a savings account offers 5% interest per annum compounded every six months, then the amount accumulated by $2,000 deposited for two years is calculated as follows. The simple interest rule applied to the first six months' period shows that the amount will earn $50 interest, and the amount deposited will have increased to $2,050 at the end of six months. During the second six months, the $2,050 will grow to $2,050(1 + \frac{5}{100} \times \frac{1}{2}) = \$2,101.25$, during the next period the amount will reach $2,153.78, and in the final six months' period the amount will reach $2,207.63.

Interest can, of course, be compounded at various other intervals of time, and the more frequent the compounding the greater the interest earned. Suppose an amount A is borrowed for T years at a rate r per annum compounded at n equally spaced intervals of time per year. Each interval of time $\frac{1}{n}$ has a simple interest rate of $\frac{r}{n}$. Thus after the first time interval the amount due has grown to $A(1 + \frac{r}{n})$, after two intervals it becomes $A(1 + \frac{r}{n})(1 + \frac{r}{n}) = A(1 + \frac{r}{n})^2$ and so on. Since there are a total of nT intervals of time, the total repayment at the end of T years will be $A(1 + \frac{r}{n})^{nT}$.

---

[4] That is at a $100r$ percentage rate.

[5] The word *compound* comes from the Latin words *com* (together) and *ponere* (to put) and is used because compound interest is a putting together of simple interest. The words used in mathematics are taken from our everyday language and given precise mathematical meanings. They are usually chosen because one of their common usages approximates their meaning within mathematics. By simply consulting a dictionary, one can sometimes gain helpful mathematical insights.

We compare different interest rates by finding their *effective rate of interest.* This is the rate of simple interest which would give the same return over *one year.* One thousand dollars borrowed for one year at a rate of 10% per annum compounded every six months would result in a repayment of $1,102.50 at the end of the year. If the same amount is borrowed for one year at 10.25% simple interest, then the amount due would also be $1,102.50. Thus we say that the rate 10% per annum compounded every six months has a 10.25% effective rate of interest. It is clear that the more frequent the compounding, the higher the effective rate of interest.

Example 1.1. By comparing effective rates of interest we find which of the following gives the highest and lowest return:

(a) 6% compounded once a year

(b) 5.8% compounded quarterly

(c) 5.9% compounded quarterly

(d) 5.8% compounded monthly

(e) 5.6% compounded daily.

In practical cases such as this it is not advisable to rush in and blindly apply a mathematical formula but to pause and examine the situation from a common sense point of view. Since (a) is compounded only once a year, its effective rate of interest is 6%. Since (b) and (c) are compounded at the same time, but (b) has a lower rate of interest, it follows that (b) will have a lower effective rate of interest. Comparing (b) and (d) we see that they have the same rate of interest but (d) is compounded more frequently and thus will have a higher effective rate of interest.

Interest rates are independent of the amount borrowed or saved, so we compare them by considering $1 borrowed for one year. For (b) the amount to be repaid is $1(1 + \frac{.058}{4})^4 = \$1.0593$ and thus its effective rate of interest is 5.93%. For (c) we have $1(1 + \frac{.059}{4})^4 = \$1.0603$, and its effective rate of interest is 6.03%. Similarly for (d), $1(1 + \frac{.058}{12})^{12} = \$1.0596$, and its effective rate of interest is 5.96%; and for (e), $1(1 + \frac{.056}{365})^{365} = \$1.0576$, and its effective rate of interest is 5.63%. Hence for the borrower (e) offers the cheapest rate, while (c) is the most expensive.

Example 1.2. A bank is offering 4% interest per annum compounded monthly to savers, and a customer wishes to save a fixed amount each month in order to accumulate a lump sum of $10,000 at the end of five years. We wish to determine how much should be saved each month.

As the customer is saving each month and also gaining interest, the amount deposited over the five years must be less than the lump sum $10,000. Since there will be a total of $12 \times 5 = 60$ deposits, the amount required each month will be less than $\$\frac{10,000}{60} = \$166.67$. Similar practical checks should be used whenever possible as they give some estimate of the expected answer and may alert us to patently false conclusions. This can be important in complicated situations. Let x denote the amount deposited each month. The first payment will be deposited for 60 months at a monthly interest rate of $\frac{.04}{12} = .0033$ and hence will amount to $x(1 + .0033)^{60}$. The second deposit will earn interest for 59 months and thus will amount to $x(1 + .0033)^{59}$. Proceeding in this way we see that the amount accumulated at the end of five years will be $\sum_{n=0}^{59} x(1.0033)^{60-n}$ and this must equal $\$10,000$. Since

$$(1.0033)^{60-n} = (1.0033)^{60}/(1.0033)^n = 1.219(.9967)^n$$

this implies

$$(1.1) \qquad x(1.219) \sum_{n=0}^{59} (.9967)^n = 10,000.$$

To calculate this sum we consider the more general problem of summing a *geometric series*.[6] If $n > m$ and

$$S = r^m + r^{m+1} + \cdots + r^n$$

then

$$rS = r^{m+1} + r^{m+2} + \cdots + r^{n+1}.$$

Hence $S(1 - r) = r^m - r^{n+1}$. If $r \neq 1$, then[7]

$$(1.2) \qquad S = \frac{r^m - r^{n+1}}{1 - r}.$$

By (1.1), and since $r^0 = 1$ for all $r \neq 0$, we have

$$x(1.219) \sum_{n=0}^{59} (.9967)^n = x(1.219)\left(\frac{(1 - (.9967)^{60})}{1 - .9967}\right) = x(66.45) = 10,000.$$

Hence the monthly deposits required are $\$\frac{10000}{66.45} = \$150.49$.

---

[6]A Dutch military engineer from Bruges, Simon Stevin (1548-1620), published *Tables for Computing Compound Interest and Annuities* in 1582, which tabulated $(1+q)^{\pm k}$ and $\sum (1+q)^{\pm k}$. He also applied mathematics to accountancy (proposing double entry bookkeeping for the public revenues), engineering (windmills, sailing craft and hydrostatics), geography (maps) and military science.

[7]Mathematics is a unified discipline, and ideas and techniques from one area often reappear, sometimes in disguise, in other areas. The identity $a^{n+1} - b^{n+1} = (a - b)(a^n + a^{n-1}b + \cdots + b^n)$, used to factorize polynomials, is essentially (1.2). When $n = 2$ this reduces to the well-known formula $a^2 - b^2 = (a - b)(a + b)$.

Up to now we considered interest rates compounded at certain fixed finite intervals of time. If we compound over smaller and smaller intervals, we obtain in the limit *continuously compounded interest.* The above shows that A, continuously compounded at an annual rate r, amounts to $A \lim_{n \to \infty} (1 + \frac{r}{n})^{nT}$ after T years. This limit has flexible mathematical properties, due to its connection, outlined in Proposition 1.3, with the exponential function, and we use it whenever possible. In particular, we assume from now on, unless otherwise stated, that *all* interest is continuously compounded. As the *exponential function* plays an essential role in many parts of our studies, we recall its basic properties.[8]

The exponential function, exp, is defined[9] for any real number x by the following power series expansion:[10]

$$(1.3) \qquad \exp(x) := \sum_{n=0}^{\infty} \frac{x^n}{n!}.$$

The exponential function maps the real numbers, $\mathbf{R}$, in a one-to-one[11] fashion onto the strictly positive real numbers. Its inverse is called the logarithm or log function. We have $\log \exp(x) = x$ for all $x \in \mathbf{R}$ and $\exp \log(x) = x$ for all $x > 0$. If $a > 0$ and b is a real number, we let $a^b := \exp(b \log a)$. Both the exponential function and its inverse are increasing differentiable functions and

$$\frac{d}{dx} \exp(x) = \exp(x) \quad \text{and} \quad \frac{d}{dx} \log(x) = \frac{1}{x}.$$

The following set of identities (see Section 7.1) are constantly used:

$$(1.4) \qquad \exp(x + y) = \exp(x)\exp(y) \qquad \log(xy) = \log x + \log y$$

$$(1.5) \qquad \exp(0) = 1 \qquad \log 1 = 0$$

$$(1.6) \qquad \exp(x - y) = \frac{\exp(x)}{\exp(y)} \qquad \log(\frac{x}{y}) = \log x - \log y$$

$$(1.7) \qquad x^y := \exp(y \log x) \qquad \log(x^y) = y \log x.$$

Note that for every property of the exponential function there is a corresponding property of the log function. The real number $\exp(1)$ is also denoted by e, and in this notation, $1 = \log \exp(1) = \log(e)$ and

$$e^x = \exp(x \log e) = \exp(x).$$

---

[8]See also Exercises 3.31 and 4.22 and Section 7.1

[9]We introduced in (1.3) the following convenient notation $A := B$, and use later the equivalent notation $B =: A$. The inclusion of " : " indicates, in both cases, that the equation is being used to *define* A by means of B.

[10]Convergent series, limits and continuous functions are defined rigorously in Chapters 3 and 4. In the meantime we rely on the reader's intuitive feelings.

[11]Functions which are one-to-one are said to be *injective*, onto functions are called *surjective* and the term *bijective* is used for functions which are both injective and surjective.

The number e is irrational and approximately equal to 2.72. We always use natural logs, that is logs to the base e.[12]

Proposition 1.3. *For any real number* r

$$\lim_{n \longrightarrow \infty} \left(1 + \frac{r}{n}\right)^n = e^r.$$

Proof. We have

$$\frac{d}{dx}\log(x) = \lim_{\Delta x \longrightarrow 0} \frac{\log(x + \Delta x) - \log x}{\Delta x} = \frac{1}{x}.$$

If we let $x = 1$ and $\Delta x = r/n$, then $\Delta x \longrightarrow 0$ as $n \longrightarrow \infty$. Since $\log 1 = 0$ this implies

$$\lim_{n \longrightarrow \infty} \frac{\log(1 + \frac{r}{n})}{\frac{r}{n}} = \lim_{n \longrightarrow \infty} \frac{n}{r}\log\left(1 + \frac{r}{n}\right) = \frac{1}{r}\lim_{n \longrightarrow \infty}\log\left(1 + \frac{r}{n}\right)^n = 1.$$

Hence $\lim_{n \to \infty} \log(1 + \frac{r}{n})^n = r$, and as exp and log are inverse functions and both are continuous[13] this implies

$$\lim_{n \longrightarrow \infty} \left(1 + \frac{r}{n}\right)^n = \exp\left(\lim_{n \longrightarrow \infty}\log\left(1 + \frac{r}{n}\right)^n\right) = \exp\left(r\right) = e^r.$$

This completes the proof. $\qquad\qquad\qquad\qquad\qquad\qquad\qquad\qquad\qquad\qquad\square$

Corollary 1.4. *An amount A earning continuously compounded interest at a constant rate r per year is worth Ae^{rT} after T years.*

Corollary 1.4 illustrates mathematically a basic functional relationship between *time* and *money*.

Example 1.5. If \$10,000 is deposited today for five years at a continuously compounded rate of 4% per annum, then it will amount to

$$\$10,000\exp(.04 \times 5) = \$12,214$$

at the end of five years.

---

[12]The number e was introduced by Leonhard Euler (1707-1783). Euler, from Basel in Switzerland, was a professor in St. Petersburg during the periods 1727-1741 and 1766-1783 and spent the intervening period in Berlin. He was the most prolific mathematician of all time and made fundamental contributions to almost all areas of pure and applied mathematics, including analysis, infinite series, differential geometry, differential equations, complex analysis, number theory, the calculus of variations, etc. He revolutionized mathematics by basing his analysis on functions rather than curves. His contributions to applied mathematics, astronomy, cartography, and engineering projects, such as ship building, were also significant. Euler went blind in 1767, but with the help of his amazing memory and some assistants, he produced almost half his scientific output while blind. He wrote so much that the St. Petersburg Academy continued to publish his unpublished work for almost fifty years after his death.

[13]See Definition 4.18 and Exercise 4.22.

This leads to an important general principle. We can *reverse* the process and say that the *present worth* or *present value* of $12,214 in five years' time is $10,000. In this way we can determine, for a given fixed rate of interest, the present worth of any amount at *any future time*. For example, if A is the present worth of $5,000 in six years' time, then, given an interest rate of 7% per annum, $Ae^{(.07)6} = \$5,000$ and $A = \$5,000e^{-.42} = \$3,285.23$. The procedure of finding the present worth or value of a future amount is called *discounting back to the present, discounting back* or just *discounting*. The present worth of a future amount is called its *discounted value*. This allows us to introduce a way of measuring, and hence comparing, the risk-free future value of money. As discounting plays an important role in pricing stock options, we summarize the above in the form of a proposition which is a mirror image of Corollary 1.4.

Proposition 1.6. *The discounted value of an amount A at a future time T, assuming a constant continuously compounded interest rate r, is given by*

$$Ae^{-rT}.$$

Example 1.7. In this example we discount back to the present in order to evaluate a project. Suppose bank interest rates are 4% per annum continuously compounded, that an initial outlay of $400,000 is required, and that the projected end of year returns are given in the following table.

year t	Profit/Loss	NPV $= Ae^{(-.04)t}$
0	$\$-400,000$	$\$-400,000$
1	$\$60,000$	$\$57,647$
2	$\$80,000$	$\$73,849$
3	$\$140,000$	$\$124,169$
4	$\$200,000$	$\$170,429$
Total	—	$\$26,094$

Thus the *Net Present Value* (NPV) of the project is $26,094. This shows that the project, assuming all estimates are correct and interest rates remain fixed, will show a greater profit than that generated by using bank deposit accounts.

The following proposition and corollary are fundamental results from the differential calculus.

Proposition 1.8. (*Mean Value Theorem*) *If the function $f : [a,b] \longrightarrow \mathbf{R}$ is continuous over $[a,b]$ and differentiable over (a,b), then there exists a point c,*

$a < c < b$, *such that*

$$f'(c) \;=\; \frac{f(b) - f(a)}{b - a}.$$

Corollary 1.9. *If $f : [a, b] \longrightarrow \mathbf{R}$ is a continuous function over $[a, b]$, differentiable over (a, b) and $f'(x) = 0$ for all $x \in (a, b)$, then f is a constant function.*

Example 1.10. In this example we use Corollary 1.9 to provide another proof of Corollary 1.4. This leads, in Example 1.12, to a way of dealing with non-constant interest rates. Suppose an amount A is deposited for T years at a constant continuously compounded annual interest rate r. For $0 \le t \le T$ let $A(t)$ denote the amount accumulated at time t. Clearly $A(0) = A$, and we wish to find $A(T)$. During the time interval $[t, t + \Delta t]$ the amount grows by $A(t + \Delta t) - A(t)$, and since Δt is small, we suppose that the continuously compounded rate over $[t, t + \Delta t]$ is approximately the same as the simple interest rate. Hence

(1.8) $$A(t + \Delta t) - A(t) \approx r \Delta t A(t)$$

where $\approx$ denotes approximately equal. This implies

$$\lim_{\Delta t \longrightarrow 0} \frac{A(t + \Delta t) - A(t)}{\Delta t} = \lim_{\Delta t \longrightarrow 0} r A(t) = r A(t),$$

and we obtain the required result by solving the *differential equation*

(1.9) $$A'(t) = r A(t).$$

We have

$$\frac{A'(t)}{A(t)} = \frac{d}{dt} (\log A(t)) = r = \frac{d}{dt} (rt)$$

and hence

(1.10) $$\frac{d}{dt} (\log A(t) - rt) = 0.$$

By Corollary 1.9 and (1.10) there exists a real number C such that $\log A(t) - rt = C$. Hence $\log A(t) = C + rt$, and applying the exponential function we obtain

$$A(t) = \exp \log A(t) = \exp(C + rt) = \exp(C) \cdot \exp(rt).$$

Since $\exp(0) = 1$ we have $A(0) = A = \exp(C)$ and

(1.11) $$A(T) = A(0) \exp(rT) = A \exp(rT).$$

To deal with variable interest rates we need a further result from the differential calculus.

Proposition 1.11. (*Fundamental Theorem of Calculus*)[14] *If f is a continuously differentiable real valued function on the interval $[a, b]$, then*

$$\int_a^b f'(t)dt = f(b) - f(a).$$

Example 1.12. We consider again the problem of calculating the growth of an initial deposit A for a period of T years given that the interest is continuously compounded at the annual rate $r(t)$ at time t. Two different approaches are included and both will be important later.

As before, let $A(t)$ denote the amount accumulated by time t. Our previous analysis shows that

(1.12) $$A(t + \Delta t) - A(t) \approx r(t)\Delta t A(t).$$

If this approximation is sufficiently accurate, then $A(t)$ is differentiable and we obtain, as in (1.9), the differential equation

(1.13) $$A'(t) = r(t)A(t).$$

Hence

$$\frac{A'(t)}{A(t)} = \frac{d}{dt}(\log A(t)) = r(t),$$

and if r is continuous, the Fundamental Theorem of Calculus implies

$$\log A(T) - \log A(0) = \int_0^T \frac{d}{dt}(\log A(t))dt = \int_0^T r(t)dt.$$

Hence

$$\log \frac{A(T)}{A(0)} = \int_0^T r(t)dt.$$

Since $A(0) = A$ this implies

(1.14) $$A(T) = A\exp(\int_0^T r(t)dt).$$

In place of using (1.12) to derive (1.13) we may also proceed as follows. Fix $t \in [0, T]$ and partition the interval $[0, t]$ into n subintervals of *equal length*, apply (1.12) to each of them, and add them together. If $[t_i, t_{i+1}]$ is the $(i + 1)^{th}$ interval in the partition and $\Delta t_i := t_{i+1} - t_i$ for $i = 0, 1, \ldots, n - 1$, then

$$A(t) - A(0) = \sum_{i=0}^{n-1} A(t_{i+1}) - A(t_i) \approx \sum_{i=0}^{n-1} r(t_i)A(t_i)\Delta t_i.$$

---

[14]An extension of the Fundamental Theorem of Calculus, the *Radon-Nikodým Theorem*, is the key result required in Chapter 8 to prove the existence of conditional expectations.

If we take finer and finer partitions we obtain, in the limit,

$$(1.15) \qquad\qquad A(t) - A(0) = \int_0^t r(s)A(s)ds.$$

Equation (1.15) is called an *integral equation*. Integrating (1.13) we obtain (1.15) and, if we know that A is differentiable, then on differentiating (1.15) we obtain (1.13). As a general rule every differential equation gives rise to an integral equation, but the converse is *not* true[15]. This apparently rather minor point will again surface when we discuss the Itô integral in Chapters 8 and 11.

This concludes our basic introduction to money and interest. Our analysis is typical of a process known as *mathematical modelling*. We started with the basic concept of interest and examined in turn three increasingly more complex situations: simple interest, compound interest and continuously compounded interest. At each stage we developed the required mathematical model before examining the next level of complexity, and as we progressed, we used more sophisticated mathematics. We were led to *linear* growth, *geometric* growth and *exponential* growth and to three basic formulae: $A(1 + rT), A(1 + \frac{r}{n})^{nT}$ and Ae^{rT}. The final result is transparent because of our gradual development of the model and because of the continuous interacting between financial and mathematical concepts.

To expose the intrinsic nature of money and interest, we deliberately over-simplified the situation. Other *financial instruments* or *securities*, that is legally enforceable agreements that give entitlement to future contingency payments or which guarantee a risk-free return based on current interest rates, also exist. They are said to be *liquid* if they can be easily traded in a well developed market. The most common type of liquid securities are *bonds*. These are issued by many different groups, governments,[16] local authorities, banks, corporations, etc., for different purposes and with different conditions attached. We confine ourselves to a few brief comments. A typical 5 year bond might have a face value of $\$1,000$, which represents the payment made on maturity. If the interest rate on the bond[17] is 7.5% per annum the holder of the bond receives at the end of each year[18] until maturity $\$1,000 \times .075 = \$75$. The purchaser of the bond makes a commitment to a certain level of interest. If interest rates increase, the value of the bond decreases and conversely. Our interest in bonds stems from their use in constructing hedging portfolios.

---

[15]Every differentiable function is continuous, and hence integrable, but not every continuous function is differentiable.

[16]War bonds were issued by the Roman Senate during the second Punic war, 218-210 BC, between Rome and Carthage.

[17]In the case of bonds it is traditional to use the effective rate of interest.

[18]Or perhaps half that amount every six months until maturity. The periodic payments are called *coupons*.

We now introduce, and use bank interest rates to illustrate, an extremely important concept, *arbitrage*. Suppose we have two banks, A and B, operating side by side. Bank A offers customers a 10% interest rate per annum on savings, while Bank B offers loans to customers at an 8% rate of interest per annum. It is not difficult to see how to take advantage of this situation. Go to Bank B, borrow as much as possible and immediately place it on deposit in Bank A. If, for example, one obtains a loan for $1,000,000$ for one year, then at the end of the year the principal in Bank A amounts to $\$1,000,000e^{.1} = \$1,105,171$, while the loan repayment to Bank B amounts to $\$1,000,000e^{.08} = \$1,083,287$. This gives a *risk-free guaranteed profit* of $\$21,884$ at the end of the year.

The word *arbitrage* is used to describe any situation, opportunity or price which allows a *guaranteed profit without risk*. The market recognizes very rapidly when arbitrage opportunities exist and takes advantage of them, thereby closing them down. In our example the *demand* on at least one of the banks would increase rapidly, and as a result, interest rates would quickly be adjusted until *equilibrium* was established.

In pricing derivatives we always aim to determine an arbitrage-free price, that is one in which neither buyer nor seller can realize risk-free profits. Prices determined in this fashion are said to be based on the *no arbitrage principle*.

1.4. The Market

So far we have considered the riskless growth of money where the return is guaranteed but modest. This does not suit everyone, and some are willing to take risks to increase the value of their money at a faster rate. We consider one such situation.

Business A is family owned, and during its fifty years in existence it has grown substantially and now has over 800 employees. The board of directors, all family members, feel that the time is right for a large-scale expansion and has identified an opportunity to take over a rival company of the same size as itself. To do so it needs *capital*, that is money, and at the same time the family wishes to maintain control of the company. A large bank loan is a possibility, but this could lead to difficulties if either interest rates rose sharply, business slowed down or the takeover turned out to be less successful than anticipated. Selling between 40% and 60% to a large number of individuals with diverse interests, who would not organize themselves into a control-seeking group, would be preferable. To achieve this the family puts a total value on the company and divides it into a large number of identical parts, say 250 million, each of which is called a *share*, and offers between 100 million and 150 million shares for sale to the public. The shares would be offered for sale on the *stock market*, a process known as a *flotation*. The non-family shareholders would collectively be entitled to 40% − 60% of the profits of the company. These are usually paid out semi-annually in the form of so much per share and are called *dividends*. As shares are auctioned daily the price is constantly changing, and shareholders may also profit by buying and selling shares. In buying and selling shares the *stockbroker*,[19] who acts as intermediary in these transactions, is paid a *commission*, which is often a percentage value of the total transaction, subject to a minimum charge. The difference in price between buying and selling shares is called *capital gains* or *losses*. During periods of relative stock price stability, dividends become the principal component of the return and are similar, in some ways, to the interest paid by banks. When share prices are volatile, that is subject to large swings, investors are usually more concerned with capital gains.

Who are the potential shareholders? The general public would have formed an opinion of the company and its future prospects, and financial experts would provide an informed opinion and give more detailed analysis. For a modest investment individuals could buy a small part of the company and share in its future prosperity and profits. Another important group of investors are fund managers, for example pension fund managers. In most companies, employees contribute weekly or monthly to a pension scheme which funds their retirement. The amounts contributed, especially in large companies, accumulate to substantial amounts, and it is crucial that the pension payments are available when required. Fund managers are appointed to see that this happens. Because of the conservative nature of their mission, fund managers usually spread their investments over all sectors of the economy. A well-managed established family business with reasonable profits and prospects would appeal to fund managers.

The flotation, if successful, would provide the company with the capital necessary for expansion. A reasonable mix of small shareholders, fund managers and a few large individual shareholders would not threaten the family's overall control. However, whereas previously they could make decisions behind closed doors, they would now have annual public general meetings and their affairs would be subject to more regulations and media attention.

This concludes our introduction to the stock market. We have discussed just one, not atypical, situation. For shareholders we have observed two important points: share prices go up and down, and these fluctuations occur continuously; thus the share price is a *function of time*. The price changes occur for many different reasons: economic, political and even psychological. Apart from buying and selling shares there are other commercial transactions involving shares, for instance, *contracts* or *options* to buy or sell shares at a given price

---

[19]Professional traders can be classified roughly as either *hedgers*, who try by eliminating risks to maintain the real value of their assets; *speculators*, who take risks in the hope of large profits; and *arbitrageurs*, who move in when they see an opportunity to make riskless profits.

at a given future date. These financial instruments are called *derivatives*, since their values are derived from underlying *assets*, in this case shares. To derive the Black-Scholes formula, which gives a arbitrage-free price for call options, we need *probability theory* and some insight into how the gambler and bookmaker approach their trade. We start with the latter in the next chapter.

1.5. Exercises

(1.1) Show that for every strictly positive real number a there exists a unique real number b such that $e^{a+b} = e^a + e^b$. What happens if $a \leq 0$? Sketch for a, an arbitrary real number, the graph of

$$f(x) = e^{a+x} - e^a - e^x.$$

(1.2) If n is a positive integer, show that $\lim_{|x| \to \infty} |x|^n e^{-x^2/2} = 0$.

(1.3) If $f : \mathbf{R} \longrightarrow \mathbf{R}$ is continuous, let $\int_{-\infty}^{+\infty} f(x)dx = \lim_{n,m \to \infty} \int_{-m}^{n} f(x)dx$ whenever this limit exists. Evaluate $\int_{-\infty}^{+\infty} x^n e^{-x^2/2}dx$, assuming that $\int_{-\infty}^{+\infty} e^{-x^2/2}dx = \sqrt{2\pi}$ and the following result: if $f, g : \mathbf{R} \longrightarrow \mathbf{R}$ are continuous, $|f(x)| \leq g(x)$ and $\int_{-\infty}^{+\infty} g(x)dx$ exists, then so does $\int_{-\infty}^{+\infty} f(x)dx$.

(1.4) Adapt the method used to prove equation (1.2) to find $\sum_{j=1}^{n} jr^j$. Verify your answer by differentiating (1.2). Find $\sum_{j=1}^{\infty} jr^j$.

(1.5) A mortgage of $\$250,000$ is to be repaid over 20 years in equal monthly installments. Find a lower bound for the repayments. Suppose the interest rate is 5.2% per annum continuously compounded. If interest is added at the beginning of each year, find the total monthly repayments. Find the total amount repaid.

(1.6) Five-year government bonds have a face value of $\$2,000$ and annual coupons worth $\$130$. If interest rates (a) increased by 1%, (b) decreased by 2% immediately after the bonds were issued, find the change in value of the bonds.

(1.7) By differentiation verify for $x > 0$ that

$$e^{-x^2/2}\frac{1}{x} = \int_x^\infty e^{-y^2/2}\left(1 + \frac{1}{y^2}\right)dy.$$

Obtain a similar formula with $1 + (1/y^2)$ replaced by $1 - (3/y^4)$. Hence show for $x > 0$ that

$$\frac{1}{\sqrt{2\pi}}e^{-x^2/2}\left(\frac{1}{x} - \frac{1}{x^3}\right) \leq \frac{1}{\sqrt{2\pi}}\int_x^\infty e^{-y^2/2}dy \leq \frac{1}{\sqrt{2\pi}}e^{-x^2/2}\frac{1}{x}.$$

Use the same approach and higher powers of x to improved this estimate.

(1.8) At what constant rate should money be continuously deposited into a
savings account in order to accumulate $10,000 at the end of 5 years
given that interest rates are 6%?

Chapter 2

Fair Games

It is not certain that everything is uncertain.
Blaise Pascal

Summary

We introduce the concept of a fair game and consider two everyday examples. From these examples we derive a number of general principles to guide our later studies.

2.1. Fair Games

Gambling for profit or pleasure is one of mankind's oldest pastimes[1] and provided the early problems that prompted the development[2] of probability theory.

---

[1] In ancient Rome people of all social classes were fond of gambling. Slaves, however, were only allowed to gamble during the Saturnalia festival, which began on December 17 and lasted for several days. If caught gambling at other times, they were thrown into a tank of cold water.

[2] Prior to 1654 references to probabilities in the literature were sparse. Luca Pacioli (1445-1517) studied games of chance in his *Summa de Arithmetica, Geometrica, Proportioni et Proportionalita*. This book, published in 1494, was one of the first printed books in mathematics and contained a comprehensive summary of the mathematics known at that time. Pacioli, a Franciscan friar from Sansepolcro (Italy), taught mathematics at many different Italian universities during the course of a long teaching career and wrote a number of influential books. In Milan he became a close friend of Leonardo de Vinci, and they collaborated on a number of projects. When Milan was captured by the French in 1499 they fled together and for a number of years afterwards shared a house in Florence. Leonardo illustrated the book *Divina Proportione* by Pacioli. Girolamo Cardano (1501-1576), from Pavia in northern Italy, wrote, while still a student, a handbook for gamblers *Book on Games of Chance* around 1520, but it was not published until 1663. Cardano, a physician, mathematician, astrologer and gambler, has been described as an unprincipled genius who appeared to have friends and enemies in equal proportion. At one stage he was imprisoned for publishing a horoscope of Jesus Christ but later became astrologer to the Papal Court. He foretold the date of his own death and, it

It is generally accepted that probability theory dates from correspondence[3] in 1654 between two eminent French mathematicians,[4] Blaise Pascal and Pierre de Fermat, about various questions on games of dice raised by the gambler Chevalier de Méré. For a further 150 years most of the main questions in probability theory were motivated by games of chance. Buying shares is a form of gambling,[5] and it is not surprising that the mathematical tools used to analyze games of chance can be adapted to study the movement of share prices. Both areas have basic concepts, such as risk, reward and hedging, in common. By examining simple games we uncover basic principles which transfer to finance. Moreover, a sequence of fair games will motivate the mathematical concept of *martingale*, a powerful and indispensable tool in our analysis.

We first explore the concept of a *fair game*. To do so we require some basic intuitive ideas about probabilities that we formally define later. Many of the terms given a precise mathematical meaning within probability theory are used colloquially, and most people have no hesitation in using terms such as *expected winnings, independent events, equally likely outcome, highly probable result, set of all outcomes,* etc., in daily conversation. The normal usage of these expressions corresponds closely to their technical mathematical meanings. This is quite helpful when explaining results in non-mathematical terms to non-experts and allows us to initially develop ideas at a non-technical intuitive level using language that will later become technical. All notation used in this chapter will later be given a precise mathematical meaning.

We consider a simple betting game between two players, John and Mark. If the game is favorable to John, then his *expected winnings*, $\mathbb{E}[W_J]$, will be at least as large as those of Mark, $\mathbb{E}[W_M]$; that is $\mathbb{E}[W_J] \geq \mathbb{E}[W_M]$. By winnings we mean *net winnings*, and thus we subtract off any losses and treat a *loss* as a win of a *negative amount*. If the game is favorable to Mark, then $\mathbb{E}[W_M] \geq \mathbb{E}[W_J]$.

---

is said, to uphold his reputation as an astrologer, took matters into his own hands on the appointed day.

[3]At the time books usually had to be printed at the author's own expense and there were no scholarly journals. Letters were the most frequent form of communication between scholars, and ideas were often spread by visiting students. The mathematical results of Fermat first appeared in his correspondence.

[4]Pascal (1623-1662) was a mathematician, philosopher, mystic, physicist, and writer, and he invented the first mechanical calculating machine. In his later years he withdrew from the world "to contemplate the greatness and the misery of man." Fermat (1601-1665), from Beaumont-de-Lomagne, France, was a lawyer and a politician who devoted his leisure hours to mathematics. He lived most of his adult life in Toulouse. To stimulate interest in mathematics Fermat did not often reveal his methods and instead challenged others to find solutions to problems he had already solved. No doubt he would have appreciated the efforts and new mathematics generated by his famous last theorem, which was finally proved by Andrew Wiles in 1994. Fermat made notable contributions to number theory, geometry and maxima and minima problems. In optics he introduced the fundamental principle, now known as *Fermat's Principle*, that light follows the shortest path.

[5]Recently, spread betting on the movement of share prices has been promoted as an alternative to buying options.

It appears reasonable to say that the game is *fair* if it is favorable to both players. Putting these two estimates together we obtain

(2.1) $$\mathbb{E}[W_J] = \mathbb{E}[W_M]$$

as a definition of a fair game between two players. If the stakes or bets placed by John and Mark are S_J and S_M, respectively, then the total input will be $S_J + S_M$. If the total output, that is the sum of all the players' winnings, is also $S_J + S_M$, we call the game a zero-sum game. In such a game we have

(2.2) $$\mathbb{E}[W_J] + \mathbb{E}[W_M] = \text{Input} - \text{Output} = 0$$

and, combining (2.1) and (2.2), we obtain

$$\mathbb{E}[W_J] = \mathbb{E}[W_M] = 0.$$

The converse is also true. We summarize the above in the following proposition.

Proposition 2.1. *A zero-sum game is a fair game if and only if the expected winnings of each player is zero.*

We now quantify the above and see the effect of changing parameters. Suppose both players bet or wager \$5 on the toss of a coin: John wins when a head (H) comes up, Mark wins when a tail (T) comes up and the winner gets \$10. Is this a fair game? Yes, provided each outcome is *equally likely*. To test this assumption we would have to toss the coin[6] a large number of times, say $1,000$, and see if we get close to 500 heads. Thus in $1,000$ games John would *expect* to win 500 and also to lose 500. His *expected winnings* are

$$500 \cdot (10 - 5) + 500 \cdot (0 - 5) = 0.$$

Since Mark's expected winnings are also 0, we have verified the fair game criterion. In tossing a balanced, fair or unbiased coin we *expect* $1/2$ of the outcomes, no matter how many games are played, to result in a head, and we interpret this later as the *probability* that a head appears. Similarly the probability of a tail appearing is $1/2$. *Expected values* have a precise mathematical definition that corresponds to our intuitive notion of a *weighted average* (see Chapter 6 for details). For example John's expected winnings are given by

$$\mathbb{E}[W_J] = \sum_{outcomes} \begin{pmatrix} \text{number of} \\ \text{games} \end{pmatrix} \times \begin{pmatrix} \text{probability of this} \\ \text{outcome} \end{pmatrix} \times \begin{pmatrix} \text{winnings on} \\ \text{this outcome} \end{pmatrix}.$$

The combination of parameters or variables which produce the above fair game are : *rewards*, *risks*, *price*[7] and *equally likely outcomes*. We look at the effect of changing these parameters in a zero-sum game. Consider the following variations:

---

[6]Statistical tests can be used to find with a predetermined degree of confidence and a predetermined error if a coin is balanced.

[7]That is the amount bet.

(A) John bets \$3 and Mark \$7,

(B) on average the coin turns up heads 80% of the time.

In anticipation of later notation we write $P(H) = 4/5$ to denote the fact that we expect $4/5$ of the outcomes[8] to be a head. Similarly $P(T) = 1/5$. We can now quantify the effect of these changes on John's expected winnings. We first make a mathematical simplification, which cannot occur in the real world of games. We consider only *one game*. If the coin is unbiased, we suppose John wins $1/2$ of the game, while if (B) applies, we suppose that John wins $4/5$ of the game. If (A) applies and the coin is unbiased, then

$$\mathbb{E}[W_J] = \frac{1}{2}(10 - 3) + \frac{1}{2}(0 - 3) = 2.$$

If only (B) applies, then

$$\mathbb{E}[W_J] = \frac{4}{5}(10 - 5) + \frac{1}{5}(0 - 5) = 3,$$

while, if both (A) and (B) apply, then

$$\mathbb{E}[W_J] = \frac{4}{5}(10 - 3) + \frac{1}{5}(0 - 3) = 5.$$

The results are not surprising since both changes benefit John. We can also work backwards and see how to change the parameters to make the game fair. The following diagram, Figure 2.1, shows the flow of John's expected winnings if he bets $\$x$ and has probability p of winning:

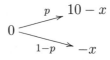

Figure 2.1

We have

$$\mathbb{E}[W_J] \quad = \quad p(10 - x) + (1 - p)(0 - x),$$

and in a fair game $\mathbb{E}[W_J] = 0$.

If (A) holds, and p is the probability that a head turns up, then

$$\mathbb{E}[W_J] = p(7) + (1 - p)(-3).$$

Hence $\mathbb{E}[W_J] = 0$ implies $p = 3/10$, and the game will be fair if a head appears on average 30% of the time.

---

[8]We see immediately in this short passage two properties of probabilities: the probability of an event will always lie between 0 and 1, and if p is the probability that an event A will occur, then $1 - p$ is the probability that A will not occur.

If (B) holds, then

$$\mathbb{E}[W_J] = \frac{4}{5}(10 - x) + \frac{1}{5}(0 - x).$$

If $\mathbb{E}[W_J] = 0$, then $(40 - 5x)/5 = 0$ and $x = 8$. This means we again have a fair game if John bets \$8. We summarize the general idea as a proposition.

Proposition 2.2. *Probabilities (or risks) and rewards (or winnings/losses) are both used in calculating the expected return. In a zero-sum game if one of these is given, then the other can be chosen to make the game fair.*

If Mark offered to play a game with a fair coin in which he bets \$7 and John bets \$3 with the winner getting \$10, then it would be in John's interest to play as many games as possible, since his expected winnings would continue to rise. John would still, however, be taking a risk as Mark might be lucky and win most of the games. This is not an opportunity to earn money without risk and illustrates the difference between *expected profit* and *guaranteed profit*.

2.2. Hedging and Arbitrage

We now consider another game in which John and Mark place a bet with a bookmaker[9] on a two-horse race. John intends to place a bet of \$400 on a horse called Lucky Heather while Mark intends to bet \$100 on the other horse, McSnappy. The situation is different from coin tossing in a number of ways. Both John and Mark may have studied the past forms of both horses, the weather conditions, the opinions of the experts, etc., and both may have opinions on the probability that their horse will win the race; but one cannot run the race a hundred times to work out "objective" probabilities that a particular horse would win a particular race. In contrast to the coin tossing game, they do not negotiate the odds on each horse. These are set by the bookmaker, who does not care what odds are given as long as he gets his percentage of the total amount wagered. In fact the bookmaker is *risk averse*, and his strategy is to eliminate any risk to his percentage share.[10] We suppose first that we are in an artificial situation and that the bookmaker knows in advance that John and Mark will be the only punters and how much they will wager. Since the total amount wagered is \$500 and the bookmaker makes a profit of 10%, that is \$50, the winner will receive \$450. John stands to profit by \$50 if Lucky Heather wins, and Mark will gain \$350 if McSnappy wins.

---

[9]A person who accepts bets on horse races (and other sporting events) is called a *bookmaker*. Members of the public who place bets or wagers are called *punters*.

[10]The risk for the (traditional) bookmaker arises from the fact that he has to set the odds *before* he knows how much will be wagered. In modern on-course betting, the *Tote*, an abbreviation for *totalisator*, eliminates this uncertainty by announcing the odds only *after* all bets have been placed. Once more we see the importance of *time*.

No objective analysis can determine if placing a bet on a particular horse is a fair game, but by placing bets, punters are *implicitly* accepting that the arrangement is fair. Probabilities may now be introduced that formally recognize such transactions as fair games.

If p is the probability in John's fair game that Lucky Heather wins, then

$$\mathbb{E}[W_J] = 50p + (-400)(1 - p) = 0$$

and $p = 8/9$, and if q is the probability that McSnappy wins in Mark's fair game, then

$$\mathbb{E}[W_M] = 350q + (-100)(1 - q) = 0$$

and $q = 2/9$. Note that John accepts $8/9$ as the probability that Lucky Heather will win, while Mark accepts $7/9$ as the probability for the *same event*. Two different games are being played, one between John and the bookmaker and the other between Mark and the bookmaker. John and Mark are operating, in language to be introduced later, in *different probability spaces*.

The bookmaker uses different terms but ones which can readily be translated into ours. A win for McSnappy will result in \$7 winnings for every \$2 bet on McSnappy and the odds on McSnappy will be given[11] as 7 to 2. A winning bet of \$8 on Lucky Heather will result in a \$1 win and hence in odds of 1 to 8.

To reverse the procedure, consider odds of 9 to 4. This results in a \$9 win for every \$4 winning bet. Thus there are $9 + 4 = 13$ possibilities, of which 4 are favorable to the punter, and the probability of a win is $4/13$.

So far the bookmaker has run no risk and is guaranteed a profit of \$50. Now suppose another bet for \$300 is placed on McSnappy at the odds of 7 to 2 quoted above. The bookmakers profit, W_B, now depends on the outcome of the race. We cannot say anything with certainty, but we can make a number of "if... then..." statements. We have

$$W_B = 50 + 300 = 350 \text{ if Lucky Heather wins}$$

and

$$W_B = 50 - 1050 = -1,000 \text{ if McSnappy wins.}$$

We introduce new notation and rewrite the above with $\mathbb{E}$ symbolizing expectation. Let

$$\mathbb{E}[W_B| \text{ Lucky Heather wins}]$$

denote the bookmaker's expected winnings *conditional* on Lucky Heather winning. We have

$$\mathbb{E}[W_B| \text{ Lucky Heather wins}] = \$350$$

---

[11]Strictly speaking we should say 7 to 2 *against*. In announcing odds it is common practice to place the larger number first, and hence odds of 1 to 8 *against* are given as 8 to 1 *on*. To keep the technical terminology to a minimum we always use odds against.

and
$$\mathbb{E}[W_B| \text{ McSnappy wins}] = -\$1,000.$$

The bookmaker now runs the risk of losing money if McSnappy wins. He may, however, take a number of steps to reduce his exposure to loss. The total amount wagered is now \$800, with \$400 bet on each horse. If all these bets had been placed initially, the bookmaker, in order to make a profit of 10%, would have set odds of 4 to 5 on both horses. This gives new winning probabilities of $5/(4+5) = 5/9$ for both horses. The bookmaker changes[12] the odds in line with the new bet, and hopefully these will attract further bets on Lucky Heather. The change in odds will apply only to *new bets*; and if the next bet is very large and on McSnappy, the bookmaker would run the risk of an even more substantial loss. He may refuse to accept the bet, but for obvious reasons, this is usually a last resort and some other strategy is required. He may place a limit on the amount that can be placed on each horse or may require punters to negotiate the odds on bets above a certain limit. Either of these house rules may help avoid an unacceptable risk but again only apply to new bets.

Another approach is to lay off part of the bet. In this case the bookmaker becomes a punter[13] and places a bet on McSnappy, since a win for McSnappy is the only outcome that leads to a loss. He may not be able to get the same odds that he himself was offering, but let us suppose that he is able to obtain odds of 3 to 1 with another bookmaker. These odds are only marginally worse than odds of 7 to 2. If he places a bet of \$x on McSnappy then we have the following conditional statements:

$$\mathbb{E}[W_B| \text{ Lucky Heather wins}] = 350 - x$$

and
$$\mathbb{E}[W_B| \text{ McSnappy wins}] = -1,000 + 3x.$$

---

[12]He may increase or lengthen the odds on Lucky Heather and reduce or shorten the odds on McSnappy.

[13]*A bookmaker who gambles will ruin himself as certainly as a licensed victualler (publican) who drinks, or a picture dealer who cannot bear to part with a good picture.* George Bernard Shaw, "The Vice of Gambling and the Virtue of Insurance", in *The World of Mathematics*, Vol.3, 1956, by James R. Newman. Shaw (1856-1950) was an Irish playwright who was interested in science and social reform, and frequently wrote on both. The words *exaggerated* and *astonishing* have been used to describe some of his scientific theories, and he had a theory on almost everything. In mathematics, however, he did not invent his own theories and developed an appreciation and some understanding of probability and statistics. The article quoted above is a superbly written accurate introduction to the basic ideas in gambling and insurance. Shaw left school at fifteen and came to mathematics relatively late in life. In the passage below he describes an unfortunately familiar experience in mathematical education, but unlike many he overcame this handicap. *Not a word was said to us about the meaning or utility of mathematics: we were simply asked to explain how an equilateral triangle could be constructed by the intersection of two circles, and to do sums in a, b, and x instead of in pence and shillings, leaving me so ignorant that I concluded that a and b must mean eggs and cheese and x nothing, with the result that I rejected algebra as nonsense, and never changed my opinion until in my advanced twenties Graham Wallas and Karl Pearson convinced me that instead of being taught mathematics I had been made a fool of.* It's a pity Shaw never wrote a mathematical textbook.

We can plot the bookmaker's winnings as a function of x for both of these outcomes (Figure 2.2, not drawn to scale) where the decreasing function represents the return when Lucky Heather wins, while the increasing function represents the return when McSnappy wins. Vertical lines through x intersect the graphs and show the bookmaker's risks. For example, if the bookmaker bets $200 on McSnappy, then he will end up either with a profit of $150 or a loss of $400.

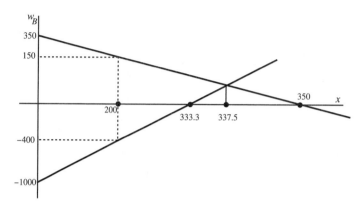

Figure 2.2

The bookmaker, now a reluctant *hedger*, wishes to remove, *in advance* of the outcome, any uncertainty regarding his final situation. To achieve this, W_B should not depend on the outcome of the race, and hence x should be chosen so that

$$\mathbb{E}[W_B| \text{ Lucky Heather wins}] = \mathbb{E}[W_B| \text{ McSnappy wins}].$$

This implies

$$350 - x = -1,000 + 3x$$

and $x = 337.50$. Hence, if the bookmaker places a bet of $337.50 on McSnappy at odds of 3 to 1, then his expected winnings are

$$\mathbb{E}[W_B] = 350 - 337.50 = 12.50$$

regardless of who wins the race. By sacrificing an uncertain, but possibly large, profit, the bookmaker removed the risk of uncertainty and, in this case, has again a guaranteed profit. Such a procedure will always allow the bookmaker to remove his exposure to uncertainty, but it may not always, as in the above example, lead to a guaranteed profit. Two important principles have emerged from the above discussion:

(1) *To remove the uncertainty associated with unpredictable future events, equate the associated rewards (or penalties) and develop a hedging strategy by working backwards.*

(2) *To reduce the potential loss due to an unfavorable event occurring, place a bet in favour of the event happening.*

Most people follow (2) in their daily lives by taking out insurance,[14] and insurance companies also *lay off bets* but call it re-insuring. In the financial world this form of playing safe is called *hedging*.

Finally we return to Mark and his original bet of $100 on McSnappy at odds of 7 to 2. We have seen that he stands to win $350 if McSnappy wins and to lose $100 otherwise. Suppose Mark, immediately after making his bet, finds another bookmaker offering odds of 4 to 1 against on Lucky Heather. If he places a bet for $90 on Lucky Heather winning at these odds, then the following hold:

$$\mathbb{E}[W_M|\text{ Lucky Heather wins}] \;=\; 360 - 100 = 260$$
$$\mathbb{E}[W_M|\text{ McSnappy wins}] \;=\; 350 - 90 = 260.$$

In other words Mark would be guaranteed $260 *regardless* of who won the race. This is an example of *arbitrage*, which occurs in betting as well as in finance.

Our description above is clearly a simplification of the real world of betting. In reality the bookmaker is continuously receiving bets, but it is not practical to change the *odds or price* each time a bet is made. Instead the bookmaker closely monitors the amounts bet on each outcome and changes the odds whenever the accumulated bets suggest it is prudent to do so.

It is worth noting that economical and suggestive notation facilitated our understanding and allowed us to express in a succinct fashion what might otherwise have become wordy and imprecise. The choice of suitable notation and terminology will be even more important in future chapters, and in anticipation of later developments we introduce what looks like a minor adjustment but one which will be seen later to be a conceptual change with important consequences. Let Ω denote the set of outcomes in the race between Lucky Heather and McSnappy. We have only two outcomes, as we are assuming that the race will not end in a dead heat. Let ω_1 denote the event that Lucky Heather wins and let ω_2 be the event that McSnappy wins. Thus $\Omega = \{\omega_1, \omega_2\}$. We can now express John's and Mark's expected winnings and the bookmaker's expected profit as *functions* on Ω. For example

$$\mathbb{E}[W_J|\cdot] : \Omega \longrightarrow \mathbf{R}$$

is John's expected winnings where

$$\mathbb{E}[W_J|\cdot](\omega_i) := \mathbb{E}[W_J|\omega_i]$$

---

[14]*It is clear that nobody who does not understand insurance and comprehend in some degree its enormous possibilities is qualified to meddle in national business. And nobody can get that far without at least an acquaintance with the mathematics of probability.* George Bernard Shaw.

is John's expected winnings when ω_i occurs.

We see later that the basic ideas developed in this chapter transfer in a transparent fashion to the problem of pricing stock options and recommend that the reader review this chapter at various stages as we proceed. We have now encountered the key financial and mathematical components required to build a model yielding a fair price for a share option: *arbitrage, hedging, probabilities* and *expected values*. To proceed we develop probability theory in order to present the share price at time t, X_t, as a *random variable* on a *probability space*. The concept of a set of fair games will reappear as a *martingale* in probability theory (Chapter 9). The central role of martingales is apparent from the following results that we partially prove later.

Proposition 2.3. (*a*) *No arbitrage opportunities for a call option exist if there exists a probability measure under which the discounted share price is a martingale.*

(*b*) *All claims on a call option can be hedged if there is at most one probability measure under which the discounted share price is a martingale.*

Combining these results we see that the existence of a *unique* probability measure under which the discounted share price is a martingale leads to a situation in which *no* arbitrage opportunities exist and *all* claims can be hedged.

2.3. Exercises

(2.1) A bookmaker receives bets of $20, $30 and $50 on three different horses in the same race. Determine the odds on each horse so that the bookmaker will make a profit of 10%. If a further bet of $50 is placed on the third horse and the bookmaker responds by placing a bet of x at odds of 2 to 3 on the same horse in order to run no risk, find x and the bookmaker's profit.

(2.2) Show that odds of a to b translate into a probability of $b/(a + b)$, while a probability p translates into odds of $(1 - p)/p$ to 1.

(2.3) Mary bets only when she is sure of winning and always bets $50. A bookmaker is offering odds of 2 to 1 on a home win in a football game, while next door another bookmaker is offering odds of 5 to 4 on an away win. Assuming that the game will continue until one team wins, what bets should Mary place in order to make the maximum guaranteed profit?

Chapter 3

Set Theory

The theory of probability, as a mathematical discipline, can and should be developed from axioms in exactly the same way as Geometry and Algebra.

Andrei Kolomogorov

Summary

After a general discussion of mathematics and infinity we define the first building blocks, σ-fields, for probability theory. Equivalence relationships and partitions are used to examine the σ-field generated by a collection of subsets of a countable sample space. Filtrations, which are later used to order the history of a share price, are introduced.

3.1. Approaching Abstract Mathematics

So far we have concentrated on the financial world and got by with very little mathematics. We now enter the world of mathematics and later model aspects of the financial world using mathematics. We do not assume familiarity with the *abstract axiomatic approach* to mathematics, but because of its central role in our investigations, begin with a simplified[1] discussion of its evolution. This may appear pedantic at the moment, but, later, it may help put in perspective our overall strategy. The pattern of development we describe is common to

---

[1]The story is partially lost in prehistory. Our description is a mixture of known facts and our personal opinion, based on the way mathematics has developed, on what may have happened.

many disciplines, and, more importantly, the *same route*, with some variation, is followed subconsciously by most individuals.

Ancient civilizations found it necessary to develop basic mathematical skills: arithmetic for counting and tabulating, and geometry for measuring. Frequent repetition of the same or very similar mathematical routines led to familiarity with *patterns* and to some intuitive feeling for the processes involved. This resulted in elementary mathematical rules of thumb.[2] Useful rules were passed on and sometimes improved. The ancient Greeks, over two and a half thousand years ago, began to organize what was then known. In collecting these intuitive rules, they observed that some rules appeared as minor variations of others and could be combined and expressed as special cases of a more general rule. This led to abstraction, which the dictionary tells us is *the formation of an idea, as of the qualities or properties of a thing, by mental separation from particular instances.* The concept of *proof* [3] arose in order to verify these abstract results, and at the same time, it was observed that many abstract results were themselves consequences of more basic results. From this emerged the desire to find the basic rules or principles from which *all* others could be derived using proofs. This enormous task, which involved organizing in a logical order a large selection of facts, was undertaken by a number of authors in succession and culminated in the thirteen books of Euclid,[4] *The Elements of Euclid*. Euclid showed that *all* geometry could be deduced from *five* basic geometric facts, called *postulates*, so simple and obvious that their validity must be assumed and on *axioms* which were regarded as higher forms of universal truth, or as primitive concepts, and which were proclaimed to be *self-evident truths which did not require proof.*[5] This was the beginning of the abstract axiomatic approach to mathematics. It ranks as one of the most remarkable achievements in the history of mankind's intellectual development.

The ancient Greeks introduced many useful concepts, techniques and conventions that we still use today. A simple but very effective innovation was their use, at times rather formal, of *definitions*. For example:

---

[2]Probably motivated by the desire to find shortcuts. Modern examples of this basic phenomenon can be found in the mathematics used by regular punters in betting offices.

[3]Thales of Miletus (c. 624-547 BC) is the first mathematician known by name and the first philosopher of the Milesian school. While visiting Egypt, he studied the practical (=non-abstract) geometry of the Egyptians and left a lasting impression on his hosts by *measuring the heights of pyramids by observation of the length of their shadow at the moment when our shadows are equal to our own height.* Afterwards he introduced geometry to Greece. As none of his writings survive, it is difficult to be certain of his mathematical achievements. Nevertheless, it is generally believed that he gave mathematics the concept of proof and proved the first theorems in geometry. He is also credited as the first recorded person to attempt to explain natural phenomena by rational rather than supernatural means.

[4]Very little is known with certainty about the life of Euclid (c. 325-265 BC) other than that he taught at Alexandria in Egypt.

[5]Some were regarded as so obvious that they were not even mentioned.

A positive integer p is a prime number if (a) $p > 1$, (b) *the only positive integer divisors of p are p and 1.*

This means a name or title is conferred on something *if* it satisfies certain specified conditions. It is common nowadays to call these conditions *axioms*. Conditions (a) and (b) above are the axioms for prime numbers and are the rules we refer to when in doubt. Definitions do not appear out of thin air but are usually the result of years of accumulated intuitive thinking, experience and experiment by many different people and are introduced for various reasons, none trivial. In the simplest cases it is economical to name an object that frequently occurs instead of constantly repeating a lengthy description. In other cases certain combinations of conditions may assume importance as a theory develops, and by naming the combination, one may emphasize its importance and enhance its role. In a small number of cases it has been found that a complete mathematical theory could be reconstructed from a number of key definitions. Note that in stating a definition we are *not* asserting that examples exist.

The abstract axiomatic[6] approach to a mathematical theory consists of starting with either a small number of definitions or postulates from which all results in the theory are derived. This approach generally leads to a more powerful and richer theory built on a more secure foundation.

A strong argument in favor of the practical usefulness of the axiomatic approach can be found in the history of probability theory, which shows some parallels with the history of Euclidean geometry. By 1900, when probability theory already contained varied and interesting results and also a degree of fuzziness about the precise meaning of certain terms, David Hilbert proposed in a list of problems which were to keep mathematicians occupied for the better part of a century that a proper axiomatic foundation be provided for probability theory. In 1933, Kolmogorov[7] published a set of axioms which were immediately

---

[6]A rather narrow view, but one that is logically correct, is to regard mathematics as a way of making explicit what is already implicit in a set of axioms. In the second half of the 13th century, Roman Lull (1235-1315) attempted to construct a general axiomatic system for all sciences, but his contemporaries found his approach incomprehensible. He influenced Gottfried Leibnitz (1646-1716), who, independently and at more or less the same time as Isaac Newton (1642-1715), developed the differential calculus. Nevertheless, it took mathematicians over two thousand years after the development of Euclidean geometry to realize that the same approach could be used to great effect in all areas of mathematics.

[7]Andrei Nikolaevich Kolmogorov (1903-1987) from Tambov, Russia, is regarded as the most influential probabilist of the twentieth century. While still an undergraduate he produced mathematical results of international importance. During a long and productive career he made fundamental contributions to logic, pure and applied probability theory, linguistics, philosophy, stochastic processes, statistics, topology, ballistics, dynamical systems, information theory, genetics, mathematical geology, algorithms, differential equations and Fourier analysis. He devoted a lot of time and energy to the development of programmes for the special needs of gifted children.

and universally recognized as being eminently suitable, and these[8] were directly responsible for the flowering of the subject over the next twenty years.

The abstraction frequently apparent in a set of axioms can initially unsettle those who associate mathematics exclusively with numbers, equations and formulae. However, greater abstraction leads to a wider variety of examples and a simplicity which helps us recognize more easily situations governed by the axioms. The first step towards understanding how a set of axioms works is to examine simple, usually very simple, situations in which they are satisfied and afterwards to derive simple consequences from the axioms. The proofs, at this initial stage, are often surprisingly easy once one understands precisely what has to be proved. As understanding grows and examples analyzed, the subject becomes more concrete and begins to reproduce the traditional signs of normal mathematical activity. When the foundations are understood it becomes easier to recognize similarities between apparently different settings and to modify one situation in order to deal with another. Added bonuses are the realization that the amount of basic mathematics required is small and that understanding unconsciously ranks in order of importance what should be remembered and what trivial facts should be filtered out. Moreover, through understanding, techniques are mastered with less effort and often in a way that is not case specific. This sharpens our intuition. The axiomatic approach does contain a degree of uncertainty not experienced when the classical approach of learning by rote and reproducing mathematical responses in carefully controlled situations is followed, but this uncertainty gradually diminishes as progress is achieved. The cause of this uncertainty is easy to identify. Over time one becomes confident that understanding has been acquired, but then a new example or result or failure to solve a problem or even to understand a solution may destroy this confidence and everything becomes confused.[9] A re-examination is required, and with clarification a better understanding is achieved and confidence returns. This cycle of effort, understanding, confidence and confusion keeps repeating itself, but with each cycle progress is achieved. To initiate this new way of thinking usually requires a change of attitude towards mathematics and this takes time. To begin the process, consider the role of proofs in mathematics. Formally they are required to verify that results are correct, but they also play an important role in helping students concentrate on the result being proved and its relationship with other parts of the subject. A proof may remove the mystery surrounding a result, it may reveal why certain hypotheses are needed, it may show why apparently similar results are not true, and it usually adds to

---

[8]The axioms for probability theory are contained in the definitions of σ-fields (Chapter 3), measurable spaces (Chapter 4) and probability spaces (Chapter 5).

[9]At such times, it may be necessary to take the advice of Winston Churchill (1874-1965): *If you are going through hell, keep going*, or to remember the words of Henry Ford (1863-1947): *If you think you can or you think you can't, you're right.*

students' confidence in applying the result. All this happens in a slow cumulative fashion, and *it may be necessary to move forward* to the next topic *with a degree of uncertainty.* Efforts at understanding are always rewarded but sometimes not immediately, and it may happen that later developments provide, subconsciously, the key insights that overcome earlier difficulties. By attempting problems of a more abstract kind and reading and re-reading proofs, one attains a higher level of understanding and appreciation.

3.2. Infinity

Our intuitions tend to be finite. Moreover, the financial world is finite and discrete; e.g. interest rates are usually given to two places of decimals. The infinite only arises in the world of mathematics where fortunately the rules are precise. Two aspects of infinity, *countability* and *limits*, continuously appear in our investigations, and a few words of preparation may later help the reader understand why certain constructions work and explain why, at times, we proceed very carefully and feel it necessary to verify minor details.

As in the previous section, it is appropriate to return to the work of the ancient Greeks. Having developed geometry they did not rest on their laurels or on the fact that Euclid's presentation allowed them to make advances that were previously inconceivable. Although truths in geometry could now be derived from five geometric postulates, it was hoped that these in turn could be replaced by even simpler postulates using only the natural numbers **N**. In this way arithmetic and geometry would be united and mathematics presented in a unified fashion.

The acceptance that all mathematical statements are either true or false[10] led to a method of proof that we also use, *proof by contradiction.*[11] The basic idea is as follows. Suppose we wish to prove that a certain statement, call it A, is true. We begin by posing as a *hypothesis*, that A is false. From this assumption we draw a number of consequences which eventually lead to a conclusion that *we know* to be false. The only possible flaw in our argument is our hypothesis, and we conclude that this hypothesis is false. Hence the statement 'A is false' is incorrect, and A must be true. This is what we required.

From **N** the ancient Greeks had constructed the positive rational numbers, and for a long time they strongly believed that all numbers were rational. Proof by contradiction was used to show that $\sqrt{2}$ was irrational, and yet, by Pythagoras' Theorem applied to a right-angled triangle with two sides of unit length,

---

[10]This is known as the *Law of the Excluded Middle.* It is accepted as a *rule of inference* or as a *Law of Thought*; that is as a logical principle that justifies deriving one truth from another, by most, but not all, mathematicians.

[11]Also known by its Latin name, *reductio ad absurdum*, and apparently first used by Zeno of Elea, c. 490-430 BC.

they knew that $\sqrt{2}$ existed as a *real* number. This led to a crisis[12] in their belief that mathematics could be built on a logical foundation. The ancient Greeks were never able to place the irrational numbers on a firm logical basis essentially because they did not develop the means to deal with *infinite processes*. As superb mathematicians they developed intuitive rules for dealing with the infinite, but their high standards of proof required results obtained in this way to be verified using their traditional methods of proof.[13] A very influential role was played by the critic Zeno, who invented subtle and profound arguments. Mathematicians at the time could not fault his logic nor refute his conclusions, which often took the form of *paradoxes* arising from the use of infinity. Zeno's arguments influenced the development of Greek geometry by forcing mathematicians to present clear and logically correct arguments[14] and his unanswerable paradoxes banished infinity from playing a role in acceptable proofs for centuries.

Remarkably this state of affairs lasted until close to the end of the 19th century when the appearance of apparent contradictions in analysis and the remarkably original work of Cantor, of which we will soon speak, forced mathematicians to re-examine the basic concepts in mathematics and to try and put on a solid logical basis the system of real numbers. This was achieved and also the dream of the ancient Greeks of uniting arithmetic and geometry.[15] We do not have the time to examine the axioms for the real numbers and shall operate with these intuitively, our main assumption being that every real number has a *decimal expansion* and conversely that every decimal expansion defines a real number. What will concern us is the practical role played by limits of real numbers. The importance of limits cannot be overstated, and it can be argued convincingly that modern mathematics began when the concept of limit was clarified in the form of a definition. *Limits* are the key to the logically consistent development of continuous functions, the differential calculus, the integral

---

[12]A crisis of similar proportions occurred at the beginning of the twentieth century when it was found that the commonly accepted definition of *sets* was logically flawed.

[13]For example, Euclid of Alexandria (c. 365-300 BC) did not say that there existed an infinite number of primes but that the number of primes exceeded any preassigned natural number. Archimedes declared that one could use, as he did when summing infinite series, the infinite to find results but that other methods should be used to justify them. See also the final remarks in Section 11.5.

[14]After the ancient Greeks there was, for many different reasons, a regression in the degree of rigor and the standard of proof within mathematics which was only recovered during the second half of the nineteenth century. For example, after the discovery of the differential calculus progress in new directions was so rapid that mathematicians did not have the time or desire to worry about foundations.

[15]The real numbers can now be derived from the natural numbers $\mathbf{N}$ or from set theory and logic. Both involve axioms. At a foundational level we now know that mathematics will always involve unprovable axioms. The absurd consequences that result from following an axiom logically and blindly has been used effectively in literature by a number of authors, for example by Jonathan Swift in *Gulliver's Travels* and by Flann O' Brien in *The Third Policeman*.

calculus and many other areas of mathematics. They appear in many different situations throughout this book and are more subtle and more powerful than they initially appear. We define, refine and constantly review the concept of limit as we proceed.

Our other topic concerning the infinite is a modern departure due to Georg Cantor. Cantor[16] developed a way of distinguishing between different infinities and introduced *cardinal numbers* in order to count the number of elements in different infinite sets. This may appear strange, and indeed many in the mathematical community at that time dismissed Cantor's remarkable discoveries, but time has shown their importance. We are obliged to take into consideration only one small aspect of Cantor's theory: that the rationals are *countable* and the real numbers are *uncountable*. Both results were proved by Cantor in 1873. We use the countability result frequently, while the uncountability result makes it necessary to use *limits*.

A set A is said to be infinite if it is not finite. For example the natural numbers $\mathbf{N} := \{1, 2, \ldots\}$, the non-negative integers $\mathbf{N}^* := \{0, 1, 2, \ldots\}$, the integers $\mathbf{Z} := \{0, \pm 1, \pm 2, \ldots\}$ and the real numbers $\mathbf{R}$ are all infinite. A set A is *countable* if either A contains a finite number of elements or there exists an infinite sequence $(x_n)_{n=1}^{\infty}$ in which every element in A appears.[17] This is the same as saying that we can count, one after another, the points in A:

$$x_1, x_2, x_3, x_4, \ldots \ .$$

Clearly $\mathbf{N}$ is countable, and since $\mathbf{Z} = \{0, +1, -1, +2, -2, \ldots\}$ it also is countable. The rational[18] numbers, $\mathbf{Q}$, are also countable, but it takes a little more effort to write them in the form of a sequence.[19] For instance the rational numbers between 0 and 1 can be displayed in the following fashion:

$$1/2, 1/3, 2/3, 1/4, 3/4, 1/5, 2/5, 3/5, 4/5, 1/6, \ldots,$$

---

[16]Georg Ferdinand Ludwig Phillipp Cantor was born in St. Petersburg in 1845, but moved to Germany in 1856 and lived there until his death in 1918. He studied in Zurich and Berlin, and was a professor of mathematics at Halle (Germany) from 1869 until he retired in 1913. Cantor is regarded as the founder of *set theory*, and his discovery and development of transfinite and ordinal numbers had profound implications for mathematics, logic and philosophy. His two main articles have been translated and published in book form, *Contributions to the Founding of the Theory of Transfinite Numbers,* by Dover Publications. This book contains an excellent introduction by Philip E.B. Jourdain and includes both an overview of Cantor's contributions and a survey of the conceptual continuity of mathematics during the nineteenth century.

[17]If we drop the terms in the sequence $(x_n)_{n=1}^{\infty}$ which have previously appeared, we obtain a new sequence which contains every element in A. This shows that an infinite set A is countable if and only if there exists a sequence, finite or infinite, in which every element appears once and once only. The same argument shows that a subset of a countable set is countable.

[18]Rational is derived from *ratio*. As $\mathbf{R}$ has already been reserved for the real numbers, we denote the rational numbers by $\mathbf{Q}$ since rationals are *quotients*, p/q, of integers with $q \neq 0$. Rational numbers are also called *fractions*, a word derived from the Latin word *fractum*, to break, e.g. $1/3$ is obtained by breaking 1 into 3 equal parts.

[19]Short proofs are outlined in Exercises 3.5. and 3.23.

and this method can be adapted to show that $\mathbf{Q}$ is countable. On the other hand, we will show that *the real numbers are uncountable*, that is not countable.

We recall, for the following proof, that any real number a can be written in a unique way as $b + c$ where b is an integer and $0 \leq c < 1$. The number b is called the integer part of a and c has a decimal expansion $c = .c_1c_2c_3c_4\ldots$ where each c_i is an integer, $0 \leq c_i \leq 9$. The decimal expansion is not necessarily unique.[20] Indeed, using geometric series, we have

$$.099999 = \sum_{n=1}^{\infty} \frac{9}{10^{n+1}} = \frac{9}{10^2} \sum_{n=0}^{\infty} \frac{1}{10^n}$$

$$= \frac{9}{100} \times \frac{1}{1 - \frac{1}{10}} = \frac{9}{100} \cdot \frac{10}{9} = \frac{1}{10} = .10000\cdots.$$

Proposition 3.1. *The real numbers* $\mathbf{R}$ *are uncountable.*

Proof. Suppose $\mathbf{R}$ is countable. Then $\mathbf{R} = (x_n)_{n=1}^{\infty}$ and each real number occurs somewhere in this sequence. For each n let $x_n = y_n + z_n$ where y_n is the integer part of x_n and $z_n = .z_n^1 z_n^2 z_n^3 \cdots$. If z_n has two expansions, we use the one containing all 9's after a certain point. The method of finding a real number which does not belong to the sequence $(x_n)_{n=1}^{\infty}$ is called a *diagonal process*,[21] a name suggested by the following display:

$$z_1 = .\underline{z_1^1} z_1^2 z_1^3 z_1^4 \cdots$$
$$z_2 = .z_2^1 \underline{z_2^2} z_2^3 z_2^4 \cdots$$
$$z_3 = .z_3^1 z_3^2 \underline{z_3^3} z_3^4 \cdots$$
$$z_4 = .z_4^1 z_4^2 z_4^3 \underline{z_4^4} \cdots$$
$$\cdot = \cdots\cdots\cdots$$
$$z_n = .z_n^1 z_n^2 z_n^3 z_n^4 \cdots \underline{z_n^n} \cdots$$
$$\cdot = \cdots\cdots\cdots\cdots\cdots\cdots.$$

Let $w_n = 6$ if $z_n^n \leq 5$ and let $w_n = 2$ if $z_n^n > 5$. We let $w = .w_1w_2w_3\cdots$. By our hypothesis there exists a positive integer n_0 such that $w = x_{n_0} = z_{n_0}$. The decimal expansion of w does not contain either a nine or a zero. Hence w and x_{n_0} have unique decimal expansions. This means, in particular, that $w_{n_0} = z_{n_0}^{n_0}$. However, by our construction, $w_n \neq z_n^n$ for all n. We have arrived at a contradiction, and thus our original assumption that $\mathbf{R}$ is countable is false. Hence $\mathbf{R}$ is uncountable. This completes the proof. □

---

[20]A real number has more than one decimal expansion if and only if it has an expansion in which all entries are 9 after a certain point.

[21]Diagonal processes are often used to construct a sequence with certain properties from a given sequence of sequences. See the proof of Proposition 11.14.

As we mentioned previously our main tool is probability theory, which itself relies on a very flexible and effective form of integration, *Lebesgue integration*. The strength and flexibility of the Lebesgue integral is based on processing a *countable* number of sets or events[22] at any one time. Thus countability is an essential and intrinsic part of the foundations on which we build our theory. Moreover, probability theory on a countable sample space is much simpler than the general theory and contains many instructive examples. This adds to our understanding and intuition, but confining ourselves to countable sample spaces would mean never arriving at the most interesting applications. For these we require a form of completeness not satisfied by $\mathbf{Q}$ but satisfied by $\mathbf{R}$.

A real number M is an *upper bound* for a set A of real numbers if $x \leq M$ for all x in A. An upper bound which is less than all other upper bounds is called a *least upper bound*. Hence U is a least upper bound for the set A if and only if it satisfies the following two conditions:

$$x \leq U \text{ for all } x \in A,$$

$$\text{if } x \leq M \text{ for all } x \in A, \text{ then } U \leq M.$$

If $x \geq m$ for all x in A, then m is called a *lower bound* for A, and a lower bound which is greater than all other lower bounds is called a *greatest lower bound* of the set A. A set A which has a lower bound and an upper bound is said to be *bounded*. Clearly, A is bounded if and only if $A \subset [a,b] := \{x \in \mathbf{R} : a \leq x \leq b\}$ for some real numbers a and b. If $(a_n)_{n=1}^{\infty}$ is an increasing sequence of real numbers, that is

$$a_1 \leq a_2 \leq a_3 \leq \cdots,$$

then a_1 is a lower bound for the set $\{a_n\}_{n=1}^{\infty}$. Hence an increasing sequence is *bounded* if and only if it has an upper bound.

The completeness result we require is given in the following proposition and leads directly to our first rigorous definition of limit.

Proposition 3.2. (*Upper Bound Principle*) *A bounded increasing sequence of real numbers has a least upper bound.*

Definition 3.3. *The limit of an increasing bounded* [23] *sequence of real numbers* $(a_n)_{n=1}^{\infty}$ *is defined to be the least upper bound of the set* $\{a_n\}_{n=1}^{\infty}$. *We denote the limit by* $\lim_{n \to \infty} a_n$ *and say that the sequence* $(a_n)_{n=1}^{\infty}$ *converges to* $\lim_{n \to \infty} a_n$.

To see that this conforms to our intuitive notion of limit,[24] let U denote the least upper bound of the increasing bounded sequence $(a_n)_{n=1}^{\infty}$. For any strictly

---

[22]Events and sample spaces are defined in the following section.

[23]For convenience we say that an increasing *unbounded* sequence of real numbers, $(a_n)_{n=1}^{\infty}$, *diverges* to $+\infty$ and write $\lim_{n \to \infty} a_n = +\infty$.

[24]Limits dispensed with the need to consider the *infinitely small*, an intuitive concept that led to foundational problems for the differential calculus. A subset A of B is *proper* if A is non-empty and $A \neq B$. The natural numbers are a proper subset of the integers and yet both have the same

positive number ϵ, *no matter how small*, the interval $(U - \epsilon, U]$ will contain a_{n_0} for some positive integer n_0. Otherwise, since $a_n \leq U$ for all n, we would have $a_n \leq U - \epsilon$ for all n. This is impossible since it would mean that the sequence has an upper bound strictly less than the least upper bound. If $n \geq n_0$, then

$$U - \epsilon < a_{n_0} \leq a_n \leq U$$

and a_n is getting closer and closer to U as n gets larger and larger.

A number of simple consequences are easily derived from Definition 3.3. If $(a_n)_{n=1}^{\infty}$ and $(b_n)_{n=1}^{\infty}$ are two bounded increasing sequences, then so also is the sequence $(a_n + b_n)_{n=1}^{\infty}$. If $\lim_{n \to \infty} a_n = m_1$ and $\lim_{n \to \infty} b_n = m_2$, then $a_n \leq m_1$ and $b_n \leq m_2$ for all n. Hence $a_n + b_n \leq m_1 + m_2$ and the sequence $(a_n + b_n)_{n=1}^{\infty}$ is convergent. Since $m_1 + m_2$ is an upper bound for $(a_n + b_n)_{n=1}^{\infty}$, we have

$$\lim_{n \to \infty} (a_n + b_n) \leq \lim_{n \to \infty} a_n + \lim_{n \to \infty} b_n.$$

If $m < m_1 + m_2$ and $2c := m_1 + m_2 - m$, then $c > 0$. Since $m_1 - c < m_1$ there exists a positive integer n_1 such that $a_{n_1} > m_1 - c$, and, similarly, there exists a positive integer n_2 such that $b_{n_2} > m_2 - c$. If $n > n_1 + n_2$, then $a_n + b_n \geq a_{n_1} + b_{n_2} > m_1 - c + m_2 - c = m$ and the least upper bound of $\{a_n + b_n\}_{n=1}^{\infty}$ is greater than any number less than $m_1 + m_2$. This shows that the least upper bound is $m_1 + m_2$ and

$$\lim_{n \to \infty} (a_n + b_n) = \lim_{n \to \infty} a_n + \lim_{n \to \infty} b_n.$$

In the same way one can show: if $a_n = c$ for all n, then $\lim_{n \to \infty} a_n = c$, and $\lim_{n \to \infty} a_n \cdot b_n = \lim_{n \to \infty} a_n \cdot \lim_{n \to \infty} b_n$ for any increasing bounded sequences $(a_n)_{n=1}^{\infty}$, $(b_n)_{n=1}^{\infty}$ such that $(a_n \cdot b_n)_{n=1}^{\infty}$ is also increasing.

As a simple application we sum a geometric series. Consider a real number r, $0 < r < 1$, and let $x_n = 1 + r + r^2 + \ldots + r^n$ for any positive integer n. Then

$$x_{n+1} = 1 + r + r^2 + \ldots + r^n + r^{n+1} = x_n + r^{n+1} > x_n$$

and $(x_n)_{n=1}^{\infty}$ is an increasing sequence of real numbers. By (1.2), $x_n = \frac{1 - r^{n+1}}{1 - r} \leq \frac{1}{1-r}$ for all n. Hence $(x_n)_{n=1}^{\infty}$ is a bounded increasing sequence of real numbers and converges. We denote the limit by $\phi(r)$ and $\sum_{n=0}^{\infty} r^n$. Since $x_{n+1} = 1 + r \cdot x_n$

---

size. This undermined the long-held belief or axiom that the whole is always *strictly greater* than *any* of its *proper* parts. Together limits and Cantor's theory gave answers within mathematics, after over two thousand years, to Zeno's paradoxes.

we have $\phi(r) = \lim_{n\to\infty} x_{n+1} = 1 + r\lim_{n\to\infty} x_n = 1 + r\phi(r)$. Hence[25] $\phi(r) = \frac{1}{1-r} = \sum_{n=0}^{\infty} r^n$.

There is a natural duality between upper and lower bounds and between increasing and decreasing sequences and we define the limit, $\lim_{n\to\infty} a_n$, of a decreasing sequence $(a_n)_{n=1}^{\infty}$, which is bounded below, to be the *greatest lower bound* of the set $\{a_n\}_{n=1}^{\infty}$. Since $\lim_{n\to\infty} a_n = -\lim_{n\to\infty}(-a_n)$ results for increasing sequences transfer to decreasing sequence and conversely and this may be useful. For example, a decreasing sequence of strictly positive numbers $(a_n)_{n=1}^{\infty}$ is bounded below and hence converges to some real number a. If $b_n = 1/a_n$ for all n, then $(b_n)_{n=1}^{\infty}$ is an increasing sequence of positive numbers. If $a > 0$, then $a_n \geq a$ and $b_n \leq 1/a$ for all n and the sequence $(b_n)_{n=1}^{\infty}$ is bounded above. Conversely, if $(b_n)_{n=1}^{\infty}$ is bounded above and m is an upper bound for the sequence, then $a_n \geq 1/m$ for all n and $a > 0$. We have shown $\lim_{n\to\infty} a_n = a > 0$ if and only if the sequence $(1/a_n)_{n=1}^{\infty}$ is bounded above. If $a_n = n$ for all n, then it is easily seen that the sequence $(a_n)_{n=1}^{\infty}$ is increasing and *not* bounded above. Hence $\lim_{n\to\infty} 1/n = 0$.

The rational numbers do not satisfy a least upper bound principle; that is we can find a bounded increasing sequence of rational numbers which does not converge to any *rational* number.[26] At this stage we have identified two important properties: countability and the upper bound principle. We have two key sets **Q** and **R**, each of which satisfies one and only one of these properties. We need both, and the key to bridging the gap is the fact that every real number can be *approximated by rationals*.[27] To see this it suffices to use decimal expansions. Approximations are useful when a satisfactory limiting procedure is available. Thus the actual bridge we use comes dressed up as a limit. The financial world, our raw material, is finite. We use countability, in the form of

---

[25]Geometric series were studied by Euclid. While calculating the area between a parabola and the x-axis, that is the quadrature of the parabola, Archimedes used the infinite series $\sum_{n=1}^{\infty}(1/4)^n$. The general form of the infinite sum, given above, was first obtained by Viète around 1593. Archimedes of Syracuse (287-212 BC) is regarded as the greatest of the ancient Greek mathematicians. His interests were many, both theoretical and practical, and included geometry, mechanics, hydrostatics (*Archimedes' Principle*), number systems, approximations and distances to the planets. He developed the *exhaustion method*, which allowed him to calculate the areas and volumes of many bodies and which was the forerunner of the *integral calculus*. His books are masterpieces of mathematical exposition, and his engineering capabilities were legendry. When challenged about his boast: *Give me a place to stand and I will move the earth*; he, *effortlessly and single handed, while comfortably seated on a chair on the beach, moved with a compound pulley a heavily weighted ship into the water from dry dock.* François Viète (1540-1603), came from la Rochelle in France. Although a qualified lawyer, most of his career was spent in the service of a succession of French kings either as a privy counsellor or as a parliamentarian. He had a lifelong interest in mathematics and devoted himself entirely to it during his political exile from 1584 to 1589. Viète wrote books on geometry and trigonometry and greatly facilitated the growth of *algebra* by introducing the practice of using letters as symbols in algebraic equations.

[26]It will converge to a real number since **Q** ⊂ **R** and **R** satisfies an upper bound principle.

[27]In mathematical terminology we say that the rationals are *dense* in the reals.

a sequence, to approach the infinite world of mathematics. We reach it by taking *limits*. In the mathematical world we use mathematical analysis to obtain mathematical results. We return to the financial world by using the infinite to approximate the finite, and on our return, interpret our mathematical results. For instance in Chapter 1 we used limits to calculate continuously compounded interest. When applied in a concrete problem a calculator is often used to produce the final answer. Calculators and computers use rational approximations in place of limits.

3.3. σ–Fields

In the previous chapter we considered two games of chance, tossing a coin and a two-horse race. The set of outcomes was small and could be analyzed case by case. Ever so slightly more complicated is throwing a die. In this case we have six outcomes, $\Omega = \{1, 2, 3, 4, 5, 6\}$. There are, in throwing a die, events of interest other than the actual number that appears, e.g. whether an even number is thrown or whether the number thrown is greater than or equal to three. These events correspond to certain subsets of Ω, and clearly other subsets of Ω could also be labeled events. To fix our notation we call an action, e.g. tossing a coin or throwing a die, an *experiment*. We denote the set of possible outcomes of the experiment by Ω and call it the *sample space*. In the financial world Ω will always be finite. For example, if Ω is the set of all prices that a certain share will take tomorrow, then Ω is finite since in the real world only a finite number of price changes are physically possible in any one day, but it is convenient, and necessary for mathematical reasons, to suppose that it may take *any* positive real number as its value.

In some cases we may suppose that all subsets of Ω are events, and it would be convenient if we could always assume this to be the case. However, in order to define and calculate *expected values*, the collection of events must satisfy certain mathematical properties, the axioms for a σ-field. Insisting that all subsets of Ω be events would mean excluding the most interesting examples from our investigations. Later, when the necessary structures are in place, we return to this point. We will also classify events by their time of occurrence using filtrations (see Section 3.5), and, in this situation, not all subsets of Ω select themselves as events.

Our main mathematical task in this chapter is to study the collections of subsets of Ω that may be taken as a suitable set of events. We introduce a precise definition of such collections and, in the remainder of this chapter, examine concrete examples and prove basic properties using the definition. This is our first experience using axioms directly, and because of this we proceed slowly and try to develop some balance between the concrete and the abstract. It may be difficult, at this stage, to appreciate the relevance of our abstract definition and simple examples to the world of finance, but this is only the first step and the first block in the foundation. Any foundation has to support all that is built on it, and we are just taking care that the foundations are secure.

As one of the main tools in this and later chapters is basic set theory, we review some, hopefully familiar, notation.

Let A, B, and $A_n, n = 1, 2, \ldots$, denote subsets of the set Ω.

$$x \in A \Leftrightarrow x \text{ is an element of } A,$$

$$x \notin A \Leftrightarrow x \text{ is not an element of } A,$$

$$A \subset B \Leftrightarrow A \text{ is a subset of } B \Leftrightarrow \text{ if } x \in A, \text{ then } x \in B,$$

$$A \cap B \Leftrightarrow \text{ intersection of } A \text{ and } B \Leftrightarrow \{x : x \text{ belongs to both } A \text{ and } B\},$$

$$A \cup B \Leftrightarrow \text{ union of } A \text{ and } B \Leftrightarrow \{x : x \in A \text{ and/or } x \in B\},$$

$$A^c \Leftrightarrow \text{ the complement of } A \Leftrightarrow \{x \in \Omega : x \notin A\},$$

$$\emptyset = \text{ empty set } = \text{ set with no elements,}$$

$$A \cap B = \emptyset \Leftrightarrow A \text{ and } B \text{ are disjoint}$$

$$\Leftrightarrow A \text{ and } B \text{ have no elements in common,}$$

$$\bigcup_{n=1}^{\infty} A_n = \{x : x \in A_n \text{ for some } n\} = \text{ union of all } A_n,$$

$$\bigcap_{n=1}^{\infty} A_n = \{x : x \in A_n \text{ for all } n\} = \text{ intersection of all } A_n.$$

The empty set is rather uninteresting, but we cannot do without it. Its role in set theory is analogous to that played by 0 in analysis. It facilitates the phrasing of many statements in a clear and efficient manner.

Definition 3.4. *A σ-field on a set Ω is a collection $\mathcal{F}$ of subsets of Ω which obeys the following rules or axioms:*

    [a] *$\Omega \in \mathcal{F}$;*
    [b] *if $A \in \mathcal{F}$, then $A^c \in \mathcal{F}$;*
    [c] *if $(A_n)_{n=1}^{\infty}$ is a sequence in $\mathcal{F}$, then $\bigcup_{n=1}^{\infty} A_n \in \mathcal{F}$.*

The points in $\mathcal{F}$ are subsets of Ω and are called *$\mathcal{F}$-events* or *$\mathcal{F}$-measurable sets*. If there is no possibility of confusion, we say event or measurable set. An event A can be considered either as a *subset* of Ω or as a *point* in $\mathcal{F}$, that is as a subset of one set or as an element of another, and we use both points of view. The pair $(\Omega, \mathcal{F})$ is called a *measurable space*. Measurable spaces are the building blocks for *probability spaces*, and without these technical rules we could not develop a powerful theory. This is true but not obvious. Note, however, that the three axioms are simple, clear and consistent.[28]

The remaining results in this chapter will help the reader gain familiarity with set theoretic calculations, an essential skill in working with σ-fields; and towards the end of the chapter, when we consider σ-fields as carriers of information, we will see that Definition 3.4 has both a practical and an intuitive content.

Definition 3.4 does not mention intersections or finite unions, but we now see that we get both quite easily.

Proposition 3.5. *Let $(\Omega, \mathcal{F})$ be a measurable space. Then*

(1) $\emptyset \in \mathcal{F}$;

(2) *if $(A_n)_{n=1}^{k}$ is a finite sequence of $\mathcal{F}$-measurable sets, then $\bigcup_{n=1}^{k} A_n \in \mathcal{F}$;*

(3) *if $(A_n)_{n=1}^{\infty}$ is a sequence of $\mathcal{F}$-measurable sets, then $\bigcap_{n=1}^{\infty} A_n \in \mathcal{F}$.*

Proof. (1) By[29] **[a]**, $\Omega \in \mathcal{F}$, and hence, by **[b]**, $\Omega^c = \emptyset \in \mathcal{F}$.

(2) Let $A_m = \emptyset$ for $m > k$. Then, by (1) and **[c]**, $\bigcup_{n=1}^{\infty} A_n \in \mathcal{F}$. Since

$$\bigcup_{n=1}^{\infty} A_n = A_1 \cup A_2 \cup \ldots \cup A_k \cup \emptyset \cup \emptyset \cup \ldots = \bigcup_{n=1}^{k} A_n,$$

this proves (2).

(3) If each $A_n \in \mathcal{F}$, then $A_n^c \in \mathcal{F}$ for all n, and hence $\bigcup_{n=1}^{\infty} A_n^c \in \mathcal{F}$. By **[b]**, $(\bigcup_{n=1}^{\infty} A_n^c)^c \in \mathcal{F}$. It suffices now to show $\bigcap_{n=1}^{\infty} A_n = (\bigcup_{n=1}^{\infty} A_n^c)^c$. We have $x \in (\bigcup_{n=1}^{\infty} A_n^c)^c$ if and only if $x \notin \bigcup_{n=1}^{\infty} A_n^c$, that is if and only if $x \notin A_n^c$ for all n. Hence $x \in (A_n^c)^c$ for all n. Since $(A_n^c)^c = A_n$ (the complement of the complement of A is again A) we have $x \in (\bigcup_{n=1}^{\infty} A_n^c)^c$ if and only if $x \in A_n$ for all n, that is if and only if $x \in \bigcap_{n=1}^{\infty} A_n$. This proves (3).[30] $\square$

Example 3.6. (a) Let $\Omega = \{1, 2, 3, 4, 5, 6\}$ and $\mathcal{F} = \{\emptyset, \{1, 2\}, \{3, 4, 5, 6\}, \Omega\}$. We wish to verify that $\mathcal{F}$ is a σ-field on Ω. This means we must show that **[a]**,**[b]** and **[c]** are satisfied by $\mathcal{F}$. Since we are given that $\Omega \in \mathcal{F}$, **[a]** is trivially satisfied. We verify **[b]** directly. We have $\emptyset^c = \Omega$, $\{1, 2\}^c = \{3, 4, 5, 6\}$, $\{3, 4, 5, 6\}^c = \{1, 2\}$ and $\Omega^c = \emptyset$. Hence **[b]** is satisfied.

---

[28]That is they do not contradict one another. To see this it suffices to give *one* example; we give many as we proceed.

[29]The boldfaced references, e.g. **[a]**, in this and the following chapter refer to the axioms in Definition 3.4.

[30]The rules $(\bigcup_{n=1}^{\infty} A_n)^c = \bigcap_{n=1}^{\infty} A_n^c$ and $(\bigcap_{n=1}^{\infty} A_n)^c = \bigcup_{n=1}^{\infty} A_n^c$ are known as *de Morgan's Laws*.

Let $(A_n)_{n=1}^{\infty}$ denote a sequence of subsets of Ω, each of which belongs to $\mathcal{F}$. We divide $\mathbf{N}$ into 4 sets. Let $N_1 = \{n : A_n = \emptyset\}$, then $\bigcup_{n \in N_1} A_n = \emptyset$; $N_2 = \{n : A_n = \{1,2\}\}$, then $\bigcup_{n \in N_2} A_n = \emptyset$ if $N_2 = \emptyset$ and equals $\{1,2\}$ otherwise; $N_3 = \{n : A_n = \{3,4,5,6\}\}$, $\bigcup_{n \in N_3} A_n = \emptyset$ if $N_3 = \emptyset$ and equals $\{3,4,5,6\}$ otherwise; $N_4 = \{n : A_n = \Omega\}$, then $\bigcup_{n \in N_4} A_n = \emptyset$ if $N_4 = \emptyset$ and equals Ω otherwise. We have

$$\bigcup_{n \in \mathbf{N}} A_n = \bigcup_{n \in N_1} A_n \cup \bigcup_{n \in N_2} A_n \cup \bigcup_{n \in N_3} A_n \cup \bigcup_{n \in N_4} A_n$$

$$= \emptyset \cup (\emptyset \text{ or } \{1,2\}) \cup (\emptyset \text{ or } \{3,4,5,6\}) \cup (\emptyset \text{ or } \Omega),$$

and clearly this is one of the 4 sets, $\{\emptyset, \{1,2\}, \{3,4,5,6\}, \Omega\}$. Hence $\mathcal{F}$ satisfies [c] and $\mathcal{F}$ is a σ-field on Ω.

(b) Given Ω we let 2^{Ω} denote the set of all subsets of Ω and call 2^{Ω} the *power set* of Ω. The collection 2^{Ω} is a σ-field on Ω. This follows since $\Omega \subset \Omega$, the complement of a subset of Ω is again a subset of Ω and the union of any sequence of subsets of Ω is also a subset of Ω, and thus the three axioms for a σ-field are satisfied. As previously mentioned the σ-field 2^{Ω} may be too large for certain mathematical constructions, but it does have certain abstract properties useful in developing the theory. A typical subset A of Ω can be chosen as follows: for each $x \in \Omega$ we have 2 choices, either $x \in A$ or $x \notin A$. In total we have $2 \times 2 \times \cdots \times 2(|\Omega|$ times) choices, where $|\Omega|$ is the number of elements in Ω, and thus we can find $2^{|\Omega|}$ different subsets of Ω. In particular, if Ω has n elements, then 2^{Ω} has 2^n elements; that is Ω has 2^n distinct subsets.[31]

(c) The σ-field 2^{Ω} is the largest σ-field of subsets of Ω. There also exists a smallest σ-field. This consists of the sets $\{\Omega, \emptyset\}$. We call this the *trivial σ-field* on Ω and denote it by $\mathcal{F}_{\emptyset}$.

Any σ-field on Ω is a subset of 2^{Ω}, and the subsets of 2^{Ω} which satisfy the axioms in Definition 3.4, are precisely the different σ-fields on Ω. This allows us to compare and take the intersection of different σ-fields on Ω. If $\mathcal{F}$ and $\mathcal{G}$ are σ-fields on Ω, we say that $\mathcal{F} \subset \mathcal{G}$ if, when we consider $\mathcal{F}$ and $\mathcal{G}$ as subsets of 2^{Ω}, we have $\mathcal{F} \subset \mathcal{G}$. This means that every element of $\mathcal{F}$ is also an element of $\mathcal{G}$. Thus

$$\mathcal{F} \subset \mathcal{G} \Leftrightarrow \text{ if } A \subset \Omega \text{ and } A \in \mathcal{F}, \text{ then } A \in \mathcal{G}.$$

For any σ-field $\mathcal{F}$ on Ω we have

$$\mathcal{F}_{\emptyset} \subset \mathcal{F} \subset 2^{\Omega}.$$

---

[31]This motivated the notation 2^{Ω}. The notation $\mathcal{P}(\Omega)$, derived from the power set of Ω, is also used in place of 2^{Ω}. See Exercise 3.28.

Let $\mathcal{F}_\alpha$ denote a σ-field on Ω for each α in some set[32] Γ. Since $\mathcal{F}_\alpha \subset 2^\Omega$ for all α we define their *intersection*

$$\bigcap_{\alpha \in \Gamma} \mathcal{F}_\alpha := \{A \subset \Omega : A \in \mathcal{F}_\alpha \text{ for all } \alpha \in \Gamma\}.$$

Our next result shows that this intersection is a σ-field on Ω.

Proposition 3.7. *If $(\mathcal{F}_\alpha)_{\alpha \in \Gamma}$ is a collection of σ-fields on Ω, then $\bigcap_{\alpha \in \Gamma} \mathcal{F}_\alpha$ is a σ-field on Ω.*

Proof. We prove[33] the special case $\Gamma = \{1, 2\}$. The general proof follows the same pattern. We must show that the three axioms in Definition 3.4 are satisfied by $\mathcal{F}_1 \cap \mathcal{F}_2$. Since $\mathcal{F}_1$ is a σ-field on $\Omega, \Omega \in \mathcal{F}_1$. Similarly, $\Omega \in \mathcal{F}_2$ and hence $\Omega \in \mathcal{F}_1 \cap \mathcal{F}_2$ and [a] is satisfied. If $A \in \mathcal{F}_1 \cap \mathcal{F}_2$, then $A \in \mathcal{F}_1$; and as $\mathcal{F}_1$ is a σ-field, $A^c \in \mathcal{F}_1$. Similarly $A^c \in \mathcal{F}_2$ and hence $A^c \in \mathcal{F}_1 \cap \mathcal{F}_2$, and [b] is satisfied.

If $(A_n)_{n=1}^\infty \subset \mathcal{F}_1 \cap \mathcal{F}_2$, then $\bigcup_{n=1}^\infty A_n \in \mathcal{F}_1$ since $\mathcal{F}_1$ is a σ-field. Similarly $\bigcup_{n=1}^\infty A_n \in \mathcal{F}_2$. Hence $\bigcup_{n=1}^\infty A_n \in \mathcal{F}_1 \cap \mathcal{F}_2$, [c] is satisfied by $\mathcal{F}_1 \cap \mathcal{F}_2$, and $\mathcal{F}_1 \cap \mathcal{F}_2$ is a σ-field. This completes the proof. $\qquad\square$

The number of elements in a σ-field may be quite large even when Ω is small; for instance if $\Omega = \{1, 2, 3, 4, 5, 6\}$, then 2^Ω has 64 elements and it can be quite tedious[34] to check certain properties for each of these 64 sets one by one. To remove some of this, usually routine, work we show how to construct a σ-field from a given collection of subsets of Ω. We call such a collection a *generating set* for the σ-field. The generating set will usually consist of a smaller and more manageable collection.

Proposition 3.8. *If $\mathcal{A}$ is a collection of subsets of Ω, then there exists a unique smallest σ-field on Ω, containing $\mathcal{A}$, which is contained in every σ-field that contains $\mathcal{A}$. We denote this σ-field by $\mathcal{F}(\mathcal{A})$ and call it the σ-field generated by $\mathcal{A}$.*

---

[32]The set Γ is an index or labeling system for the collection of sets under consideration; it has nothing to do with Ω. If we are just considering two σ-fields, $\mathcal{F}_1$ and $\mathcal{F}_2$, then $\Gamma = \{1, 2\}$ and we write $\mathcal{F}_1 \cap \mathcal{F}_2$. If we are considering a sequence of σ-fields $(\mathcal{F}_n)_{n=1}^\infty$, we write $\bigcap_{n=1}^\infty \mathcal{F}_n$.

[33]Our proofs fall into a number of categories. We prefer to include complete proofs and do so whenever possible. In certain cases, as for instance in the proof of this proposition, the general proof follows the same pattern as the proof of a special case, while the special case avoids technical complications which add nothing to our understanding. In such situations we prefer to prove the special case and leave the general case as an exercise. The reader should consider writing out the proof of Proposition 3.5 for three σ-fields and then writing out a full proof. In other cases, for instance in proving the existence of conditional expectations (Chapter 8), the general proof may be beyond the scope of our methods, but we still may be able to prove an interesting special case. In a few rare instances we do not even prove a special case and only include some general remarks. In all cases we inform the reader of the option being followed.

[34]See Example 3.10.

Proof. Let $\mathfrak{B}$ denote the set of all σ-fields on Ω which contain $\mathcal{A}$, that is

$$\mathfrak{B} = \{\mathcal{G} : \mathcal{G} \text{ is a } \sigma\text{-field on } \Omega \text{ and } \mathcal{A} \subset \mathcal{G}\}.$$

Since $2^{\Omega} \in \mathfrak{B}, \mathfrak{B}$ is non-empty. By Proposition 3.7

$$\mathcal{F}(\mathcal{A}) := \bigcap_{\mathcal{G} \in \mathfrak{B}} \mathcal{G}$$

is a σ-field on Ω. Moreover, as $\mathcal{A} \subset \mathcal{G}$ for all $\mathcal{G} \in \mathfrak{B}, \mathcal{A} \subset \bigcap_{\mathcal{G} \in \mathfrak{B}} \mathcal{G} = \mathcal{F}(\mathcal{A})$. Since we are taking the intersection of *all* σ-fields containing $\mathcal{A}$, $\mathcal{F}(\mathcal{A})$ is contained in every σ-field that contains $\mathcal{A}$.

If $\mathcal{F}_1$ and $\mathcal{F}_2$ are σ-fields on Ω containing $\mathcal{A}$, then $\mathcal{F}_1 \in \mathfrak{B}$ and $\mathcal{F}_2 \in \mathfrak{B}$. By Proposition 3.7, $\mathcal{F}_1 \cap \mathcal{F}_2 \in \mathfrak{B}$, and $\mathcal{F}(\mathcal{A}) \subset \mathcal{F}_1 \cap \mathcal{F}_2$. If $\mathcal{F}_1$ and $\mathcal{F}_2$ are contained in every σ-field that contains $\mathcal{A}$, then $\mathcal{F}_i \subset \mathcal{F}(\mathcal{A}), i = 1, 2$. By Exercise 3.12, $\mathcal{F}_1 = \mathcal{F}_2 = \mathcal{F}(\mathcal{A})$. This completes the proof. $\square$

Our next proposition is a small refinement of Proposition 3.8.

Proposition 3.9. *If $\mathcal{A}, \mathcal{A}_1$ and $\mathcal{A}_2$ are subsets of 2^{Ω}, then the following hold.*

(a) *If $\mathcal{A}_1 \subset \mathcal{A}_2$, then $\mathcal{F}(\mathcal{A}_1) \subset \mathcal{F}(\mathcal{A}_2)$.*

(b) *If $\mathcal{A}$ is a σ-field, then $\mathcal{F}(\mathcal{A}) = \mathcal{A}$.*

(c) *$\mathcal{F}(\mathcal{F}(\mathcal{A})) = \mathcal{F}(\mathcal{A})$.*

(d) *If $\mathcal{A}_1 \subset \mathcal{F}(\mathcal{A}_2)$, then $\mathcal{F}(\mathcal{A}_1) \subset \mathcal{F}(\mathcal{A}_2)$.*

Proof. (a) We have $\mathcal{A}_1 \subset \mathcal{A}_2 \subset \mathcal{F}(\mathcal{A}_2)$. Since $\mathcal{F}(\mathcal{A}_2)$ is a σ-field and $\mathcal{F}(\mathcal{A}_1)$ is the smallest σ-field containing $\mathcal{A}_1$, this implies $\mathcal{F}(\mathcal{A}_1) \subset \mathcal{F}(\mathcal{A}_2)$.

(b) If $\mathcal{A}$ is a σ-field, then it must be the smallest σ-field containing $\mathcal{A}$. Hence $\mathcal{A} = \mathcal{F}(\mathcal{A})$.

(c) Let $\mathcal{A} = \mathcal{F}(\mathcal{A})$ in (b).

(d) By (a), $\mathcal{F}(\mathcal{A}_1) \subset \mathcal{F}(\mathcal{F}(\mathcal{A}_2))$, and by (c), $\mathcal{F}(\mathcal{F}(\mathcal{A}_2)) = \mathcal{F}(\mathcal{A}_2)$. $\square$

Example 3.10. Let $\Omega = \{1, 2, \ldots, 10\}$ and let $\mathcal{A} = \{\{2, 3, 4\}, \{4, 5, 6, 7\}\}$. Our aim is to describe the σ-field, $\mathcal{F}(\mathcal{A})$, generated by $\mathcal{A}$ using directly the axioms for a σ-field. We first note that since $\mathcal{F}(\mathcal{A})$ is a σ-field, it contains $\emptyset$ and Ω. We now take the two given sets, their complements and union and obtain

$$\{2, 3, 4\},$$

$$\{4, 5, 6, 7\},$$

$$\{1, 5, 6, 7, 8, 9, 10\} = \{2, 3, 4\}^c,$$

$$\{1, 2, 3, 8, 9, 10\} = \{4, 5, 6, 7\}^c,$$

$$\{2, 3, 4, 5, 6, 7\} = \{2, 3, 4\} \cup \{4, 5, 6, 7\},$$

and we have found 7 sets in $\mathcal{F}(\mathcal{A})$.

Are there any more? We continue applying [**b**] and obtain

$$\{1, 8, 9, 10\} = \{2, 3, 4, 5, 6, 7\}^c.$$

At this stage we have a collection that satisfies [**b**] and are obliged to use [**c**] and take unions. This yields the following sets in $\mathcal{F}(\mathcal{A})$:

$$\{1, 2, 3, 4, 8, 9, 10\} = \{2, 3, 4\} \cup \{1, 8, 9, 10\},$$
$$\{1, 4, 5, 6, 7, 8, 9, 10\} = \{1, 8, 9, 10\} \cup \{4, 5, 6, 7\},$$

and their complements

$$\{5, 6, 7\} = \{1, 2, 3, 4, 8, 9, 10\}^c,$$
$$\{2, 3\} = \{1, 4, 5, 6, 7, 8, 9, 10\}^c.$$

We have located 12 subsets of Ω which lie in $\mathcal{F}(\mathcal{A})$. Continuing with unions and complements we obtain

$$\{2, 3, 5, 6, 7\} = \{2, 3\} \cup \{5, 6, 7\},$$
$$\{1, 2, 3, 5, 6, 7, 8, 9, 10\} = \{1, 5, 6, 7, 8, 9, 10\} \cup \{2, 3\},$$
$$\{1, 4, 8, 9, 10\} = \{2, 3, 5, 6, 7\}^c,$$

and

$$\{4\} = \{1, 2, 3, 5, 6, 7, 8, 9, 10\}^c,$$

and this gives 16 subsets of Ω which belong to $\mathcal{F}(\mathcal{A})$.

We are making progress but, since Ω has $2^{10} = 1024$ subsets, there are signs that the amount of work required may increase substantially, and it is also possible we may become confused in keeping track of the sets in $\mathcal{F}(\mathcal{A})$ already counted. We require a more systematic way of counting. In this kind of situation it is worth pausing and reorganizing what we already know. We list the sets known to lie in $\mathcal{F}(\mathcal{A})$ by size and obtain

sets with 0 elements ,	$\emptyset$,
sets with 1 element ,	$\{4\}$,
sets with 2 elements ,	$\{2, 3\}$,
sets with 3 elements ,	$\{2, 3, 4\}, \{5, 6, 7\}$,
sets with 4 elements ,	$\{1, 8, 9, 10\}, \{4, 5, 6, 7\}$,
sets with 5 elements ,	$\{2, 3, 5, 6, 7\}, \{1, 4, 8, 9, 10\}$.

At this stage a pattern is emerging, and we may take advantage of some elementary observations. We have listed 9 sets, of which 7 contain 4 or less elements. If we take their complements, we get 7 more sets with 6 or more elements and putting these together with the 2 sets with 5 elements, we obtain the 16 sets already identified. Let $\mathfrak{C}$ denote these 16 sets. We have $\mathcal{A} \subset \mathfrak{C} \subset \mathcal{F}(\mathcal{A})$, and by Proposition 3.9(b) and (c), $\mathfrak{C} = \mathcal{F}(\mathcal{A})$ if $\mathfrak{C}$ is a σ-field. By construction $\mathfrak{C}$ satisfies [**a**] and [**b**], and it suffices to show that $\mathfrak{C}$ satisfies [**c**]. By inspection all of the above sets can be written as unions of the following 4 sets in $\mathcal{F}(\mathcal{A})$:

$$\{4\}, \{2,3\}, \{5,6,7\}, \{1,8,9,10\}, \quad (*).$$

Since

$$
\begin{aligned}
\{4\}^c &= \{2,3\} \cup \{5,6,7\} \cup \{1,8,9,10\}, \\
\{2,3\}^c &= \{4\} \cup \{5,6,7\} \cup \{1,8,9,10\}, \\
\{2,3,4\}^c &= \{5,6,7\} \cup \{1,8,9,10\}, \\
\{5,6,7\}^c &= \{4\} \cup \{2,3\} \cup \{1,8,9,10\}, \\
\{1,8,9,10\}^c &= \{4\} \cup \{2,3\} \cup \{5,6,7\}, \\
\{4,5,6,7\}^c &= \{2,3\} \cup \{1,8,9,10\},
\end{aligned}
$$

all 16 sets in $\mathfrak{C}$ are unions of the 4 sets in $(*)$. It suffices to show that arbitrary unions of the four sets in $(*)$ belong to $\mathfrak{C}$. Since the union of all 4 sets is Ω and the union of any 3 is the complement of the remaining one and $\mathfrak{C}$ is closed by complements, we have reduced the problem to showing that the union of any 2 of the sets in $(*)$ belongs to $\mathfrak{C}$. We verify this directly. We have

$$
\begin{aligned}
\{4\} \cup \{2,3\} &= \{2,3,4\} \in \mathfrak{C}, \\
\{4\} \cup \{5,6,7\} &= \{4,5,6,7\} \in \mathfrak{C}, \\
\{4\} \cup \{1,8,9,10\} &= \{1,4,8,9,10\} \in \mathfrak{C}, \\
\{2,3\} \cup \{5,6,7\} &= \{2,3,5,6,7\} \in \mathfrak{C}, \\
\{2,3\} \cup \{1,8,9,10\} &= \{1,2,3,8,9,10\} = \{4,5,6,7\}^c \in \mathfrak{C}, \\
\{5,6,7\} \cup \{1,8,9,10\} &= \{2,3,4\}^c \in \mathfrak{C}.
\end{aligned}
$$

Hence $\mathfrak{C}$ is a σ-field and $\mathfrak{C} = \mathcal{F}(\mathcal{A})$.

The ad-hoc methods used in Example 3.10 are very basic and could be termed first principles. The main point of the example was to obtain some familiarity with set manipulation and counting and to prepare the reader for the simple abstract results that we establish in the next section. These provide a simple, efficient method for describing certain σ-fields.

3.4. Partitions

The results in this section apply, in particular, to all σ-fields on a countable set and thus are relevant to many of our more illustrative examples in later chapters. A partition of a set Ω is a collection of non-overlapping subsets of Ω whose union covers the whole space. We repeat this in a formal fashion.

Definition 3.11. *A collection of subsets of* $\Omega, (A_\alpha)_{\alpha \in \Gamma}$, *is called a partition of* Ω *if*

(3.1) $A_\alpha \cap A_\beta \; = \; \emptyset \; \text{if } \alpha \neq \beta,$

(3.2) $\bigcup_{\alpha \in \Gamma} A_\alpha \; = \; \Omega.$

Condition (3.1) says that the sets in the partition are *pairwise disjoint* while (3.2) says that they cover the whole space. If the indexing set Γ is finite, we usually write $(A_n)_{n=1}^k$; and if Γ is countable, we write $(A_n)_{n=1}^\infty$.

Proposition 3.12. *If* $\mathcal{P} = (A_n)_{n=1}^\infty$ *is a countable partition of* Ω, *then the* σ-*field*, $\mathcal{F}(\mathcal{P})$, *consists of all sets of the form* $\bigcup_{n \in M} A_n$ *where* M *ranges over all subsets of* $\mathbf{N}$.

Proof. Let $\mathcal{G}$ denote all subsets of Ω which can be written in the form $\bigcup_{n \in M} A_n$, $M \subset \mathbf{N}$. We first show that $\mathcal{G}$ is a σ-field. Since $\Omega = \bigcup_{n \in \mathbf{N}} A_n$, **[a]** is satisfied. If $B = \bigcup_{n \in M} A_n$, then $B^c = \bigcup_{n \in M^c} A_n$ and **[b]** is satisfied. Suppose $B_m = \bigcup_{n \in M_m} A_n$ for every positive integer m. Let $M = \bigcup_m M_m$. Then

$$\bigcup_{m=1}^\infty B_m = \bigcup_{m=1}^\infty \bigcup_{n \in M_m} A_n = \bigcup_{n \in M} A_n$$

and **[c]** is satisfied. Hence $\mathcal{G}$ is a σ-field. Clearly $\mathcal{P} \subset \mathcal{G}$. By Proposition 3.9(a), $\mathcal{F}(\mathcal{P}) \subset \mathcal{F}(\mathcal{G})$, and by Proposition 3.9(b), $\mathcal{G} = \mathcal{F}(\mathcal{G})$. Since every subset M of $\mathbf{N}$ is countable, $\mathcal{G} \subset \mathcal{F}(\mathcal{P})$. Hence $\mathcal{F}(\mathcal{P}) \subset \mathcal{F}(\mathcal{G}) = \mathcal{G} \subset \mathcal{F}(\mathcal{P})$ and $\mathcal{G} = \mathcal{F}(\mathcal{P})$. This completes the proof. $\square$

We now generalize Proposition 3.11 so that we can associate a partition of Ω with every σ-field on Ω when Ω is countable. To do so we require *equivalence relationships*.

Definition 3.13. *A relationship between elements of a set* Ω *is called an equivalence relationship if the following axioms hold:*

(3.3) $x \sim x \, (reflexive),$

(3.4) $x \sim y \Leftrightarrow y \sim x \, (symmetric),$

(3.5) $x \sim y \text{ and } y \sim z \Leftrightarrow x \sim z \, (transitive),$

where we have written $x \sim y$ *if* x *and* y *are equivalent.*

We call $[x] := \{y \in \Omega : x \sim y\}$ the *equivalence class* containing x.

Example 3.14. Let $\Omega = \mathbf{Z}$ and for $n, m \in \mathbf{Z}$ let $n \sim m$ if $n - m$ is an even integer (note that 0 is an even integer). It is an easy exercise to verify that $\sim$ defines an equivalence relationship. Since $2 - 1 = 1$ is odd, 1 and 2 belong to different equivalence classes. If n is odd, then $n-1$ is even and $n \sim 1$; while if n is even, then $n-2$ is even and $n \sim 2$. Since every integer is either even or odd this covers all possibilities. We have shown that there are just 2 equivalence classes, $[1]$ and $[2]$. The equivalence class $[1]$ consists of all odd integers, while the equivalence class $[2]$ consists of all even integers. Thus the equivalence classes partition the integers. We show that this is always the case.

Lemma 3.15. *If $\sim$ is an equivalence relationship on Ω, then for x and y in Ω*

    (a) $[x] = [y] \Leftrightarrow x \sim y$,

    (b) *either $[x] = [y]$ or $[x] \cap [y] = \emptyset$ (that is two equivalence classes either coincide or are totally disjoint).*

Proof. (a) Suppose $[x] = [y]$. By reflexivity $x \in [x] = [y]$ and hence $x \in [y]$ and $x \sim y$.

Conversely, suppose $x \sim y$. If $z \in [x]$, then $z \sim x$, and since $x \sim y$, transitivity implies $z \sim y$ and hence $z \in [y]$. Since z was an arbitrary element of $[x]$, this shows $[x] \subset [y]$. The same argument shows that $[y] \subset [x]$. Hence $[x] = [y]$, and this proves (a).

(b) It suffices to show that $[x] \cap [y] \neq \emptyset$ implies $[x] = [y]$. If $z \in [x] \cap [y]$, then $z \sim x$ and $z \sim y$. By (3.4) and (3.5) this implies $x \sim y$. Hence, by (a), $[x] = [y]$, and this completes the proof. $\qquad\qquad\square$

Lemma 3.15 is significant because it establishes a correspondence between equivalence relationships on Ω and partitions of Ω. Since $x \in [x]$ each point in Ω is in some equivalence class, and as equivalence classes are disjoint, by Lemma 3.15(b) we obtain a partition of Ω. Conversely, if we are given a partition of Ω, $(A_\alpha)_{\alpha \in \Gamma}$, we obtain an equivalence relationship by letting $x \sim y$ if x and y belong to the same A_α. This shows that *partitions* and *equivalence relationships* are precisely the same concept. They just appear different.

We show in the following proposition how a collection of sets which generates a σ-field also generates an equivalence relationship and thus a partition. Although our next proposition appears very abstract, the proof gives a practical method for constructing $\mathcal{F}(\mathcal{A})$ from $\mathcal{A}$ and leads to a useful way of displaying and comparing σ-fields.

Proposition 3.16. *Let $\mathcal{A}$ denote a collection of subsets of Ω. Let $x \sim y$ if for all $B \in \mathcal{A}$ we have $x \in B$ if and only if $y \in B$. Then $\sim$ is an equivalence relationship on Ω. If the equivalence relationship generates a countable partition $(B_n)_{n=1}^\infty$ of Ω, then $\mathcal{F}(\mathcal{A})$ consists of all sets of the form $\bigcup_{n \in M} B_n$ where M ranges over all subsets of $\mathbf{N}$.*

Proof. We first show that $\sim$ is an equivalence relationship on Ω. We have

$$x \sim x \text{ since, if } B \in \mathcal{A}, \text{ then } x \in B \text{ if and only if } x \in B.$$

Hence (3.3) holds. Since

$$\begin{aligned}
x \sim y \quad &\Leftrightarrow \quad \text{if } B \in \mathcal{A}, \text{ then } x \in B \text{ if and only if } y \in B, \\
&\Leftrightarrow \quad \text{if } B \in \mathcal{A}, \text{ then } y \in B \text{ if and only if } x \in B, \\
&\Leftrightarrow \quad y \sim x
\end{aligned}$$

(3.4) holds. If $x \sim y, y \sim z$ and $B \in \mathcal{A}$, then $x \in B \Leftrightarrow y \in B$ and $y \in B \Leftrightarrow z \in B$. Hence $x \in B \Leftrightarrow z \in B$ and thus $x \sim z$. We have established that $\sim$ is an equivalence relationship.

Note that we are *not* assuming that each point in Ω belongs to some $B \in \mathcal{A}$. Indeed, if x and y belong to Ω and neither belongs to *any* $B \in \mathcal{A}$, then the condition, $x \in B \Leftrightarrow y \in B$ for all $B \in \mathcal{A}$, is satisfied[35] and $x \sim y$. On the other hand, if $x \in B$ for some $B \in \mathcal{A}$, and $y \notin B$ for any $B \in \mathcal{A}$, then $x \nsim y$. This implies that $(\bigcup B : B \in \mathcal{A})^c$ is an equivalence class, a useful practical observation.

Our collection of equivalence classes gives rise to a partition $\mathcal{P}$ of Ω. We suppose from now on that this partition is countable and let $\mathcal{P} = (B_n)_{n=0}^{\infty}$, where $B_0 = (\bigcup B : B \in \mathcal{A})^c$. To complete the proof we must show that $\mathcal{F}(\mathcal{P}) = \mathcal{F}(\mathcal{A})$. If $B \in \mathcal{A}$ and $x \in B$, then any $y \in [x]$ also belongs to B. Hence $[x] \subset B$ and each $B \in \mathcal{A}$ is a union of equivalence classes. Since the set of distinct equivalence classes is countable, any union of equivalence classes belongs to $\mathcal{F}(\mathcal{P})$ by Proposition 3.12. Hence $B \in \mathcal{F}(\mathcal{P})$ and $\mathcal{F}(\mathcal{A}) \subset \mathcal{F}(\mathcal{P})$.

To show $\mathcal{F}(\mathcal{P}) \subset \mathcal{F}(\mathcal{A})$ it suffices to show that $B_{n_0} \in \mathcal{F}(\mathcal{A})$ for all n_0. First suppose $n_0 > 0$. By the above there exists $B \in \mathcal{A}$ such that $B_{n_0} \subset B$. If $B = B_{n_0}$ then $B_{n_0} \in \mathcal{F}(\mathcal{A})$. Otherwise there exists a positive integer $n_1 \neq n_0$ such that $B_{n_1} \subset B$. If $x \in B_{n_0}$ and $y \in B_{n_1}$, then there exists $C \in \mathcal{A}$ such that either $x \in C$ and $y \notin C$ or $y \in C$ and $x \notin C$. Let

$$D_1 := \begin{cases} B \cap C & \text{if } x \in C, \\ B \cap C^c & \text{if } x \notin C. \end{cases}$$

Then $D_1 \in \mathcal{F}(\mathcal{A})$, $B_{n_0} \subset D_1$ and $B_{n_1} \cap D_1 = \emptyset$. We may use, whenever $n_i \neq n_0$ and $B_{n_i} \subset B$, the same construction to find sets $D_i \in \mathcal{F}(\mathcal{A})$ such that $B_{n_0} \subset D_i$ and $B_{n_i} \cap D_i = \emptyset$. This implies

$$\bigcap_{n_i \neq n_0} D_i = B_{n_0} \in \mathcal{F}(\mathcal{A}).$$

---

[35]This is subtle and based on the fact that the elements in the *empty set* satisfy *all* properties. If no one lives on Mars, then everyone who lives on Mars has red hair. Think about it.

Since $\mathcal{F}(\mathcal{A})$ is a σ-field, $B_0 = (\bigcup_{n=1}^{\infty} B_n)^c \in \mathcal{F}(\mathcal{A})$. Hence $\mathcal{F}(\mathcal{P}) \subset \mathcal{F}(\mathcal{A})$, and this completes the proof. $\qquad\square$

When Ω is countable every partition of Ω gives rise to a countable partition. We have thus shown that there exists a correspondence[36] between σ-fields and partitions of Ω whenever Ω is countable. This is not true for uncountable sets, for instance $\mathbf{R}$, but we will get a similar correspondence between countable partitions of arbitrary Ω and σ-fields generated by random variables with *countable range*.

Example 3.17. (Example 3.8 revisited). We describe, as before, the σ-field on $\Omega = \{1, 2, \ldots, 10\}$ generated by the sets $\{2, 3, 4\}$ and $\{4, 5, 6, 7\}$. We have to identify the equivalence classes given in the previous proposition. We noted in the proof that $(\bigcup A : A \in \mathcal{A})^c$ is an equivalence class. In our case this is the set $\{1, 8, 9, 10\}$. We can thus confine our attention to the subset $\{2, 3, 4, 5, 6, 7, \}$. Two elements are equivalent if and only if they are always together. We may rephrase this and say that two elements are not equivalent if they can be separated by some set $A \in \mathcal{A}$. Clearly $\{2, 3\}$ are always together and so also are $\{5, 6, 7\}$. Since each of the original sets is a union of equivalence classes and $\{2, 3, 4\} = \{2, 3\} \cup \{4\}$, the set $\{4\}$ is an equivalence class. We have found all the equivalence classes and thus the required partition of Ω. The equivalence classes are $\{1, 8, 9, 10\}, \{2, 3\}, \{4\}, \{5, 6, 7\}$. The partition of Ω is displayed in Figure 3.1.

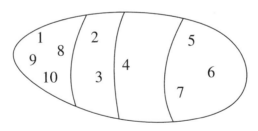

Figure 3.1

Note that we have 4 equivalence classes and the number of sets that can be constructed using these sets is $2^4 = 16$. In addition, we have got some extra information from the proof. A σ-field which contains only a finite number of sets contains 2^n sets for some positive integer n.

If $\mathcal{P}_1$ and $\mathcal{P}_2$ are partitions of the same set Ω, we say that $\mathcal{P}_2$ is *finer* than $\mathcal{P}_1$ if every set in $\mathcal{P}_2$ is obtained by *subdividing* sets in $\mathcal{P}_1$ or, equivalently, if all

---

[36]This correspondence is one-to-one if we restrict ourselves to partitions by non-empty sets. For all practical purposes this restriction is unimportant.

sets in $\mathcal{P}_1$ are obtained by *combining* sets in $\mathcal{P}_2$. If $\mathcal{P}_2$ is finer than $\mathcal{P}_1$, we write $\mathcal{P}_1 \subset \mathcal{P}_2$. For example we have $\mathcal{P}_1 \subset \mathcal{P}_2$ in the following diagram (Figure 3.2). It is easily seen that

$$\mathcal{F}(\mathcal{P}_1) \subset \mathcal{F}(\mathcal{P}_2) \Leftrightarrow \mathcal{P}_1 \subset \mathcal{P}_2$$

and thus we have, particularly when Ω is small, a practical visual way of comparing σ-fields.

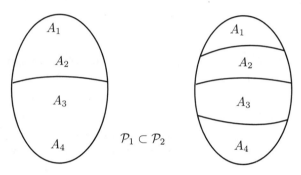

Figure 3.2

3.5. Filtrations and Information

In the previous sections we studied the elements in a σ-field from a set theoretic point of view. We now consider them as *events* and associated with events[37] we may have *information*[38] such as the event has occurred, the event will never occur, the event may only occur at a certain time, etc. We have already seen the importance of *time* in the financial world, and information is equally important. The two are not unrelated, as an increase in time generally leads to an increase in information.

The sample space Ω is the set of all possible outcomes of some experiment $\mathfrak{E}$, while the σ-field $\mathcal{F}$ represents the events that are observed and that can be recorded when the experiment is performed. In other words, it is the information we receive on performing the experiment. Thus after the experiment we can observe whether or not $A \in \mathcal{F}$ occurred. If $\mathcal{F}_1$ and $\mathcal{F}_2$ are two σ-fields on Ω, then $\mathcal{F}_1 \subset \mathcal{F}_2$ if and only if $\mathcal{F}_2$ contains *more* information than $\mathcal{F}_1$; that is complete information about all $\mathcal{F}_2$ events includes complete information about

---

[37]Two closely related area within mathematics are *probability theory* and *measure theory*. Probability theory, by far the older, had to await the development of measure theory to secure its current mathematical foundations. Probability theory and measure theory share, for the most part, a common notation with a few notable exceptions. For example probabilists use *almost surely* while measure theorists use, with the same meaning, *almost everywhere* (see Chapter 6 for details).

[38]Our comments regarding *information* are purely informal and are introduced solely to help the reader gain some intuitive feeling for σ-fields and random variables. In particular, our remarks are unconnected with the subject known as *Information Theory*.

all $\mathcal{F}_1$ events. As a simple artificial example, suppose a die is thrown and that

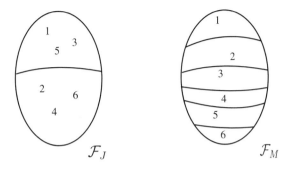

Figure 3.3

afterwards John is told if an even or odd number appeared while Mark is told the actual number that appeared. Clearly Mark has more information than John. We can represent the information known to both as the events in the σ-fields $\mathcal{F}_J$ and $\mathcal{F}_M$, and we compare them in Figure 3.3.

We will be interested in distinguishing between events by their time of occurrence or non-occurrence. We again consider a rather simple case, but one that contains useful lessons. Let Ω denote the set of all outcomes resulting from tossing a coin three times in succession. We display the set Ω in the obvious way (Figure 3.4).

H	H	H
H	H	T
H	T	H
H	T	T
T	H	H
T	H	T
T	T	H
T	T	T

Figure 3.4

If A is the event that a head appears on the first toss and B is the event that a head appears on the second toss, then we can distinguish between these events only by time. We identify $\mathcal{F}$, the set of all events that may occur, with the set of all subsets of Ω. Let $\mathcal{F}_i, i = 1, 2, 3$ denote the events that have been decided (or determined) by the end of the ith toss. Since we have more information at the end of the $(i + 1)^{th}$ toss than at the end of the ith toss,

$$\mathcal{F}_1 \subset \mathcal{F}_2 \subset \mathcal{F}_3.$$

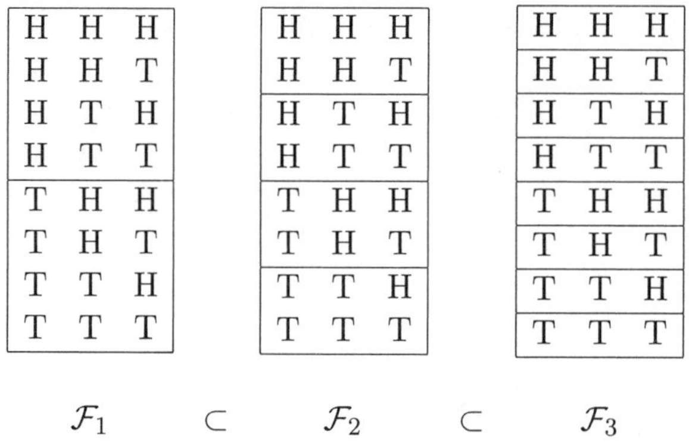

H	H	H
H	H	T
H	T	H
H	T	T
T	H	H
T	H	T
T	T	H
T	T	T

H	H	H
H	H	T
H	T	H
H	T	T
T	H	H
T	H	T
T	T	H
T	T	T

H	H	H
H	H	T
H	T	H
H	T	T
T	H	H
T	H	T
T	T	H
T	T	T

$$\mathcal{F}_1 \quad \subset \quad \mathcal{F}_2 \quad \subset \quad \mathcal{F}_3$$

Figure 3.5

We consider $\mathcal{F}_i$ the *history* of the system up to time i. It is natural to write the events determined after the first toss as $\{H, T\}$ since either one of these events has occurred and nothing more. We might write $\{HH, HT, TH, TT\}$ as the history up to the end of the second toss and we would also be correct. However, this does not allow us to compare, as σ-fields, the events associated with the first and the first two tosses, as we would be considering σ-fields on *different sets*. To do so we must identify the events H, T, HH, HT, TH, TT with subsets of the same set. We choose Ω as the universal or global set, as it contains all information on the process. We identify H, the event that a head appears on the first toss, with the subset $\widetilde{H}$ of Ω consisting of all points beginning with H (see Figure 3.5). The information provided by knowing that $\widetilde{H}$ has occurred is precisely the same as knowing that a head appeared on the first toss.

This gives us the set of σ-fields in Figure 3.5 and leads to the following definition.

Definition 3.18. *Let $(\Omega, \mathcal{F})$ be a measurable space.*

(a) *A discrete filtration on $(\Omega, \mathcal{F})$ is an increasing sequence of σ-fields $(\mathcal{F}_n)_{n=1}^{\infty}$ such that*

$$\mathcal{F}_1 \subset \mathcal{F}_2 \subset \cdots \subset \mathcal{F}_i \subset \cdots \subset \mathcal{F}.$$

(b) *A continuous filtration on $(\Omega, \mathcal{F})$ is a set of σ-fields $(\mathcal{F}_t)_{t \in I}$, where I is an interval in $\mathbf{R}$, such that for all $t, s \in I, t < s$, we have*

$$\mathcal{F}_t \subset \mathcal{F}_s \subset \mathcal{F}.$$

We call $\mathcal{F}_n$ (respectively $\mathcal{F}_t$) the history up to time n (respectively time t).

We mention briefly an important example that we consider later and that makes concrete the rather abstract notion of a filtration. Let Ω denote the set of all possible future prices that may be taken by a given share. Let $\mathcal{F}$ denote the set of events we may associate with the share price. We have two natural filtrations adapted to the share price: $(\mathcal{F}_n)_{n=1}^{\infty}$ where $\mathcal{F}_n$ is the history up to the end of the nth day and $(\mathcal{F}_t)_{t \geq 0}^{\infty}$ where $\mathcal{F}_t$ is the history up to time t.

The interpretation of elements in a σ-field as events allows us to upgrade our ideas on set theoretic operations and lends credibility to the axioms for a σ-field. Given two $\mathcal{F}$ events in Ω, A and B, then $A \cap B$ occurs if and only if *both occur*; $A \cap B = \emptyset$ if and only if A and B are *mutually exclusive*, that is both cannot happen; $A \cup B$ occurs if *either* A or B or both occur, while if $A_\alpha \in \mathcal{F}$ for all α, then $\bigcup_\alpha A_\alpha = \Omega$ if and only if at least one A_α occurs whenever the experiment $\mathfrak{E}$ is performed.

The first axiom for a σ-field states that we can tell when the experiment has been performed. The second states that if we have all information about an event A, then we also know all about A^c. For example, if we know the number of heads that appeared when a coin was tossed 10 times, then we also know the number of times a head did not appear. Thus the second axiom is quite reasonable and intuitive. Similarly, information on each one of a finite number of events can be combined to make a statement about the union of these events, and the finite version of the final axiom for a σ-field is acceptable to our everyday experience. Combining an infinite countable number of events is not intuitive and is introduced, as we shall see later, for mathematical reasons.

3.6. Exercises

(3.1) Show that there exists a rational number between any two different real numbers.

(3.2) Show (a) that a subset of a countable set is countable and (b) a union of countable sets is countable.

(3.3) Let $(a_\alpha)_{\alpha \in \Gamma}$ denote a set of positive real numbers. If $\sum_{\alpha \in \Gamma} a_\alpha < \infty$, show that $\{\alpha \in \Gamma : a_\alpha \neq 0\}$ is countable.

(3.4) If $f : A \longrightarrow B$ is an *injective* (that is one-to-one) function and B is countable, show that A is countable. If $g : C \longrightarrow D$ is a *surjective* (that is onto) function and C is countable, show that D is countable.

(3.5) Use the first part of the previous exercise and the function $f : \mathbf{N} \mapsto \mathbf{N} \times \mathbf{N}$, $f(n,m) := 2^n \cdot 3^m$ to show that $\mathbf{N} \times \mathbf{N}$ is countable. Use this result, the second part of the previous exercise, and the function $g : \mathbf{N} \times \mathbf{N} \mapsto \mathbf{Q}^+$, $g(n,m) = n/m$ to show that the strictly positive rational numbers are countable. Hence show that $\mathbf{Q}$ is countable.

(3.6) If A and B are sets, let $A \times B = \{(x,y) : x \in A, y \in B\}$. If A and B are countable, show that $A \times B$ is countable. Show, by induction or otherwise, that the product of any finite number of countable sets is countable.

(3.7) If Ω is a countable infinite set, show that the set of all finite subsets of Ω is countable and that the set of all subsets of Ω is uncountable.

(3.8) Let $\mathcal{A}$ be a collection of subsets of Ω which is closed under the formation of finite unions and complements: that is if $(A_i)_{i=1}^n \subset \mathcal{A}$, then $\bigcup_{i=1}^n A_i \in \mathcal{A}$; and if $A \in \mathcal{A}$, then $A^c \in \mathcal{A}$. Show that $\mathcal{A}$ is a σ-field if and only if for any increasing sequence $(A_n)_{n=1}^\infty \subset \mathcal{A}$, $A_n \in \mathcal{A}$ for all n, we have $\bigcup_{n=1}^\infty A_n \in \mathcal{A}$.

(3.9) Show that a set of real numbers which is bounded above has a *unique* least upper bound, and a set which is bounded below has a *unique* greatest lower bound.

(3.10) Show that $\sqrt{2}$ is irrational. By using the decimal expansion of $\sqrt{2}$ show that $\mathbf{Q}$ does not satisfy an upper bound principle.

(3.11) Show that $\lim_{n \to \infty} 1/(n^2 + n) = 0$.

(3.12) If A and B are sets, show that $A = B$ if and only if $A \subset B$ and $B \subset A$.

(3.13) If A and B are subsets of Ω, show that

$$A \subset B \Leftrightarrow B^c \subset A^c.$$

(3.14) Let $(A_n)_{n=1}^\infty$ denote a sequence of subsets of the set Ω. Show that

$$\bigcup_{n=1}^\infty (\bigcap_{m \geq n}^\infty A_m) = \{x : x \text{ belongs to all but a finite number of } A_n\}$$

$$\bigcap_{n=1}^\infty (\bigcup_{m \geq n}^\infty A_m) = \{x : x \text{ belongs to an infinite number of } A_n\}.$$

(3.15) Find, using only the axioms for a σ-field, the σ-field generated by the subsets $\{1, 2, 3\}, \{2, 3, 4, 5\}, \{3, 5, 9\}$ of $\{1, 2, \ldots, 10\}$.

(3.16) Give examples of σ-fields $\mathcal{F}_1$ and $\mathcal{F}_2$ such that $\mathcal{F}_1 \cup \mathcal{F}_1$ is not a σ-field.

(3.17) Give examples of σ-fields $\mathcal{F}_1$ and $\mathcal{F}_2$ such that $\mathcal{F}_1 \not\subset \mathcal{F}_2$ and $\mathcal{F}_2 \not\subset \mathcal{F}_1$.

(3.18) Show, using only the axioms for a σ-field, that there does not exist a σ-field which contains only 6 elements.

(3.19) Let $\mathcal{A}$ denote the collection of all subsets of Ω which contain a single element. Show that the σ-field generated by $\mathcal{A}, \mathcal{F}(\mathcal{A})$, consists of all subsets of Ω which are either countable or whose complement is countable. Show that $\mathcal{F}(\mathcal{A}) = 2^\Omega$ if Ω is countable.

(3.20) Let $x \sim y$ for $x, y \in \mathbf{R}$ if $x - y$ is rational. Show that $\sim$ is an equivalence relationship. Show that this equivalence relationship does not lead to a countable partition of $\mathbf{R}$.

(3.21) Let $x \sim y$ for $x, y \in \mathbf{R}$ if $x - y$ is an irrational number. Show that $\sim$ is not an equivalence relationship.

(3.22) If $\mathcal{F}$ is the σ-field generated by a finite partition of Ω, show that $\mathcal{F}$ has 2^n elements for some positive integer n.

(3.23) For elements of $\mathbf{N} \times \mathbf{N}$ let $(n, m) \sim (p, q)$ if $nq = pm$. Show that $\sim$ is an equivalence relationship. Find a surjective mapping ϕ from $\mathbf{N} \times \mathbf{N}$ onto the positive rational numbers such that $\phi(n, m) = \phi(p, q)$ if and only if $(n, m) \sim (p, q)$. Hence show that $\mathbf{Q}$ is countable.

(3.24) List all σ-fields on $\Omega = \{1, 2, 3, 4\}$ and find 4 distinct σ-fields $(\mathcal{F}_i)_{i=1}^4$ such that $\mathcal{F}_1 \subset \mathcal{F}_2 \subset \mathcal{F}_3 \subset \mathcal{F}_4$.

(3.25) Let Ω denote the set of all outcomes when a coin is tossed a countably infinite number of times, that is $\Omega = \{(x_n)_{n=1}^\infty : x_n = H \text{ or } T\}$. Show that Ω is uncountable.

(3.26) Let $(a_n)_{n=1}^\infty$ denote a sequence of real numbers. Show that $(a_n)_{n=1}^\infty$ is an increasing sequence if and only if the sequence $(-a_n)_{n=1}^\infty$ is decreasing. Show that $(a_n)_{n=1}^\infty$ has an upper bound if and only if $(-a_n)_{n=1}^\infty$ has a lower bound. Find the relationship between the least upper bound of $(a_n)_{n=1}^\infty$ and the greatest lower bound of $(-a_n)_{n=1}^\infty$.

(3.27) If $(a_n)_{n=1}^\infty$ is a bounded sequence, show that there exists a smallest closed interval $[a, b]$ that contains all a_n. Show that b is the least upper bound and a the greatest lower bound of the sequence.

(3.28) Show that there exists a one-to-one correspondence between the subsets of the set Ω and the collection of mappings from Ω into $\{0, 1\}$.

(3.29) Give examples of increasing sequences of real numbers $(a_n)_{n=1}^\infty$ and $(b_n)_{n=1}^\infty$ such that $(a_n \cdot b_n)_{n=1}^\infty$ is a decreasing sequence.

(3.30) Let $\mathcal{A}$ denote a collection of subsets of Ω such that the complement, finite intersection and increasing countable union of sets in $\mathcal{A}$ belong to $\mathcal{A}$. If $\Omega \in \mathcal{A}$, show that $\mathcal{A}$ is a σ-field.

(3.31) If $x \geq 0$, show that the series $\sum_{n=0}^\infty x^n/n!$ converges.

(3.32) Prove, by contradiction, that the set $S = \{n^2 : n \in \mathbf{N}\}$ is not bounded above.

(3.33) A subsequence of $(x_n)_{n=1}^\infty$ is a sequence of the form $(x_{\phi(j)})_{j=1}^\infty$ where $\phi : \mathbf{N} \mapsto \mathbf{N}$ is strictly increasing; that is $i < j$ implies $\phi(i) < \phi(j)$ (n_j is frequently written in place of $\phi(j)$). Show that a subsequence of a subsequence of $(x_n)_{n=1}^\infty$ is a subsequence of $(x_n)_{n=1}^\infty$.

Chapter 4

Measurable Functions

If language is not correct, then what is said is not what is meant; and if what is said is not what is meant then what ought to be done remains undone.

Confucius, c. 550-478 BC

Summary

Measurable functions are defined and shown to be stable under the operations of addition, composition and pointwise limits. Simple functions are examined and continuous functions are shown to be measurable. Measurable functions on the σ-fields generated by countable partitions and by functions with countable range are characterized.

4.1. The Borel Field

Our next goal is to develop the tools to measure the likelihood that the events, collected into a σ-field in the previous chapter, occur. While we will work directly with the measurable space $(\Omega, \mathcal{F})$, distinct advantages can be gained by transferring our investigations to the richly endowed real numbers. To be successful such transfers, which occur frequently within mathematics, must preserve the structure under consideration. This means that both the source and target spaces must be endowed with similar structures and the mappings, which make the transfer, must preserve the main ingredients in the structures. Thus in linear algebra we use linear mappings, which preserve vector addition and scalar multiplication, to transfer one vector space into another. Later we shall see that continuous mappings preserve convergent sequences.

The structure we are considering here is a σ-field, and the appropriate mappings are called *measurable functions* in this chapter and later, when we have placed a measure on $(\Omega, \mathcal{F})$, *random variables*. We first need to choose a σ-field on $\mathbf{R}$. The most natural subsets of $\mathbf{R}$ which can be measured are intervals and, at a minimum, our σ-field must contain the intervals. On the other hand, by Definition 4.5, the smaller the σ-field on $\mathbf{R}$, the larger the collection of measurable functions. For these reasons we use the σ-field generated by the intervals. We proceed to formally carry out this programme.

Let O and C denote, respectively, the open and closed intervals in $\mathbf{R}$. As usual, $(a, b) = \{x : a < x < b\}$ and $[a, b] = \{x : a \leq x \leq b\}$.

Definition 4.1. *The Borel field on* $\mathbf{R}, \mathcal{B}(\mathbf{R})$, *is the* σ-*field generated by the open intervals in* $\mathbf{R}$. *Subsets of* $\mathbf{R}$ *which belong to* $\mathcal{B}(\mathbf{R})$ *are called Borel sets.*

The Borel[1] σ-field on $[a, b]$, a closed interval in $\mathbf{R}$, is defined as

$$\{B \cap [a, b] : B \in \mathcal{B}(\mathbf{R})\}.$$

Our next proposition shows that we could just as easily have used closed intervals in the above definition.

Proposition 4.2. *The Borel field is generated by the closed intervals.*

Proof. Since $[a, b] = \bigcap_{n=1}^{\infty}(a - \frac{1}{n}, b + \frac{1}{n})$, Proposition 3.5 implies that $[a, b]$ is a Borel set. Hence $\mathsf{C} \subset \mathcal{F}(\mathsf{O}) = \mathcal{B}(\mathbf{R})$ and, by Proposition 3.9(d), $\mathcal{F}(\mathsf{C}) \subset \mathcal{F}(\mathsf{O})$. On the other hand $(a, b) = \bigcup_{n=1}^{\infty}[a + \frac{1}{n}, b - \frac{1}{n}]$ and hence $(a, b) \subset \mathcal{F}(\mathsf{C})$. By Proposition 3.9(d) this implies $\mathcal{F}(\mathsf{O}) \subset \mathcal{F}(\mathsf{C})$. Hence $\mathcal{F}(\mathsf{C}) = \mathcal{F}(\mathsf{O}) = \mathcal{B}(\mathbf{R})$. This completes the proof. $\square$

Example 4.3. Every countable subset $A = (x_n)_{n=1}^{\infty}$ of $\mathbf{R}$ is a Borel set. It suffices to note that every one point subset $\{x\}$ of $\mathbf{R}$ is a closed interval, $\{x\} = [x, x]$, and hence

$$A = \bigcup_{n=1}^{\infty} [x_n, x_n] \in \mathcal{F}(\mathsf{C}) = \mathcal{B}(\mathbf{R}).$$

A counting process can be used to show that the number of Borel subsets of $\mathbf{R}$ is strictly less than the total number of subsets of $\mathbf{R}$. This shows that

---

[1]Emile Borel (1871-1956) was a French mathematician who made important contributions to real analysis, probability theory and game theory. His original ideas influenced many people, including Lebesgue, and form important points of departure for a number of theories that are standard today. His final book, *Les paradoxes de l'infini*, was a gem written when he was 75. He was actively involved in politics, serving as a parliamentary deputy from 1924 to 1936 and as Minister for the Navy from 1925 to 1940.

there exist subsets of **R** which are *not* Borel sets. Sometimes, it is necessary to verify that a given set is Borel.

4.2. Measurable Functions

We follow standard notation from probability theory and use X, Y, Z, etc., to denote measurable functions and random variables. From now on the symbol ω is used to denote a typical point in Ω; this helps remind us where we are.

Inverse images of sets play a role in defining measurable functions. If $f : A \longrightarrow B$ and $C \subset B$, we let

$$f^{-1}(C) = \{x \in A : f(x) \in C\}$$

and call $f^{-1}(C)$ the inverse image[2] of C by f. Thus $f^{-1}(C)$ consists of all points in the domain of f mapped by f into C. The three main properties of inverse images are equations (4.1), (4.2) and (4.12). These are proved below and hold for all sets and all mappings.

Proposition 4.4. *Let $X : \Omega \longrightarrow \mathbf{R}$ denote a real-valued function. The collection of sets $X^{-1}(B)$, where B ranges over the Borel subsets of $\mathbf{R}$, is a σ-field on Ω. We denote this σ-field by $\mathcal{F}_X$ and call it the σ-field generated by X.*

Proof. We verify the three conditions in Definition 3.4.

(a) Since $\mathbf{R}$ is a Borel set, $\Omega = X^{-1}(\mathbf{R}) \in \mathcal{F}_X$, and axiom [a] for a σ-field is satisfied by $\mathcal{F}_X$.

(b) If $A \in \mathcal{F}_X$, then $A = X^{-1}(B)$ for some Borel set B in $\mathbf{R}$. Since $\mathcal{B}(\mathbf{R})$ is a σ-field, B^c is Borel and

$$\omega \in X^{-1}(B)^c \quad \Leftrightarrow \quad \omega \notin X^{-1}(B) \Leftrightarrow X(\omega) \notin B$$
$$\Leftrightarrow \quad X(\omega) \in B^c \Leftrightarrow \omega \in X^{-1}(B^c).$$

Hence

(4.1) $$(X^{-1}(B))^c = X^{-1}(B^c),$$

$A^c = X^{-1}(B^c) \in \mathcal{F}_X$ and $\mathcal{F}_X$ satisfies axiom [b] for a σ-field.

(c) Let $(A_n)_{n=1}^{\infty}$ denote a sequence in $\mathcal{F}_X$. If $A_n = X^{-1}(B_n)$ for all n, then $(B_n)_{n=1}^{\infty}$ is a sequence of Borel sets and, as the Borel sets form a σ-field,

---

[2]Be careful. The notation $f^{-1}(C)$ does not refer, in this situation, to an inverse function for f (which may or may not exist).

$\bigcup_{n=1}^{\infty} B_n$ is also a Borel set. We have

$$\omega \in X^{-1}(\bigcup_{n=1}^{\infty} B_n) \quad \Leftrightarrow \quad X(\omega) \in \bigcup_{n=1}^{\infty} B_n$$

$$\Leftrightarrow \quad X(\omega) \in B_n \text{ for some } n$$

$$\Leftrightarrow \quad \omega \in X^{-1}(B_n) \text{ for some } n$$

$$\Leftrightarrow \quad \omega \in \bigcup_{n=1}^{\infty} X^{-1}(B_n).$$

Hence

$$(4.2) \qquad\qquad X^{-1}(\bigcup_{n=1}^{\infty} B_n) = \bigcup_{n=1}^{\infty} X^{-1}(B_n)$$

and $\bigcup_{n=1}^{\infty} A_n = \bigcup_{n=1}^{\infty} X^{-1}(B_n) \in \mathcal{F}_X$. This shows that axiom [c] for σ-fields is satisfied by $\mathcal{F}_X$ and completes the proof. $\qquad\qquad\qquad\qquad\qquad\qquad\square$

Definition 4.5. *A mapping* $X : \Omega \longrightarrow \mathbf{R}$, *where* $(\Omega, \mathcal{F})$ *is a measurable space, is called* $\mathcal{F}$ *measurable if* $X^{-1}(B) \in \mathcal{F}$ *for every Borel subset* $B \subset \mathbf{R}$.

For simplicity we say X is measurable if $\mathcal{F}$ is understood. The following result is immediate from the definition and Proposition 4.4, but since we use it so frequently, we state it as a proposition. It says that all events connected with X are $\mathcal{F}$ events and, moreover, when the experiment $\mathfrak{E}$ is performed the result will contain complete information about X (see Section 3.5).

Proposition 4.6. *A mapping* $X : \Omega \longrightarrow \mathbf{R}$ *is* $\mathcal{F}$ *measurable if and only if* $\mathcal{F}_X \subset \mathcal{F}$.

Borel sets can be quite complicated, and it may be difficult to apply Definition 4.5 directly; so, before giving any examples, we prove a result which implies that it suffices to consider the inverse image of intervals.

Proposition 4.7. *If the collection* $\mathcal{A}$ *of subsets of* $\mathbf{R}$ *generates the Borel field, then* $X : \Omega \longrightarrow \mathbf{R}$ *is* $\mathcal{F}$ *measurable if and only if* $X^{-1}(A) \in \mathcal{F}$ *for all* $A \in \mathcal{A}$.

Proof. First suppose that X is measurable. Let $X^{-1}(\mathcal{A}) = \{X^{-1}(A) : A \in \mathcal{A}\}$. Since $\mathcal{A} \subset \mathcal{B}(\mathbf{R})$, $X^{-1}(\mathcal{A}) \subset \mathcal{F}_X$. If X is measurable, then $\mathcal{F}_X \subset \mathcal{F}$ and $X^{-1}(\mathcal{A}) \subset \mathcal{F}_X \subset \mathcal{F}$.

Conversely, suppose $X^{-1}(\mathcal{A}) \subset \mathcal{F}$. Let $\mathcal{G} = \{A \subset \mathbf{R} : X^{-1}(A) \in \mathcal{F}\}$. Our hypothesis says that $\mathcal{A} \subset \mathcal{G}$. Since $X^{-1}(\mathbf{R}) = \Omega$ we have $\mathbf{R} \in \mathcal{G}$. If $A \in \mathcal{G}$, then, by (4.1) and since $\mathcal{F}$ is a σ-field, $(X^{-1}(A))^c = X^{-1}(A^c) \in \mathcal{F}$. Hence $A^c \in \mathcal{G}$. If $(A_n)_{n=1}^{\infty} \subset \mathcal{G}$, then, by (4.2), $X^{-1}(\bigcup_{n=1}^{\infty} A_n) = \bigcup_{n=1}^{\infty} X^{-1}(A_n)$. Since $X^{-1}(A_n) \in \mathcal{F}$ for all n and $\mathcal{F}$ is a σ-field, this implies $X^{-1}(\bigcup_{n=1}^{\infty} A_n) \in \mathcal{F}$. Hence $\bigcup_{n=1}^{\infty} A_n \in \mathcal{G}$ and $\mathcal{G}$ is a σ-field. By Proposition 3.9(a) and (b),

$\mathcal{B}(\mathbf{R}) = \mathcal{F}(\mathcal{A}) \subset \mathcal{G}$. This shows that $X^{-1}(A) \in \mathcal{F}$ for all A Borel. Hence X is measurable, and this completes the proof. $\qquad\square$

Example 4.8. Our first example of a measurable function is both simple and useful. The *indicator* [3] function of a set A in Ω, $\mathbf{1}_A$, is defined as follows:

$$\mathbf{1}_A(\omega) = \begin{cases} 1 & \text{if } \omega \in A, \\ 0 & \text{if } \omega \notin A. \end{cases}$$

The value of $\mathbf{1}_A$ at ω indicates whether or not ω belongs to A. When we examine $\mathbf{1}_A^{-1}(B)$ for $B \in \mathbf{R}$ we are considering all points mapped into B, and the only relevant information is whether or not 0 or 1 or both belong to B. For any $B \subset \mathbf{R}$ we have the following possibilities:

$$\mathbf{1}_A^{-1}(B) = \begin{cases} \emptyset & \text{if } \{0,1\} \cap B = \emptyset, \\ A & \text{if } \{0,1\} \cap B = \{1\}, \\ A^c & \text{if } \{0,1\} \cap B = \{0\}, \\ \Omega & \text{if } \{0,1\} \cap B = \{0,1\}. \end{cases}$$

If $\mathcal{F}$ is a σ-field on Ω, then $\emptyset$ and Ω are in $\mathcal{F}$, while $A \in \mathcal{F}$ if and only if $A^c \in \mathcal{F}$. Hence $\mathcal{F}_{\mathbf{1}_A} = \{\emptyset, A, A^c, \Omega\}$ and $\mathbf{1}_A$ is $\mathcal{F}$ measurable if and only if $A \in \mathcal{F}$.

The calculus of indicator functions is closely related to the set theory operations of union and intersection. If A and B are sets, both contained in a larger set Ω and $\omega \in \Omega$, then $(\mathbf{1}_A \cdot \mathbf{1}_B)(\omega) = \mathbf{1}_A(\omega) \cdot \mathbf{1}_B(\omega) = 1$ if $\omega \in A \cap B$ and equals 0 otherwise. Hence

$$(4.3) \qquad\qquad \mathbf{1}_{A \cap B} = \mathbf{1}_A \cdot \mathbf{1}_B.$$

Similarly one sees that

$$(4.4) \qquad\qquad \mathbf{1}_{A \cup B} = \mathbf{1}_A + \mathbf{1}_B - \mathbf{1}_{A \cap B}.$$

If

$$X = \sum_{i=1}^{n} x_i \mathbf{1}_{A_i} \text{ and } Y = \sum_{j=1}^{m} y_j \mathbf{1}_{B_j},$$

then

$$(4.5) \qquad X \cdot Y = \Big(\sum_{i=1}^{n} x_i \mathbf{1}_{A_i}\Big) \cdot \Big(\sum_{j=1}^{m} y_j \mathbf{1}_{B_j}\Big) = \sum_{i,j=1}^{n,m} x_i y_j \mathbf{1}_{A_i \cap B_j};$$

---

[3]The term *characteristic* function is also used for *indicator* function within *mathematics* but not usually by probabilists. In *probability theory* and *statistics* the *characteristic function* φ_X of a random variable X is the function from $\mathbf{R}$ into $\mathbf{C}$ (the complex numbers) defined by $\varphi_X(t) := \mathbb{E}[\exp(itX)]$ for all $t \in \mathbf{R}$, where $i = \sqrt{-1}$. The most efficient modern proof of the *Central Limit Theorem*, Proposition 7.19, uses characteristic functions.

and if $(A_i)_{i=1}^n$ and $(B_j)_{j=1}^m$ are partitions of Ω, then $(A_i \cap B_j)_{i,j=1}^{n,m}$ is also a partition of Ω and

$$(4.6) \qquad X + Y = \sum_{i,j=1}^{n,m} (x_i + y_j) \mathbf{1}_{A_i \cap B_j}.$$

Our next proposition and Example 4.8 can be combined to give further examples of measurable functions. In proving Proposition 4.9 we make essential use of the countability of the rational numbers and the fact that between any two distinct real numbers we can find a rational number.[4]

Proposition 4.9. *If c is a real number and X and Y are $\mathcal{F}$ measurable functions defined on Ω, then $X + Y, X - Y, X \cdot Y$, and cX are $\mathcal{F}$ measurable. If $Y(\omega) \neq 0$ for all $\omega \in \Omega$, then X/Y is also measurable.*

Proof. We prove this result for the sum of two functions. The remaining results follow the same pattern and are left as an exercise for the reader. By Exercise 4.1 and Proposition 4.7 it suffices to show that

$$\{\omega \in \Omega : X(\omega) + Y(\omega) < q\} = (X + Y)^{-1}((-\infty, q)) \in \mathcal{F}$$

for any $q \in \mathbf{Q}$. If $\omega \in \Omega$ and $X(\omega) + Y(\omega) < q$, then $X(\omega) - q < -Y(\omega)$ and we can find a rational number p such that $X(\omega) - q < p < -Y(\omega)$. Hence

$$(4.7) \qquad X(\omega) < q + p \text{ and } Y(\omega) < -p.$$

Conversely, if there exists rational numbers p and q satisfying (4.7), then

$$X(\omega) + Y(\omega) < q + p - p = q.$$

Hence

$$\{\omega \in \Omega : X(\omega) + Y(\omega) < q\} = \bigcup_{p \in \mathbf{Q}} (\{\omega : X(\omega) < q + p\} \cap \{\omega : Y(\omega) < -p\})$$

and, as X and Y are measurable and $\mathbf{Q}$ is countable, the third axiom for a σ-field and Proposition 3.5 imply $\{\omega : X(\omega) + Y(\omega) < q\} \in \mathcal{F}$. Hence $(X + Y)^{-1}((-\infty, q)) \in \mathcal{F}$, and this completes the proof. $\qquad \square$

Example 4.10. Let $\mathcal{F}$ denote the σ-field on $\Omega = \{1, 2, 3, 4, 5, 6\}$ generated by $\{1, 2\}, \{1, 4\}$ and $\{2, 3, 5\}$ and let

$$(4.8) \qquad X = 2\mathbf{1}_{\{1,2\}} + 3\mathbf{1}_{\{1,3,5\}} - 2\mathbf{1}_{\{3,5\}}.$$

---

[4]If a and b are real numbers with $a < b$, then, since $\lim_{n \to \infty} 2^n(b - a) = +\infty$, we can choose a positive integer n_0 such that $2^{n_0}(b-a) > 1$. Hence there exists an integer c such that $2^{n_0}a < c < 2^{n_0}b$. If $p = c/2^{n_0}$, then $p \in \mathbf{Q}$ and $a < p < b$.

Direct calculation gives

$$
\begin{aligned}
X(1) &= \mathbf{2}\mathbf{1}_{\{1,2\}}(1) + \mathbf{3}\mathbf{1}_{\{1,3,5\}}(1) - \mathbf{2}\mathbf{1}_{\{3,5\}}(1) \\
&= 2 + 3 - 0 = 5, \\
X(2) &= \mathbf{2}\mathbf{1}_{\{1,2\}}(2) + \mathbf{3}\mathbf{1}_{\{1,3,5\}}(2) - \mathbf{2}\mathbf{1}_{\{3,5\}}(2) \\
&= 2 + 0 - 0 = 2, \\
X(3) &= 2 \cdot 0 + 3 \cdot 1 - 2 \cdot 1 = 1, \\
X(4) &= 2 \cdot 0 + 3 \cdot 0 - 5 \cdot 0 = 0, \\
X(5) &= 0 + 3 - 2 = 1, \\
X(6) &= 0 + 0 + 0 = 0.
\end{aligned}
$$

Hence $X(1) = 5, X(2) = 2, X(3) = X(5) = 1, X(4) = X(6) = 0$, and we can rewrite X as follows:

$$
(4.9) \qquad\qquad X = \mathbf{5}\mathbf{1}_{\{1\}} + \mathbf{2}\mathbf{1}_{\{2\}} + \mathbf{1}_{\{3,5\}}.
$$

The representation (4.9) has useful features not present in the original (4.8). We can read the values of X from (4.9) and obtain

$$
\begin{aligned}
X^{-1}(\{0\}) &= \{\omega : X(\omega) = 0\} = \{4, 6\}, \\
X^{-1}(\{1\}) &= \{\omega : X(\omega) = 1\} = \{3, 5\}, \\
X^{-1}(\{2\}) &= \{\omega : X(\omega) = 2\} = \{2\}, \\
X^{-1}(\{5\}) &= \{\omega : X(\omega) = 5\} = \{1\}.
\end{aligned}
$$

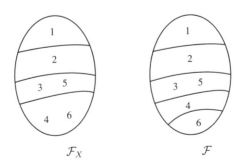

Figure 4.1

We call $X^{-1}(\{c\})$ where c is a real number[5] a *level set* of X. We have found a partition of $\Omega, \mathcal{P}_X$, into level sets of X. By Example 4.3, every finite subset of $\mathbf{R}$ is Borel. Hence the σ-field generated by the partition $\mathcal{P}_X$ is contained in the σ-field generated by $X, \mathcal{F}_X$. If $\mathcal{P}_X$ does not generate $\mathcal{F}_X$, then it is generated by some finer partition of Ω. If, for instance, $\{4\} \in \mathcal{F}_X$, then $\{4\} = X^{-1}(B)$

---

[5]A function is constant on each of its level sets. Conversely, if X is constant on A and not *constant* on any *strictly larger* set, then A is a level set of X. Hence level sets are *maximal* sets where X is constant. Some texts omit maximality in the definition of level sets.

for some Borel set B in $\mathbf{R}$. Hence $X(4) \in B$ and since $X(4) = 0$ this implies that $0 \in B$. Since $X(6) = 0$ we have $6 \in X^{-1}(B)$, and this contradicts the fact that $\{4\} = X^{-1}(B)$. The same analysis shows that $\{3\} \notin \mathcal{F}_X$. Hence the partition $\mathcal{P}_X$ generates $\mathcal{F}_X$ and as $\mathcal{F}_X \subset \mathcal{F}$ (see Figure 4.1) the function X is $\mathcal{F}$ measurable.

Example 4.11. A finite linear combination of indicator functions is called a *simple function*. Any simple function X on Ω can be written in the form

$$(4.10) \qquad\qquad X = \sum_{i=1}^{n} c_i \mathbf{1}_{A_i}$$

where $c_i \in \mathbf{R}$ and $A_i \subset \Omega$ for all i. The previous example suggests that the σ-field $\mathcal{F}_X$ is generated by the level sets of X. To find these level sets we need to rewrite (4.10) in a more suitable form, and as this will involve a partition of Ω there must be an equivalence relationship in the background. The definition of level sets suggests how to proceed. We let $\omega_1 \sim \omega_2$ if $X(\omega_1) = X(\omega_2)$ for points ω_1 and ω_2 in Ω. It is easily seen that $\sim$ is an equivalence relationship on Ω and, by our construction, the equivalence classes are level sets of X. Since the values taken by X are finite sums from the set $(c_i)_{i=1}^{n}$, X has *finite* range. This means we have only a finite number of equivalence classes and a finite partition of Ω into *non-empty* sets and shows that *simple* functions are precisely those functions with *finite range*.

Let $\mathcal{P}_X$ denote the partition $(B_j)_{j=1}^{m}$ of Ω generated by the above equivalence relationship and let $X(\omega) = d_j$ if $\omega \in B_j, j = 1, 2, \ldots, m$. Clearly $d_j \neq d_k$ if $j \neq k$. We now have a new representation of X:

$$(4.11) \qquad\qquad X = \sum_{j=1}^{m} d_j \mathbf{1}_{B_j},$$

and as $B_j = X^{-1}(\{d_j\})$ for all j, this allows us to read off the values taken by X at different points. We refer to (4.11) as the *canonical representation* of X. As in the previous example $\mathcal{P}_X$ generates the σ-field $\mathcal{F}_X$. We have established the following:

The level sets of a real-valued function with finite range partition the domain into a finite number of non-empty sets, and the σ-field generated by this partition coincides with the σ-field generated by the function.

If X is a real-valued function on Ω with representation (4.10), then X is $\mathcal{F}$ measurable *if* $A_i \in \mathcal{F}, 1 \leq i \leq n$. However, using the canonical representation, (4.11), we can make a more precise statement, namely, that X is $\mathcal{F}$ measurable *if and only if* $B_j \in \mathcal{F}, 1 \leq j \leq m$, and hence, if and only if the level sets of X belong to $\mathcal{F}$.

Our main application of simple measurable functions will be given in Chapter 6 when we show that any *measurable function can be approximated by simple measurable functions*. The results in the next example, in which we use indicator functions to modify functions on part of their domains, will be used in Chapter 6 to approximate *unbounded* measurable functions by *bounded* measurable functions. We first introduce some notation.

Definition 4.12. *A real-valued function X on Ω is positive if $X(\omega) \geq 0$ for all $\omega \in \Omega$. It is said to be strictly positive if $X(\omega) > 0$ for all $\omega \in \Omega$. The function X is negative (respectively strictly negative) if $X(\omega) \leq 0$ (respectively $X(\omega) < 0$) for all $\omega \in \Omega$.*

Example 4.13. If X is a real-valued function defined on the set Ω, let $A = \{\omega : X(\omega) \geq 0\}$ and $B = \{\omega : X(\omega) \leq 0\}$. Let $X^+ = X \cdot \mathbf{1}_A$ and $X^- = -X \cdot \mathbf{1}_B$. We have

$$X^+(\omega) = \begin{cases} X(\omega) & \text{if } X(\omega) \geq 0, \\ 0 & \text{if } X(\omega) < 0, \end{cases}$$

$$X^-(\omega) = \begin{cases} -X(\omega) & \text{if } X(\omega) \leq 0, \\ 0 & \text{if } X(\omega) \geq 0, \end{cases}$$

and call X^+ the positive part and X^- the negative part of X. It is easily seen that X^+ and X^- are *both* positive functions, that $X = X^+ - X^-$ and $|X| = X^+ + X^-$.

For example, if $\Omega = \{1, 2, 3, 4, 5, 6\}$, and

$$X = 2\mathbf{1}_{\{1,3,5\}} + 3\mathbf{1}_{\{4\}} - 4\mathbf{1}_{\{2,6\}},$$

then

$$X^+ = 2\mathbf{1}_{\{1,3,5\}} + 3\mathbf{1}_{\{4\}}, X^- = 4\mathbf{1}_{\{2,6\}},$$

and

$$|X| = 2\mathbf{1}_{\{1,3,5\}} + 3\mathbf{1}_{\{4\}} + 4\mathbf{1}_{\{2,6\}}.$$

If $\mathcal{F}$ is a σ-field on Ω and X is measurable, then, since $A = X^{-1}(\{x : x \geq 0\})$ and $B = X^{-1}(\{x : x \leq 0\})$ are in $\mathcal{F}_X$, it follows that X^+, X^-, and $|X|$ are $\mathcal{F}_X$ measurable.

We summarize in our next proposition ideas that are implicit in the last few examples.

Proposition 4.14. *Let $\mathcal{F}$ denote a σ-field on Ω and let X and Y denote real-valued functions on Ω.*

(a) *If $\mathcal{F}$ is generated by a countable partition $(A_n)_{n=1}^{\infty}$, then X is $\mathcal{F}$ measurable if and only if X is constant on each A_n. In particular, each $\mathcal{F}$ measurable function has countable range.*

(b) *If X has countable range, then*

$$X = \sum_{n=1}^{\infty} x_n \mathbf{1}_{B_n}$$

for some sequence of distinct real numbers $(x_n)_{n=1}^{\infty}$ and some pairwise disjoint[6] sequence of subsets $(B_n)_{n=1}^{\infty}$ of Ω. The function X is $\mathcal{F}$ measurable if and only if $B_n \in \mathcal{F}$ for all n. Moreover,

$$X^+ = \sum_{\{n:x_n \geq 0\}} x_n \mathbf{1}_{B_n}, \ X^- = \sum_{\{n:x_n \leq 0\}} -x_n \mathbf{1}_{B_n}, \ |X| = \sum_{n=1}^{\infty} |x_n| \mathbf{1}_{B_n}.$$

(c) *If X has countable range, then Y is $\mathcal{F}_X$ measurable if and only if Y is constant on the level sets of X.*

Proof. Suppose X is $\mathcal{F}$ measurable. For each n choose ω_n in A_n and let $x_n = X(\omega_n)$. Then $X^{-1}(\{x_n\})$ is $\mathcal{F}$ measurable and contains ω_n. Since the set A_n cannot be subdivided into proper $\mathcal{F}$ subsets, $A_n \subset X^{-1}(\{x_n\})$. Hence $X(\omega) = X(\omega_n)$ for all $\omega \in A_n$ and X is constant on each A_n. Since $\mathcal{F}$ is generated by a countable partition of Ω, X has countable range. Conversely, if X is constant on each A_n, then X has countable range and for any $B \subset \mathbf{R}$, $X^{-1}(B) = \bigcup_{n \in M} A_n$ for some $M \subset \mathbf{N}$ and $X^{-1}(B) \in \mathcal{F}$. This proves (a).

Let $(x_n)_{n=1}^{\infty}, x_n \neq x_m$ when $n \neq m$, denote the range[7] of X. If $B_n = X^{-1}(\{x_n\})$, we obtain the representation of X given in (b). The remaining results in (b) follow from (a). We obtain (c) from (a) by letting $\mathcal{F} = \mathcal{F}_X$. This completes the proof. $\square$

The countability hypotheses *cannot be removed* in this proposition, and the result is not true for arbitrary σ-fields.[8]

Example 4.15. If X is a real-valued function on Ω and f is a real-valued function of a real variable, we form the composition[9] $f(X)$; where $f(X)(\omega) =$

---

[6]A sequence of sets $(B_n)_{n=1}^{\infty}$ is pairwise disjoint if $B_n \cap B_m = \emptyset$ for all $n \neq m$.

[7]We consider here the case where X has an infinite countable range. The finite range case is essentially covered in Example 4.11.

[8]If $X(x) = x$ for all $x \in \mathbf{R}$, then X is injective and every level set of X contains just one point. Hence every $Y : \mathbf{R} \longrightarrow \mathbf{R}$ is constant on the level sets of X. Moreover, since $X^{-1}((a,b)) = (a,b)$ for all $(a,b) \subset \mathbf{R}, \mathcal{F}_X = \mathcal{B}(\mathbf{R})$. If Proposition 4.14 extended to arbitrary σ-fields, this would imply that every real-valued function on $\mathbf{R}$ was Borel measurable, and using $\mathbf{1}_A$ and Example 4.8 this would mean that every subset of $\mathbf{R}$ was a Borel set. It is known, as we mentioned previously, that this is not the case.

[9]The notation $f \circ X$ is also used in place of $f(X)$.

$f(X(\omega))$ for all $\omega \in \Omega$. For $B \in \mathbf{R}$ we have

$$
\begin{aligned}
f(X)^{-1}(B) &= \{\omega \in \Omega : f(X)(\omega) \in B\} \\
&= \{\omega \in \Omega : f(X(\omega)) \in B\} \\
&= \{\omega \in \Omega : X(\omega) \in f^{-1}(B)\} \\
&= \{\omega \in \Omega : \omega \in X^{-1}(f^{-1}(B))\}.
\end{aligned}
$$

We have proved the following useful formula;

(4.12) $$(f(X))^{-1}(B) = X^{-1}(f^{-1}(B)).$$

If $f : \mathbf{R} \to \mathbf{R}$ is Borel measurable, that is $f^{-1}(B) \in \mathcal{B}$ for all B Borel, then $X^{-1}(f^{-1}(B)) \in \mathcal{F}_X$ and $\mathcal{F}_{f(X)} \subset \mathcal{F}_X$. If, in addition, X is $\mathcal{F}$ measurable, $\mathcal{F}_X \subset \mathcal{F}$ and $f(X)$ is $\mathcal{F}$ measurable.

We briefly interpret measurable functions vis-a-vis our comments at the end of Chapter 3 that the total observable information available from an experiment is encoded in the σ-field of events $\mathcal{F}$ on the sample space Ω. The real-valued function X on Ω may be regarded as a *carrier* of information in the same way as a satellite relays messages from one source to another. The receiver will hopefully extract from the Borel set B information regarding $X^{-1}(B)$. An important requirement when transmitting information is accuracy. If X is not measurable, then $X^{-1}(B)$ is not an observable event and information transmitted may be false. For this reason we require X to be measurable. If X is measurable, then information transferred will be about events in $\mathcal{F}_X$. Complete information will be transferred if $\mathcal{F}_X = \mathcal{F}$, and at times this may be desirable. On the other hand, $\mathcal{F}$ may be extremely large and we may only be interested in extracting certain information. In such cases, if X secures the required information, we may consider X as a file storing the information about all events in $\mathcal{F}_X$. In the case of a filtration, $(\mathcal{F}_n)_{n=1}^{\infty}$, we obtain a filing system.

4.3. Convergence

Different modes of convergence of random variables will be required in later chapters, e.g. almost sure convergence, convergence in measure, $\mathbf{L}^2$-convergence, etc. One way or another, *every* type of convergence we use depends on *convergent sequences of real numbers*. In Chapter 3 we defined when *increasing* and *decreasing* sequences of real numbers converge. We use these definitions now to define convergence of an arbitrary sequence of real numbers. In Chapters 6, 9 and 11 we augment this discussion while constructing the Lebesgue integral, considering martingale convergence, and developing the Itô integral.

We denote by $lub(\{a_n\}_{n=1}^{\infty})$ and $glb(\{a_n\}_{n=1}^{\infty})$, respectively, the *least upper bound* and the *greatest lower bound* of the set $\{a_n\}_{n=1}^{\infty}$.

Definition 4.16. *A sequence of real numbers $(a_n)_{n=1}^{\infty}$ converges to the real number a if there exists an increasing sequence $(b_n)_{n=1}^{\infty}$ and a decreasing sequence $(c_n)_{n=1}^{\infty}$ such that $a = lub(\{b_n\}_{n=1}^{\infty}) = glb(\{c_n\}_{n=1}^{\infty})$ and*

$$(4.13) \qquad\qquad b_n \le a_n \le c_n$$

for all n.

To show *consistency* between the different definitions, we need to prove that an increasing sequence converges to a by Definition 3.3 if and only if it also converges[10] to a by Definition 4.16. Suppose $(a_n)_{n=1}^{\infty}$ is an increasing sequence that converges to a by Definition 3.3. Let $b_n = a_n$ for all n and let $c_n = a$ for all n. Then $(b_n)_{n=1}^{\infty}$ is an increasing sequence and $(c_n)_{n=1}^{\infty}$ is a decreasing sequence and both converge to a. Since $b_n \le a_n \le c_n$, this shows that $(a_n)_{n=1}^{\infty}$ converges to a by Definition 4.16.

Conversely, suppose $(a_n)_{n=1}^{\infty}$ is an increasing sequence that converges to a by Definition 4.16. In the notation of Definition 4.16 we have $a_n \le c_n \le c_1$ for all n. Hence $\{a_n\}_{n=1}^{\infty}$ is bounded above and converges by Definition 3.3 to $a' \in \mathbf{R}$. By (4.13), $a = lub(\{b_n\}_{n=1}^{\infty}) \le lub(\{a_n\}_{n=1}^{\infty}) = a'$. If $m \ge n$, $a_n \le a_m \le c_m$, and as $(c_n)_{n=1}^{\infty}$ is decreasing, we have

$$a_n \le glb\{c_m\}_{m=n}^{\infty} = glb\{c_m\}_{m=1}^{\infty} = a$$

for all n. Hence $a' = lub\{a_n\}_{n=1}^{\infty} \le a$ and $a' = a = \lim_{n\to\infty} a_n$. A similar argument works for decreasing sequences.

We have defined convergence of sequences using the *order* structure on the real numbers, as increasing and decreasing sequences play such an important role in probability theory. The usual definition, the $\epsilon - \delta$ definition (part (c) of Lemma 4.17), uses the *metric* structure of the real numbers. Routine use of $\epsilon - \delta$, as generations of students will confirm, comes slowly. Both approaches have advantages, and we show they are equivalent.

Lemma 4.17. *The following are equivalent for $(x_n)_{n=1}^{\infty} \subset \mathbf{R}$ and $x \in \mathbf{R}$.*

    (a) $\lim_{n\to\infty} x_n = x$,

    (b) *for every open interval (a,b) containing x there exists a positive integer n_0 such that $x_n \in (a,b)$ for all $n \ge n_0$,*

    (c) *for every $\epsilon > 0$ there exists a positive integer[11] $n(\epsilon)$ such that $|x_n - x| < \epsilon$ whenever $n \ge n(\epsilon)$.*

---

[10]Otherwise there would be ambiguity that could only be resolved by specifying, in each particular case, which of the two definitions we were using.

[11]The notation $n(\epsilon)$ indicates that the integer chosen may, and generally will, depend on ϵ. That is, different choices of ϵ will generally require different choices of integers. If we wrote n in place of $n(\epsilon)$ it could be incorrectly interpreted as saying that the same n could be chosen for all ϵ. Similarly in the proof of Proposition 4.19 we use ϵ_x to indicate that the choice depends on x.

Proof. Suppose (a) holds. Let $(z_n)_{n=1}^{\infty}$ and $(y_n)_{n=1}^{\infty}$ denote, respectively, an increasing and a decreasing sequence, both of which converge to x, such that $z_n \leq x_n \leq y_n$ for all n. If $x \in (a, b)$, then $a < x < b$. Since $x = lub\{z_n\}_{n=1}^{\infty} = glb\{y_n\}_{n=1}^{\infty}$, we can find integers n_1 and m_1 such that $z_{n_1} > a$ and $y_{m_1} < b$. If $n \geq n_0 := n_1 + m_1$, then $a < z_{n_1} \leq z_n \leq x_n \leq y_n \leq y_{m_1} < b$. Hence (a) implies (b).

Suppose (b) holds. If $\epsilon > 0$, then $(x - \epsilon, x + \epsilon)$ is an open interval containing x. By (b) there exists a positive integer n_0 such that $x_n \in (x - \epsilon, x + \epsilon)$ for all $n \geq n_0$. Let $n_\epsilon = n_0$. Since $x_n \in (x - \epsilon, x + \epsilon)$ if and only if $|x - x_n| < \epsilon$, (b) implies (c).

Suppose (c) holds. It follows, on taking $\epsilon = 1$, that all except possibly a finite number of terms in the sequence $(x_n)_{n=1}^{\infty}$ lie in the interval $(x - 1, x + 1)$ and hence the sequence is bounded. Let $M = lub\{x_n\}_{n=1}^{\infty}$ and $m = glb\{x_n\}_{n=1}^{\infty}$. By induction choose an increasing sequence of positive integers $(n_j)_{j=1}^{\infty}$ such that $|x_n - x| < 1/j$ for all $n \geq n_j$. Let $y_n = x + (1/j)$ and $z_n = x - (1/j)$ for $n_j \leq n < n_{j+1}$ and all $j \geq 1$, and let $y_n = M + 2$ and $z_n = m - 2$ for $1 \leq n < n_1$. Then $z_n \leq x_n \leq y_n$ for all n, $(y_n)_{n=1}^{\infty}$ is decreasing to x and $(z_n)_{n=1}^{\infty}$ is increasing to x. Hence $\lim_{n \to \infty} x_n = x$ and (c) implies (a). This completes the proof. □

We next introduce continuous functions.

Definition 4.18. *A function $f : A \subset \mathbf{R} \longrightarrow \mathbf{R}$ is continuous if*

$$\lim_{n \to \infty} f(x_n) = f(\lim_{n \to \infty} x_n)$$

whenever $(x_n)_{n=1}^{\infty}$ converges to a point in A.

Continuous functions are those functions which *commute with limits* or which *preserve convergent sequences*. The following proposition characterizes continuous real-valued functions so that the relationship between continuous and measurable functions becomes transparent. Countability of the rationals plays a key role in the proof.

Proposition 4.19. *A function $f : \mathbf{R} \longrightarrow \mathbf{R}$ is continuous if and only if $f^{-1}((a, b))$ is a countable union of open intervals for every $(a, b) \subset \mathbf{R}$.*

Proof. We show that every continuous function f satisfies the condition in the proposition. As we shall not use the converse, we leave it as an exercise. Let (a, b) be an arbitrary open interval in $\mathbf{R}$ and let $x \in f^{-1}((a, b))$. Then $a < f(x) < b$.

We first prove, by contradiction, that we can find an open interval containing x which belongs to $f^{-1}((a, b))$. Suppose otherwise. Then for every positive integer n, $(x - \frac{1}{n}, x + \frac{1}{n}) \not\subset f^{-1}((a, b))$ and we can choose $x_n \in (x - \frac{1}{n}, x + \frac{1}{n})$ such that $f(x_n) \notin (a, b)$. Since $|x_n - x| < \frac{1}{n}$, Lemma 4.17 implies

$\lim_{n\to\infty} x_n = x$. Since $f(x) \in (a,b)$ and $f(x_n) \notin (a,b)$ for all n, Lemma 4.17 implies $\lim_{n\to\infty} f(x_n) \neq f(x)$. This contradicts the fact that f is continuous. Hence, for every $x \in f^{-1}((a,b))$, there exists a positive number ϵ_x such that $(x - \epsilon_x, x + \epsilon_x) \subset f^{-1}((a,b))$.

For every x choose rational numbers p_x and q_x such that $x - \epsilon_x < p_x < x < q_x < x + \epsilon_x$. Then (p_x, q_x) is an open interval with rational end-points such that $x \in (p_x, q_x) \subset f^{-1}((a,b))$. If we take the union over all $x \in f^{-1}((a,b))$, we obtain

$$f^{-1}((a,b)) = \bigcup_{x \in f^{-1}((a,b))} \{x\} \subset \bigcup_{x \in f^{-1}((a,b))} (p_x, q_x) \subset f^{-1}((a,b))$$

and, by Exercise 3.12,

$$f^{-1}((a,b)) = \bigcup_{x \in f^{-1}((a,b))} (p_x, q_x).$$

Since $\mathbf{Q}^2 = \mathbf{Q} \times \mathbf{Q}$ is countable there are only a countable number of intervals in $\mathbf{R}$ with rational end-points. Hence the number of intervals in the above union is countable and there exist sequences of rationals $(p_n)_{n=1}^{\infty}$ and $(q_n)_{n=1}^{\infty}$ with $p_n < q_n$ for all n such that

$$f^{-1}((a,b)) = \bigcup_{n=1}^{\infty} (p_n, q_n).$$

This completes the proof.   □

Proposition 4.7 and the previous proposition combine to give immediately the following result.

Corollary 4.20. *If $f : \mathbf{R} \longrightarrow \mathbf{R}$ is continuous then f is Borel measurable.*

If $X : \Omega \longrightarrow \mathbf{R}$ is $\mathcal{F}$ measurable and $f : \mathbf{R} \longrightarrow \mathbf{R}$ is continuous, then $f(X)$ is measurable by Example 4.15 and Corollary 4.20. For example, $\exp(X)$ is measurable if X is measurable.

We now introduce our first notion of convergence for a sequence of functions. This definition merely transfers, in a very simple way, a concept involving real numbers to real-valued functions and is no more difficult to deal with than convergence of a sequence of real numbers. Familiarity with this concept is preparation for the more advanced types of convergence we encounter later.

Definition 4.21. *A sequence of real-valued functions $(X_n)_{n=1}^{\infty}$ defined on a set Ω converges pointwise to a real-valued function X if*

$$X_n(\omega) \longrightarrow X(\omega) \ \text{as} \ n \longrightarrow \infty$$

for all $\omega \in \Omega$.

Our first application shows that we do not lose measurability even when taking very weak limits. This result does not extend to continuous functions.[12] The approach used in the following proposition will be developed and used extensively in Chapter 6.

Proposition 4.22. *If the sequence $(X_n)_{n=1}^{\infty}$ of measurable functions on $(\Omega, \mathcal{F})$ converges pointwise to X, then X is measurable.*

Proof. For (a, b) an open interval in $\mathbf{R}$ let $\mathbf{Q}_{(a,b)} := \{\{p, q\} : p, q \in \mathbf{Q}, a < p < q < b\}$; that is $\mathbf{Q}_{(a,b)}$ is the set of all *pairs* of rational numbers which lie in (a, b). The set $\mathbf{Q}_{(a,b)}$ is countable since $\mathbf{Q}^2$ is countable. If $\omega \in \Omega$ and $X(\omega) \in (a, b)$, then $p < X(\omega) < q$ for some $\{p, q\} \in \mathbf{Q}_{(a,b)}$. Since $X_n(\omega) \longrightarrow X(\omega)$ as $n \longrightarrow \infty$ there exists an integer n_0 such that $p < X_n(\omega) < q$ for all $n \geq n_0$. Hence $\omega \in \bigcap_{n \geq n_0} X_n^{-1}((p, q))$ and

$$X^{-1}\big((a, b)\big) \subset \bigcup_{n_0=1}^{\infty} \bigcup_{\{p,q\} \in \mathbf{Q}_{(a,b)}} \Big(\bigcap_{n \geq n_0} X_n^{-1}((p, q)) \Big).$$

Conversely, suppose $\omega \in X_n^{-1}((p, q))$ for some $\{p, q\} \in \mathbf{Q}_{(a,b)}$ and all n greater than some positive integer n_0. Since $X_n(\omega) \longrightarrow X(\omega)$ as $n \longrightarrow \infty$ this implies $p \leq X(\omega) \leq q$ and $X(\omega) \in (a, b)$. This shows that

$$X^{-1}\big((a, b)\big) = \bigcup_{n_0=1}^{\infty} \bigcup_{\{p,q\} \in \mathbf{Q}_{(a,b)}} \Big(\bigcap_{n \geq n_0} X_n^{-1}((p, q)) \Big).$$

Proposition 3.5 implies, since each X_n is measurable, that $\bigcap_{n \geq n_0} X_n^{-1}((a, b)) \in \mathcal{F}$ and, by the third axiom for a σ-field, $X^{-1}((a, b)) \in \mathcal{F}$. By Proposition 4.7, X is measurable. This completes the proof. $\square$

Example 4.23. Let $\mathbf{Q} = (q_n)_{n=1}^{\infty}$. For each positive integer n let $X_n = \mathbf{1}_{\{q_1, q_2, \ldots, q_n\}}$. By Examples 4.3 and 4.8, X_n is measurable. The pointwise limit of the sequence $(X_n)_{n=1}^{\infty}$ is easily seen to be $\mathbf{1}_{\mathbf{Q}}$. By Proposition 4.22 or Example 4.8, $\mathbf{1}_{\mathbf{Q}}$ is measurable. The function $\mathbf{1}_{\mathbf{Q}}$ is an example of an everywhere discontinuous measurable function.

Our final result is similar to Proposition 4.22 but has the advantage of not requiring in advance the existence of a limit. To state this result we need some further pointwise properties of a sequence of real-valued functions.

---

[12]If

$$f_n(x) = \begin{cases} 0 & \text{if } x \leq 0, \\ nx & \text{if } 0 \leq x \leq 1/n, \\ 1 & \text{if } x \geq 1/n, \end{cases}$$

then $(f_n)_{n=1}^{\infty}$ is a sequence of continuous functions that converges pointwise to the non-continuous function f where $f(x) = 0$ if $x \leq 0$ and $f(x) = 1$ when $x > 0$. See Exercise 7.6.

Definition 4.24. Let $(X_n)_{n=1}^\infty$ denote a sequence of real-valued functions defined on the set Ω. Then

    (a) $(X_n)_{n=1}^\infty$ is pointwise bounded if for each $\omega \in \Omega$ there exists a real number M_ω such that $|X_n(\omega)| \le M_\omega$ for all n,

    (b) $(X_n)_{n=1}^\infty$ is increasing if for each $\omega \in \Omega$ the sequence $(X_n(\omega))_{n=1}^\infty$ is an increasing sequence of real numbers.

Proposition 4.25. An increasing pointwise bounded sequence of measurable functions $(X_n)_{n=1}^\infty$ on $(\Omega, \mathcal{F})$ converges pointwise to a measurable function.

Proof. Since $(X_n(\omega))_{n=1}^\infty$ is an increasing bounded sequence of real numbers, the upper bound principle implies that the sequence converges. Hence $(X_n)_{n=1}^\infty$ is a pointwise convergent sequence, and an application of Proposition 4.22 completes the proof. $\qquad\square$

4.4. Exercises

(4.1) Let $\mathcal{A}_1 = \{(-\infty, a) : a \in \mathbf{R}\}$ and $\mathcal{A}_2 = \{(-\infty, q) : q \in \mathbf{Q}\}$. Show that $\mathcal{F}(\mathcal{A}_1) = \mathcal{F}(\mathcal{A}_2) = \mathcal{B}(\mathbf{R})$.

(4.2) If X and Y are real-valued measurable functions on the measurable space $(\Omega, \mathcal{F})$ and $c \in \mathbf{R}$, show that $X \cdot Y, X - Y, cX$ are always measurable, and that X/Y is measurable if $Y(\omega) \neq 0$ for all $\omega \in \Omega$.

(4.3) Give an example of a measurable function X on $(\Omega, \mathcal{F})$ such that X is not $\mathcal{F}_{X^2}$ measurable.

(4.4) Show that a real-valued function X defined on a set Ω satisfies $X = X^2$ if and only if X is an indicator function.

(4.5) Let $\Omega := \{f : \mathbf{R} \mapsto \mathbf{R}\}$. If $f, g \in \Omega$, let $f \sim g$, if $f(q) = g(q)$ for all $q \in \mathbf{Q}$. Show that $\sim$ is an equivalence relationship on Ω. Show that any two different continuous functions are in different equivalence classes. Find an equivalence class which does not contain any continuous function.

(4.6) Let Ω denote an arbitrary set and let $\mathcal{F} = 2^\Omega$. Show that any $X : \Omega \longrightarrow \mathbf{R}$ is $\mathcal{F}$ measurable.

(4.7) Let $\mathcal{F}$ denote a σ-field on Ω generated by a countable partition $(A_n)_{n=1}^\infty$. Find a measurable function X such that $\mathcal{F} = \mathcal{F}_X$.

(4.8) If $\Omega = \mathbf{R}, \mathcal{F} = \mathcal{B}(\mathbf{R})$ and $X = 2\mathbf{1}_{[0,4]} - 3\mathbf{1}_{[2,5]} + 4\mathbf{1}_{[3,6]}$, show that X is Borel measurable and find a finite partition of $\mathbf{R}$ which generates $\mathcal{F}_X$.

(4.9) Let $\Omega = \mathbf{N}$ and let

$$X = 3\mathbf{1}_{\{1,2,3\}} + 4\mathbf{1}_{\{1,4,5,6\}} - 2\mathbf{1}_{\{2,8,10\}}.$$

Write X in the form $X = \sum_{i=1}^n a_i \mathbf{1}_{A_i}$ where $a_i \neq a_j$ and $A_i \cap A_j = \emptyset$ for $i \neq j$. Find $\mathcal{F}_X$.

(4.10) Let $\Omega = \{1, 2, \ldots, 7\}$ and let $\mathcal{F}$ be the σ-field generated by $\{1, 2, 3, 4\}$ and $\{3, 4, 5, 6\}$. Let X be defined on Ω by

$$X(1) = X(2) = 2, X(3) = X(4) = 4, X(5) = X(6) = X(7) = 6$$

and let $Y = (X - 3)^2$. Find $\mathcal{F}_X$ and $\mathcal{F}_Y$. Sketch diagrams illustrating $\mathcal{F}, \mathcal{F}_X$ and $\mathcal{F}_Y$. Is $X, \mathcal{F}$ measurable? Write Y as a finite sum of indicator functions. Is $X, \mathcal{F}_Y$ measurable? Is $Y, \mathcal{F}_X$ measurable?

(4.11) If $\lim_{n \to \infty} x_n = x$, show that any subsequence of $(x_n)_{n=1}^{\infty}$ converges to x.

(4.12) Show that the function $\mathbf{1}_{\mathbf{Q}}$ is nowhere continuous.

(4.13) If $f : \mathbf{R} \mapsto \mathbf{R}$ is differentiable, show that f' is Borel measurable.

(4.14) Let $X(\omega) = \omega$ if $\omega \in \mathbf{Q}$ and equal to zero otherwise. Show that X is Borel measurable. Write X as an infinite sum of indicator functions.

(4.15) Let $(X_n)_{n=0}^{\infty}$ denote a sequence of functions. Show that $X_n \longrightarrow X$ pointwise as $n \longrightarrow \infty$ if and only if $X_n^+ \longrightarrow X^+$ and $X_n^- \longrightarrow X^-$ pointwise as $n \longrightarrow \infty$.

(4.16) If $(X_n)_{n=1}^{\infty}$ is an increasing sequence of measurable functions on the measurable space $(\Omega, \mathcal{F})$, show that $\{\omega \in \Omega : \lim_{n \to \infty} X_n(\omega) < \infty\} \in \mathcal{F}$.

(4.17) Show that a sequence of real numbers converges to x if and only if every subsequence of $(x_n)_{n=1}^{\infty}$ contains a subsequence converging to x.

(4.18) If X is a measurable function on $(\Omega, \mathcal{F})$ and $g : \mathbf{R} \longrightarrow \mathbf{R}$ is a Borel measurable function, show that $g(X)^+ = g^+(X)$ and $g(X)^- = g^-(X)$.

(4.19) Let $X_n(x) = (-1)^n/n$ for all positive integers n and all $x \in \mathbf{R}$. Let $X(x) = 0$ for all $x \in \mathbf{R}$. Show that $X_n \longrightarrow X$ pointwise as $n \longrightarrow \infty$. Let $f = \mathbf{1}_{(-\infty, 0]}$. Show that $f(X_n)(x) \not\to f(X)(x)$ as $n \longrightarrow \infty$ for any $x \in \mathbf{R}$.

(4.20) If X is a measurable function on the measurable space $(\Omega, \mathcal{F})$, find a Borel measurable function $f : \mathbf{R} \longrightarrow \mathbf{R}$ such that $X^+ = f(X)$.

(4.21) If $(a_n)_{n=1}^{\infty}$ and $(b_n)_{n=1}^{\infty}$ are two sequences of real numbers which both converge to the real number d and $(c_n)_{n=1}^{\infty}$ is a sequence of real numbers satisfying $a_n \leq c_n \leq b_n$ for all n, show that $\lim_{n \to \infty} c_n = d$ by (a) using Definition 4.16 and (b) using Lemma 4.17.

(4.22) Show that the exponential function is continuous and differentiable and that $\frac{d}{dx}(\exp(x)) = \exp(x)$.

(4.23) Let $f : (a, b) \subset \mathbf{R} \mapsto \mathbf{R}$ and $a < c < b$. We say $\lim_{x \to c} f(x) = \alpha$ if $\lim_{n \to \infty} f(x_n) = \alpha$ for any sequence $(x_n)_{n=1}^{\infty} \subset (a, b)$ for which $x_n \neq c$ and $\lim_{n \to \infty} x_n = c$. Show $\lim_{x \to c} f(x)$ exists if and only if $\lim_{n \to \infty} f(x_n)$ exists for every sequence $(x_n)_{n=1}^{\infty}$, $x_n \neq c$ for all n, which converges to c. Show that f is continuous at c if and only if $\lim_{x \to c} f(x) = f(c)$.

(4.24) Let $f : (a, b) \subset \mathbf{R} \mapsto \mathbf{R}$ and $a < c < b$. If there exists a real number α such that $\lim_{n \to \infty} f(x_n) = \alpha$ for any sequence $(x_n)_{n=1}^{\infty}, x_n < x$ all

n and $\lim_{n \to \infty} x_n = x$, then we say that f is left continuous at x and let $\lim_{y \to x^-} f(x) := f(x^-) := \alpha$. We define $\lim_{y \to x^+} f(x) = f(x^+)$ in an analogous fashion. Show that f is continuous at x if and only if $f(x^+) = f(x) = f(x^-)$.

(4.25) If $f, g : A \subset \mathbf{R} \mapsto \mathbf{R}$ are continuous, show that $f \pm g, f \cdot g, f^+, f^-$ and $|f|$ are continuous.

Chapter 5

Probability Spaces

As far as the laws of mathematics refer to reality,
they are not certain, and as far as they are
certain, they do not refer to reality.

Albert Einstein

Summary

Probability spaces and random variables are defined using σ-fields and measurable functions. A first model for pricing a call option is constructed and independent random variables are introduced.

5.1. Probability Spaces

In this chapter we assign probabilities to the events in a σ-field and define probability spaces using Kolmogorov's axioms. This conceptual construction, like all mathematical constructions, has no *absolute* physical meaning. This appears, initially, as a restriction, but fundamentally it is a freedom which allows scope for unlimited applications. The same mathematics can often be used to *model* very different phenomena,[1] with intuitive interpretations adapted to the situation under consideration. This could not happen if each mathematical concept was tied to a specific physical event. However, when developing purely mathematical ideas it is useful, and perhaps essential, to be guided by some intuitive physical interpretation. While modelling we operate in a twilight zone

---

[1] In Chapter 10 we will see that the same mathematical model describes the diffusion of gas and the movement of share prices.

between mathematics and reality and *make assumptions* based on our perceptions of both reality and mathematics. If the initial assumptions in a model are accurate and comprehensive, then so are the conclusions.

In Chapter 2 we gave two different interpretations of probabilities. The classical interpretation, although idealistic, does promote an intuitive understanding: if an event A is observed as the result of an experiment $\mathfrak{E}$ and if the experiment could be performed[2] a large number of times, say n times, then we expect, as n tends to infinity, that the *proportion of times* that A occurs will converge to $P(A)$, the probability assigned to the event A. In the second model a bookmaker used weighted averages or expected values to introduce probabilities and create a *fair game*.

The intuitive rules in probability theory were suggested by limits of proportions. Since proportions lie between 0 and 1 we expect $P(\Omega) = 1$ and $0 \leq P(A) \leq 1$ for any event A. If $(A_i)_{i=1}^{k}$ are k mutually exclusive events; that is no two of them can occur, or equivalently $A_i \cap A_j = \emptyset$ for $i \neq j$, and n_i is the number of times A_i occurs in n experiments, then $A_1 \cup \cdots \cup A_k$ occurs $n_1 + \cdots + n_k$ times. In the limit this suggests

(5.1) $$P(\bigcup_{i=1}^{n} A_i) = \sum_{i=1}^{n} P(A_i).$$

In particular, if A occurs m times in n experiments, then A^c, the event that A does not happen, occurs $n - m$ times, and (5.1) applied to the disjoint union $A \cup A^c$ implies

(5.2) $$P(A^c) = 1 - P(A).$$

Kolmogorov's axioms in Definition 5.1 are based on (5.1) and (5.2). Axiom (5.4), which extends (5.1) to infinite sums, introduces limits into the process and allows us to avail of the power of the Lebesgue integral.[3] In many ways this axiom plays the role of an upper bound principle, a remark that is clarified by Proposition 5.3.

---

[2] Scientific successes between 1700 and 1900 gave rise to the philosophy of determinism, which claimed that the future could be predicted from a complete knowledge of the present. However, twentieth century quantum theory showed that the universe is basically probabilistic, especially at the subatomic level, and one can never measure precisely both the position and velocity of a particle. This is the *Heisenberg Uncertainty Principle*, which proved unacceptable to the father of relativity theory, Albert Einstein, who remarked, *God does not play dice*. Quantum theory uses probability theory to show that it is impossible to repeat, even once, exactly the same experiment and thus an interpretation of $P(A)$, based on a large number of identical experiments, is an ideal. While probability theory may have uncovered an inherent instability in the universe, it also appears to explain, by the *Central Limit Theorem*, the apparent stability that is a feature of everyday life. Philosophical debates about the meaning of probabilities do not in any way affect the mathematical theory or the applications.

[3] Developed in Chapter 6.

Definition 5.1. *A probability space is a triple* $(\Omega, \mathcal{F}, P)$ *where* Ω *is a set (the sample space),* $\mathcal{F}$ *is a* σ-*field on* Ω *and* P, *the probability measure, is a mapping from* $\mathcal{F}$ *into* $[0, 1]$ *such that*

$$(5.3) \qquad\qquad P(\Omega) = 1,$$

and if $(A_n)_{n=1}^{\infty}$ *is any sequence of pairwise disjoint events in* $\mathcal{F}$, *then*

$$(5.4) \qquad\qquad P(\bigcup_{n=1}^{\infty} A_n) = \sum_{n=1}^{\infty} P(A_n).$$

We call $P(A)$ the probability that A will occur. The convergent[4] series in (5.4) has all positive[5] terms, and hence we can rearrange the terms in *any order*. Convergence implies that $P(A_n) \to 0$ as $n \longrightarrow \infty$. If $A_n = \emptyset$ for all n, then $(A_n)_{n=1}^{\infty}$ is a pairwise disjoint sequence of measurable sets, and hence $P(\emptyset) = 0$.

If $(A_i)_{i=1}^{n}$ is a finite sequence of pairwise disjoint measurable sets and we let $A_m = \emptyset$ for all $m > n$, then $(A_i)_{i=1}^{\infty}$ is a pairwise disjoint sequence of measurable sets. By (5.4), $P(\bigcup_{i=1}^{\infty} A_i) = \sum_{i=1}^{\infty} P(A_i)$. Since $\bigcup_{i=1}^{\infty} A_i = \bigcup_{i=1}^{n} A_i$ and $\sum_{i=1}^{\infty} P(A_i) = \sum_{i=1}^{n} P(A_i)$, this proves (5.1) and hence (5.2).

If A and B are sets, let $B \backslash A = \{\omega : \omega \in B, \omega \notin A\} = \{\omega : \omega \in B, \omega \in A^c\} = B \cap A^c$. If A and B are measurable, then so also is $A \backslash B$. The Venn diagram in Figure 5.1 gives the following pairwise disjoint decompositions

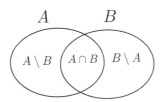

Figure 5.1

---

[4]By definition, an infinite series $\sum_{n=1}^{\infty} a_n$ converges to the real number s if $\lim_{n \to \infty} s_n = s$ where $s_n = \sum_{i=1}^{n} a_i$ is the nth partial sum of the series. If the series converges, then $\lim_{n \to \infty} s_n = \lim_{n \to \infty} s_{n-1} = s$ and hence $a_n = s_n - s_{n-1} \to 0$ as $n \to \infty$. In particular, the only convergent series with $a_n = c$ for all n is the series with all entries equal to zero, that is $c = 0$.

[5]By the upper bound principle a series with *all positive terms* converges if and only if its partial sums are bounded above. This implies that any rearrangement of a convergent series with positive entries is also convergent and all rearrangements converge to the same sum (see Exercise 5.25 and Section 7.1). This is not the case for every convergent series. The series $\sum_{n=1}^{\infty} (-1)^n / n$ converges, but the terms can be rearranged so that the resulting series no longer converges. Since any rearrangement of a sequence of sets $(A_n)_{n=1}^{\infty}$ has the same union, the left-hand side of (5.4) is independent of the order in which the union is taken and the same *must be true* for the right-hand side. This implies that the series in (5.4) can be rearranged in *any* order to give the same sum. *Positivity* guarantees that this happens.

$$A = (A \backslash B) \cup (A \cap B),$$
$$B = (B \backslash A) \cup (A \cap B),$$
$$A \cup B = (A \backslash B) \cup (B \backslash A) \cup (A \cap B).$$

By (5.1), $P(A) = P(A \backslash B) + P(A \cap B)$ and $P(B) = P(B \backslash A) + P(B \cap A)$. Hence

$$P(A \cup B) = P(A \backslash B) + P(B \backslash A) + P(A \cap B) = P(A) + P(B) - P(A \cap B).$$

In particular, $P(A) \leq P(B)$ whenever $A \subset B$.

Example 5.2. Suppose Ω is finite and all outcomes are equally likely, for example if a fair or unbiased die is thrown, then all 6 outcomes are equally likely. If $\Omega = \{\omega_1, \omega_2, \ldots, \omega_n\}$ and $\mathcal{F}$ consists of all subsets of Ω, then

$$P(\{\omega_1\}) = P(\{\omega_2\}) = \cdots = P(\{\omega_n\}).$$

By (5.3), $P(\Omega) = 1$ and, by (5.1), $P(\Omega) = \sum_{i=1}^{n} P(\{\omega_i\}) = nP(\{\omega_i\}) = 1$. Hence $P(\{\omega_i\}) = 1/n$ for all i. If $A \subset \Omega$ has m elements, then

$$P(A) = \sum_{\omega \in A} P(\{\omega\}) = \frac{m}{n} = \frac{\text{number of elements in A}}{\text{number of elements in } \Omega}.$$

A sequence $(A_n)_{n=1}^{\infty}$ of subsets of Ω is said to be *increasing* (respectively *decreasing*) if $A_m \subset A_n$ for all $m < n$ (respectively all $n < m$). Let $A = \bigcup_{n=1}^{\infty} A_n$ (respectively $A = \bigcap_{n=1}^{\infty} A_n$) if $(A_n)_{n=1}^{\infty}$ is increasing (respectively decreasing). In both cases we call $(A_n)_{n=1}^{\infty}$ a *convergent* sequence of sets and write $A = \lim_{n \to \infty} A_n$. Convergent sequences of sets feature later in monotone classes (see Section 7.7).

Proposition 5.3. *If $(\Omega, \mathcal{F}, P)$ is a probability space and $(A_n)_{n=1}^{\infty}$ is a convergent sequence of measurable sets, then*

$$\lim_{n \to \infty} P(A_n) = P(\lim_{n \to \infty} A_n).$$

Proof. Suppose $(A_n)_{n=1}^{\infty}$ is an increasing[6] sequence. Our first step is to generate a pairwise disjoint sequence with the same limit. For convenience let $A_0 = \emptyset$. Let $B_1 = A_1 = A_1 \backslash A_0, B_2 = A_2 \backslash A_1$ and $B_n := A_n \backslash A_{n-1}$ (see Figure 5.2).

The sequence $(B_n)_{n=1}^{\infty}$ consists of pairwise disjoint sets and $\bigcup_{n=1}^{\infty} B_n = \bigcup_{n=1}^{\infty} A_n$. By (5.4)

$$P(\bigcup_{n=1}^{\infty} A_n) = P(\bigcup_{n=1}^{\infty} B_n) = \sum_{n=1}^{\infty} P(B_n).$$

---

[6]If $(A_n)_{n=1}^{\infty}$ is increasing, then $0 \leq P(A_n) \leq P(A_{n+1}) \leq 1$ and $(P(A_n))_{n=1}^{\infty}$ is an increasing bounded sequence. The upper bound principle implies that the sequence converges. Proposition 5.3 gives more information by identifying the limit.

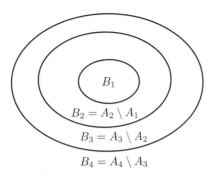

Figure 5.2

Since $A_n = A_{n-1} \cup B_n$ and $A_{n-1} \cap B_n = \emptyset$, $P(A_n) = P(A_{n-1}) + P(B_n)$ for all n, and

$$P(\lim_{n \longrightarrow \infty} A_n) = \sum_{n=1}^{\infty} P(B_n) = \sum_{n=1}^{\infty} (P(A_n) - P(A_{n-1}))$$

$$= \lim_{n \longrightarrow \infty} \sum_{m=1}^{n} (P(A_m) - P(A_{m-1})) = \lim_{n \longrightarrow \infty} P(A_n).$$

This result applied to $(A_n^c)_{n=1}^{\infty}$ and (5.2) prove the result for a decreasing sequence and completes the proof. $\square$

Proposition 5.3 is equivalent to axiom (5.4) when P is *finitely* additive on $\mathcal{F}$. Specifically, if $P(\bigcup_{i=1}^{n} A_i) = \sum_{i=1}^{n} P(A_i)$ for any pairwise disjoint *finite* sequence $(A_i)_{i=1}^{n} \subset \mathcal{F}$, then $P(\lim_{n\to\infty} B_n) = \lim_{n\to\infty} P(B_n)$ for any increasing sequence $(B_n)_{n=1}^{\infty} \subset \mathcal{F}$ if and only if P satisfies (5.4).

Example 5.4. The following probability measure was discovered by the French applied mathematician Poisson[7] in 1837 in order to model the frequency of *rare events* in a large number of trials. Let $\Omega = \{0, 1, 2, \ldots\}$, $\mathcal{F} = 2^{\Omega}$ and α denote a strictly positive number. If $A \subset \Omega$, let $P(A) = \sum_{n \in A} e^{-\alpha} \alpha^n / n!$. Since $\alpha > 0$ and $e^{-\alpha} > 0$, $P(A) \geq 0$. Moreover,

$$P(A) \leq \sum_{n=0}^{\infty} \frac{e^{-\alpha} \alpha^n}{n!} = e^{-\alpha} \sum_{n=0}^{\infty} \frac{\alpha^n}{n!} = e^{-\alpha} e^{\alpha} = 1.$$

---

[7]Siméon Poisson, 1781-1840, made fundamental contributions to almost all areas of applied mathematics under investigation during his lifetime. He had a deep theoretical insight into physical phenomena such as the movement of planets, mechanics, electricity, magnetism, heat, vibrations, etc., and was a very clear expositor. He was also very clumsy, and this affected his career in a number of ways: he had to abandon his first apprenticeship in medicine because of lack of coordination, he could not apply for a position in the civil service because of his inability to draw diagrams and, for the same reason, he could not pursue to any extent his study of geometry. Through the efforts of Laplace, see Chapter 7, he obtained a position in a physics institute and, wisely, did not attempt to verify his theoretical conclusions by experiment.

Hence $0 \leq P(A) \leq 1$ for all $A \subset \Omega$, and $P(\Omega) = 1$. If $(A_j)_{j=1}^{\infty}$ is any sequence of pairwise disjoint subsets of Ω, then

$$\sum_{j=1}^{\infty} P(A_j) = \sum_{j=1}^{\infty} \sum_{n \in A_j} \frac{e^{-\alpha}\alpha^n}{n!} = \sum_{n \in \bigcup_{j=1}^{\infty} A_j} \frac{e^{-\alpha}\alpha^n}{n!} = P(\bigcup_{j=1}^{\infty} A_j).$$

Hence (5.4) is satisfied and P is a probability measure.

This probability measure was forgotten until Bortkiewicz[8] applied it to model, very accurately, the number of soldiers killed by horsekicks in the Prussian cavalry in the late nineteenth century. Today it is one of the most important tools in both theoretical probability theory and applied statistics,[9] where it is used to model such diverse phenomena as radioactive decay, chromosome interchanges in cells, telephone calls, traffic, queues, etc.

We complete this section by returning to a claim we made earlier: *that the σ-field 2^{Ω} of all subsets of Ω may be too large in certain circumstances.* Let $\mathcal{F}$ denote a σ-field of subsets of the closed interval $[0,1]$ and let $2^{[0,1]}$ denote the set of all subsets of $[0,1]$. It can be shown that there is *no* mapping $P : \mathcal{F} \longrightarrow [0,1]$ which satisfies *all* three of the following properties:

1. $\mathcal{F} = 2^{[0,1]}$,
2. $P\left(\bigcup_{n=1}^{\infty} A_n\right) = \sum_{n=1}^{\infty} P(A_n)$ for any pairwise disjoint sequence in $\mathcal{F}$,
3. $P\{[a,b]\} = b - a$ for $[a,b] \subset [0,1]$.

It is necessary to modify at least one of these conditions. Condition 3 is *the* essential property of Lebesgue measure, see Proposition 7.15, while condition 2 is necessary if we are to obtain a probability measure. This means we have to modify condition 1, that is the domain of P. The smallest σ-field on $[0,1]$ that satisfies conditions 2 and 3 is the Borel field on $[0,1]$, and this is adequate for our purposes.[10]

---

[8]Like Cantor, Ladislaus Bortkiewicz, 1868-1931, was born in St. Petersburg and ended his career as a professor in Germany. He was the first to make practical use of Poisson's probability measure. In 1898 he published a paper on the subject, *The Law of Small Numbers*, a title suggested perhaps by the terminology, *The Law of Large Numbers*, introduced earlier by Poisson for another important result. The probabalist William Feller believed this terminology delayed the realization of the fundamental role of Poisson's measure. Bortkiewicz was a professor of statistics and economics and contributed to actuarial science and economics.

[9]As a typical application, consider the following. If the average number of accidents per week in a given location is 3, we use the above with $\alpha = 3$. The model predicts $P(\{0\}) \times 52 = e^{-3} \times 52 = 2.58$ as the expected number of accident-free weeks and $P(\{2\}) \times 52 = e^{-3} \cdot 3^2 \cdot 52/2! = 11.56$ as the expected number of weeks with precisely two accidents.

[10]There is also a largest natural σ-field on $[0,1]$ satisfying (2) and (3): the σ-field of Lebesgue measurable subsets of $[0,1]$. All sets that can be *constructed* by ordinary logic are Lebesgue measurable. Nevertheless, it can be shown by adding the *axiom of choice* to the usual axioms for set theory that there are subsets of $[0,1]$ which are not Lebesgue measurable. See Exercise 5.27.

5.2. Call Options 1

In this section we present the *binomial model*, our first model for pricing *options*. We use the basic ideas on interest rates and fair games from Chapters 1 and 2. An intuitive notion of expected value as a weighted average is sufficient for this model, but to develop it further we need a more mathematically sophisticated definition. This forms the main topic in the next chapter.

A *call option* is an option to buy a certain *asset*, the underlying *security*, on or before a certain date, the *maturity date* or the *exercise date*, for a certain price. If the call option is for a fixed quantity of shares, then the price *per share* at maturity, if the option is taken up or exercised, is called the *strike price* or *exercise price*. An option to *sell* is called a *put option*, and when the option is replaced by an *obligation* to buy or sell, it is called a *forward contract* or a *futures contract*. If the option can only be exercised *at* the maturity date, it is called a *European Option*; while if it can be exercised at *any* time prior to the maturity date, it is called an *American Option*. We only consider European options in this book and use the term option in place of European option from now on.

Options have been around for centuries, but call options were first traded on the stock markets only in 1973 and put options in 1977. Today they are responsible for the largest volume of business on the markets and, moreover, many other financial transactions, e.g. insurance, can be viewed indirectly as a combination of options. Options can be viewed as a means of transferring *risk*, either to *hedge* and reduce exposure to risk or to speculate and, in the process, accept exposure to risk. As our primary objective is to lay the mathematical foundations for pricing options, we do not dwell on their interesting economic and financial background. In Chapters 8 and 10 we develop the binomial model and eventually arrive at the *Black-Scholes formula*. The mathematics involved appears quite complicated initially, and the effort required to master it would not be justified if the applications were confined to those given here. However, this model has been refined and others developed using as a foundation the mathematics presented here. As a result, a thorough examination of the model we consider, simple though it may appear initially, leads us to essential ideas and important mathematical concepts and techniques.

Example 5.5. Suppose interest rates are 12% continuously compounded, and a certain stock's share price is $20 today. If the share price can take only one of the two values $18 or $27 in six months' time and the seller takes no commission, what is the *fair price* per share for a call option with strike price $21 and maturity date six months? Figure 5.3 summarizes the situation.

The situation is similar to that of the punter and bookmaker in Chapter 2. In this case the seller plays the role of bookmaker and the buyer is the punter.

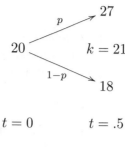

$$t = 0 \qquad\qquad t = .5$$

Figure 5.3

The buyer has a choice. He can buy shares or buy a call option. He assumes the market price for shares is *fair* and that a *fair price* for a call option will be based on the fair share price. If he buys today at \$20, he can sell in six months' time at either \$18 or \$27. To compare these prices in six months' time with the selling price today, we discount back to the present using the given interest rate. The discounted value of a single share will either be \$27 $\times$ $e^{-.12 \times .5}$ or \$18 $\times$ $e^{-.12 \times .5}$. We seek, as the bookmaker did in Chapter 2, the probability p of the stock rising that will make this a *fair game*. The expected discounted return from buying shares directly is

$$27e^{-.06}p + 18e^{-.06}(1 - p).$$

For a fair game, this should equal the initial investment of \$20. Hence

$$27e^{-.06}p + 18e^{-.06}(1 - p) = 20$$

or

$$(27 - 18)p + 18 = 20e^{.06}$$

and

$$p = \frac{20e^{.06} - 18}{9} = .3596.$$

This establishes for the buyer a *standard* to judge the actual price of a call option. If the share price increases, we see, on discounting back to the present, that the buyer of the option will receive \$6$e^{-.06}$. The buyer receives 0 if the share price falls, and the option will not be exercised. The total expected return is

$$p \cdot 6 \cdot e^{-.06} + (1 - p) \cdot 0 \cdot e^{-.06} = 6 \cdot (.3596) \cdot e^{-.06} = 2.032.$$

For a fair price this should equal the initial outlay, the price f of the option. Hence from the buyer's point of view $f = 2.032$ is a fair price.

We now consider the seller's point of view on a fair price. She is taking no commission, expects no profit and is unwilling to take any risk or any loss. Being in a similar position to the bookmaker in Chapter 2, she adopts the same strategy and lays off the bet, in this case by buying a quantity Δ of stock. *Risk* is avoided if her financial situation is independent of the share price at all times. We suppose she starts with zero capital and that the call option is for just one share. Let g denote the price she will charge for the option. To buy Δ shares today she borrows $\$(20\Delta - g)$. If at the end of six months, the share price goes up, she will receive $\$27\Delta$ by selling her shares, pay the difference between the share and strike price $\$(27 - 21) = \$6$ to the buyer, and repay the loan with interest. Her financial position will be

$$27\Delta - 6 - (20\Delta - g)e^{.06}.$$

If, on the other hand, the share price goes down, she will end up with

$$18\Delta - (20\Delta - g)e^{.06}.$$

For a no-risk no-loss situation these must both equal the starting sum of zero. We have two equations:

$$27\Delta - 6 - (20\Delta - g)e^{.06} = 0,$$

$$18\Delta - (20\Delta - g)e^{.06} = 0$$

and two unknowns Δ and g. Subtracting we obtain $9\Delta = 6$; and $\Delta = 2/3$. Moreover

$$\frac{18 \times 2}{3} - (\frac{20 \times 2}{3} - g)e^{.06} = 0$$

and

$$g = \frac{40}{3} - 12e^{-.06} = 2.032.$$

Hence $f = g$, and the buyer and seller agree on a price which both regard as fair. Note that both operated *independently* and yet both arrived at the same fair price. Is it an arbitrage-free price? Suppose the price was raised to $\$2.20$. In this case the seller borrows $\$(\frac{2}{3} \times 20 - 2.20) = \$11.13$ to buy $\frac{2}{3}$ of a share. If the share price goes up in six months, she receives $\$\frac{27 \times 2}{3} = \$18$ by selling the shares. She then pays the buyer $\$6$, pays off the loan of $\$11.13e^{.06}$ and ends up with

$$\frac{2}{3} \times 27 - 6 - 11.13e^{.06} = .18.$$

If the share price goes down, the seller's final position is

$$\frac{2}{3} \times 18 - 11.13e^{.06} = .18.$$

In either case she is guaranteed a profit and runs no risk, and if the call option was for 20,000 shares, this would give a profit of $\$3,600$. Similarly any other price above the fair price leads to *arbitrage*.

If the price is lower than \$2.032, say \$1.80, the buyer[11] borrows 2/3 of a share, sells it for \$13.333, buys a call option for one share and invests the balance of \$11.533 in bonds. If the share price goes up, he receives

$$11.533 e^{.06} + 6 - \frac{2}{3}(27) = .246$$

in six months; and if the share price goes down, he obtains

$$11.533 e^{.06} - \frac{2}{3}(18) = .246.$$

In both cases he makes a profit of \$.246 without running any risk. The same argument shows that any price lower than the above fair price leads to arbitrage, and we conclude that \$2.032 is an arbitrage-free price for a call option on one share.

As a *put option* will be exercised only if the share price is below the strike price at maturity, the expected return, is $p \cdot (0) \cdot e^{-.06} + (1 - p) \cdot (3) \cdot e^{-.06} = 3(.6404) \cdot e^{-.06} = 1.809$. It is easily verified that this is an arbitrage-free price and that the seller can hedge the risk.

Before discussing a more abstract version of the above example, we introduce some terminology. The *payoff* on an option is the amount received when the option is exercised. For example, on a call option the payoff will be the difference between the share price and the strike price if this is positive; otherwise it will be zero. A *claim* is a payment which *may* be demanded at some future time according to a contract. Thus the buyer of a call option is really buying the right to make a *claim*, while the seller is making a *contract*. The seller of the option in the previous example sets up a *portfolio* at time 0 consisting of risky and non-risky *assets* to hedge the claim. The risky assets were the shares and the non-risky assets the borrowings, which from now on we suppose are obtained in the form of *bonds* rather than bank loans. An individual is said to have a *long position* on shares owned and a *short position* on shares not owned but contracted to provide if required. The portfolio is riskless if, at all times, its value is independent of the changes in the price of the risky asset. An *arbitrage opportunity* exists if it is possible to construct a portfolio with value V_t at time t such that $V_0 = 0$, $V_t \geq 0$ for all t and $V_T > 0$ for some $T > 0$.

Proposition 5.6. *Suppose the interest rate is r, the share price of a certain stock is S at time 0 and that at a future time T it will either be Su or Sd*

---

[11]In the real world borrowing a share would lead to charges of some kind, similar to the transaction charges on buying shares, but in our simplified model we are assuming there are no charges. Note that borrowing a share is not the same as borrowing money, as shares cannot be lodged to earn interest. Shares, however, do have uses while in a person's possession, e.g. as security on a loan, and this justifies some charges. When 100 shares are borrowed for 3 months, then, assuming no dividends are paid during that period, 100 shares must be returned. The value of the shares being returned may not be the same as the value of the shares received initially, but 100 shares are still just 100 shares.

where[12] $0 < d < 1 < e^{rT} < u$. The risk neutral probability p that the share price will go up is

$$(5.5) \qquad\qquad p \;=\; \frac{e^{rT} - d}{u - d}.$$

The arbitrage-free price for a call option, C_T, with strike price k, $Sd < k < Su$, and maturity date T is

$$(5.6) \qquad\qquad C_T \;=\; \frac{Su - k}{u - d} \cdot (1 - e^{-rT}d).$$

The seller's portfolio for hedging the call option consists of Δ shares and B bonds where

$$(5.7) \qquad \Delta = \frac{Su - k}{Su - Sd} \quad \text{and} \quad B = -de^{-rT}\left(\frac{Su - k}{u - d}\right).$$

The arbitrage-free price for a put option[13], P_T, with strike price k, $Sd < k < Su$, and maturity date T is

$$(5.8) \qquad P_T = \frac{Sd - k}{u - d}(1 - e^{-rT}u) = \frac{k - Sd}{u - d} \cdot (e^{-rT}u - 1).$$

The call-put parity formula

$$(5.9) \qquad\qquad C_T - P_T \;=\; S - ke^{-rT}$$

gives the relationship between the prices of call and put options and the price of a contract to buy a share at time T at price k.

Proof. If p is the probability that the share price moves up, then the expected return from buying one share is

$$p \cdot Su + (1 - p) \cdot Sd.$$

If p is chosen so that the price is fair to the buyer, then the expected return discounted back to the present, equals S. Hence

$$S = e^{-rT}(p \cdot Su + (1 - p) \cdot Sd) = e^{-rT}S(p \cdot (u - d) + d)$$

---

[12]Note that u and d represent the fraction by which the share price will either move up or down at time T. In normal times it is reasonable to suppose that $d < 1 < u$. We require only $d < u$, but keep $d < 1 < u$ so that we can write about the share price going *up* and *down*. If \$1 is deposited in a bank, then it will amount to \$$e^{rT}$ by time T. If \$1 worth of shares are purchased, then it will either increase to u or decrease to d. Since deposits are riskless while shares are not, we may suppose $u > e^{rT}$.

[13]Consider C_T and P_T as functions of u and d with domain $\{(u,d) : u > 0, d > 0\}$, that is let $C_T = C_T(u,d)$ and $P_T = P_T(u,d)$, and interpret $C_T(u,d)$ as an obligation to buy, if the share price is Su at time T, and $P_T(u,d)$ as an obligation to sell, if the share price is Sd at time T. The obligation to buy if the share price falls, $C_T(d,u)$, will result in a loss equal to the amount received if one has an obligation to sell if the share price rises, $-P_T(u,d)$. Hence $C_T(d,u) = -P_T(u,d)$ and we obtain (5.8) from (5.6).

and

$$p \;=\; \frac{e^{rT} - d}{u - d}.$$

Since $u - d > e^{rT} - d$, we have $0 < \frac{e^{rT}-d}{u-d} < 1$ and p can be *interpreted* as a probability. We call p the *risk neutral probability*, enforced by interest rates, that the share price will go up. This proves (5.5).

Let f_B and f_S denote, respectively, the prices of a call option for one share considered fair by the buyer and seller. The buyer's expected return at time T is

$$(Su - k) \cdot p + 0 \cdot (1 - p),$$

and discounting back to the present this should give the initial investment, that is the buyer's fair price. Hence

$$f_B = e^{-rT} \cdot (Su - k) \cdot p \;=\; e^{-rT} \cdot (Su - k) \cdot \frac{e^{rT} - d}{u - d}$$

$$= \frac{(Su - k)}{u - d} \cdot (1 - e^{-rT}d).$$

Note that f_B was calculated from information available at time 0.

We are assuming that the seller takes no commission and that her main concern is to suffer neither risk nor loss. If the seller has zero capital initially, then we require, regardless of whether the share price goes up or down, that she ends up with zero capital. By assembling a *portfolio* to hedge any claim, she will achieve her aim. She receives f_S initially for the option and borrows $\Delta S - f_S$ to buy Δ shares. The seller's portfolio at time 0 consists of borrowings of $\$(\Delta S - f_S)$ bonds and Δ shares. She has a *long position* on shares and a *short position* on bonds.[14] The *portfolio is riskless* if its value *at all times* is independent of changes in the share price.

If the share price goes up, then the seller's portfolio at time T involves the following considerations:

receives ΔSu from selling Δ shares

pays $Su - k$ to settle the claim

repays borrowings of $e^{rT} \cdot (\Delta S - f_S)$.

If the share price goes down, then the seller's portfolio at time T involves the following considerations:

receives ΔSd from selling Δ shares

repays borrowings of $e^{rT} \cdot (\Delta S - f_S)$.

---

[14]To remember these recall that being *short* of money means, colloquially, that you don't have it. In finance, being short means not only that you don't have it but, in addition, that you owe it.

This implies
$$\Delta Su - (Su - k) - e^{rT} \cdot (\Delta S - f_S) = \Delta Sd - e^{rT} \cdot (\Delta S - f_S) = 0.$$

Hence
$$\Delta Su - (Su - k) = \Delta Sd$$

and

(5.10)
$$\Delta = \frac{Su - k}{S(u - d)}.$$

Since
$$\Delta Sd - e^{rT} \cdot (\Delta S - f_S) = 0$$

we have, by (5.10),

(5.11)
$$\Delta S - f_S = e^{-rT} \Delta Sd = de^{-rT} \cdot \frac{Su - k}{u - d}$$

and

$$
\begin{aligned}
f_S &= \Delta S - e^{-rT} \cdot \Delta Sd \\
&= \Delta S \cdot (1 - e^{-rT} d) \\
&= \frac{Su - k}{u - d} \cdot (1 - e^{-rT} d).
\end{aligned}
$$

We have shown that $f_B = f_S$ and, though motivated by different considerations, both buyer and seller arrive at the same price for the option and both regard the common price as fair. It is now an exercise to show that the price we have found is an arbitrage-free price. This proves (5.6), and by (5.10), we have also proved one half of (5.7). By the above the borrowing at time 0 is $\Delta S - f_S$, and by (5.11), we obtain the required formula for B. This proves (5.7). By (5.5)

$$1 - p = \frac{(u - d) - (e^{rT} - d)}{u - d} = \frac{u - e^{rT}}{u - d}$$

and the buyer's expected discounted return from buying a *put* is

$$e^{-rT}(1 - p)(k - Sd) = e^{-rT}\left(\frac{u - e^{rT}}{u - d}\right)(k - Sd) = \frac{Sd - k}{u - d}(1 - ue^{-rT}).$$

We can show, as above, that the seller arrives at the same price and that this is the arbitrage-free price for a put. This establishes (5.8). Moreover,

$$
\begin{aligned}
C_T - P_T &= \left(\frac{Su - k}{u - d}\right) \cdot (1 - e^{-rT} d) - \left(\frac{Sd - k}{u - d}\right) \cdot (1 - e^{-rT} u) \\
&= \frac{(Su - k) - (Sd - k)}{u - d} - \frac{k}{u - d}(1 - de^{-rT} - 1 + ue^{-rT}) \\
&= \frac{(Su - Sd)}{u - d} - \frac{k(ue^{-rT} - de^{-rT} d)}{u - d} \\
&= S - ke^{-rT}.
\end{aligned}
$$

This proves (5.9). One may also establish (5.9) by financial arguments. Set up a portfolio at $t = 0$, by buying a call option for 1 share, selling a put option for 1 share, and investing ke^{-rT} in bonds. The value of the portfolio at $t = 0$ is $C_T - P_T + ke^{-rT}$. If the share price rises, the portfolio is worth $(Su - k) + ke^{-rT}e^{rT} = Su$; and if the share price goes down, its value is $(Sd - k) + ke^{-rT}e^{rT} = Sd$. In both cases the value of the portfolio at time T coincides with the share price. Since the same is true at all times the portfolio is worth S at time 0. This implies $C_T - P_T + ke^{-rT} = S$ as required.

The expected discounted return on a contract to buy a share at price k at time T is

$$e^{-rT}[p(Su - k) + (1 - p)(Sd - k)] = e^{-rT}[pSu + (1 - p)Sd - k].$$

We have already seen that $e^{-rT}[pSu + (1 - p)Sd] = S$. Hence the value of the contract at $t = 0$ is $S - ke^{-rT}$. Again it is possible to see this directly. The price of a share at time 0 is S. Paying an amount k at time T is equivalent to paying ke^{-rT} at time 0, and hence the balance due at $t = 0$ is $S - ke^{-rT}$. This completes the proof.   □

Example 5.7. In this example we see how options can be used to *hedge* and to *speculate*. Consider a stock with share price $20 today that will either be $35 or $5 in one month's time.[15] Suppose the interest rate[16] is 2%. We consider call and put options with strike price $18. From our earlier results the risk neutral probability of the share price rising is .501, the price of a call option is $8.505 and a put option costs $6.475.

We consider the situation of two investors. In all cases we display prices discounted back to the present. Anne-Marie has 1,000 shares, and if she holds on to them, she will either incur a profit of $14,942 or a loss of $15,008. She is not comfortable with the potentially large loss and decides to buy a *put option* for all her shares to minimize her exposure to loss.

share price in 1 month	keep shares	buy put option
$35	+$14,942	+$8,467
$5	-$15,008	-$8,505

The put option costs $6,475. If the share price increases, she will not exercise her option and her profit will be reduced to $8,467. If the share price

---

[15]This is an unusually large swing in a short period. It may be that some important news is imminent, e.g. a possible merger, the result of a legal investigation or the awarding of a large and lucrative contract.

[16]Since the time frame is very short and the interest rate is low, a good and rapid estimate can be obtained by assuming the interest rate is 0.

decreases, she will exercise her options and sell her shares. Her present worth will then be $\$(18,000e^{-.02/12} - 6,475) = \$11,495$ and she will have lost $\$8,505$. She has thus reduced her exposure to loss at the cost of reducing her potential profit. The above table summarizes her situation.

Brian is an investor who would like to invest $\$1,000$ either in the form of shares or options. If he buys 50 shares, he will either make a profit of $\$747$ or a loss of $\$750$. His $\$1,000$ will buy a *call option* for 117.58 shares. In this case he will lose the full $\$1,000$ if the share price falls and will make a profit of $\$(117.58 \times 17 \times e^{-.02/12} - 1,000) = \$996$ if the share price increases. By buying a call option instead of shares, the potential profits and losses have *both* increased. We summarize the above situation for Brian and include the case if he buys a put option.

share price in 1 month	buy shares	buy call option	buy put option
$35	+$747	+$996	-$1,000
$5	-$750	-$1,000	+$1,004

We summarize the important general principles that arose in the previous proposition and examples.

1. *The buyer uses the market price of the share to determine a fair price for the option.*

2. *The seller considers the price to be fair if it is possible to hedge any claim.*

3. *The analysis shows how to construct a portfolio of shares and bonds to hedge any claim on an option.*

These ideas will be further developed and the assumptions modified later to obtain a more realistic model. To proceed we need further results from probability theory and, in particular, the concept of independence.

5.3. Independence

Events do not occur in isolation, and information about an event A combined with knowledge about the relationship between events A and B may often be used to gain information about B. For example, if we know that A has occurred and that A and B are mutually exclusive, then we know that B has not occurred. Mathematically it is more convenient to start with events that are unrelated, that is *independent* events. For example, if a coin is tossed and a die is thrown, then, clearly, the outcomes do not influence one another and are independent. Independence translates into a relationship between probabilities well known to anyone who has ever bet on a horse. If horse A in race 1 is quoted at odds of 5 to 1 and horse B in race 2 at odds of 4 to 1, then the odds on the double, that both horses win, is 29 to 1. To arrive at this figure we reason as follows. Suppose a \$1 wager is placed on horse A in the first race. If A wins, then the punter wins \$5 and his original stake has increased to \$6. If this is now placed on horse B in the second race and horse B wins, he receives \$30, that is \$29 and the original \$1. Hence the odds on the double are 29 to 1 . Odds of 5 to 1 on A in the first race mean that $P(A$ wins race 1$) = \frac{1}{6}$, odds of 4 to 1 on B in the second race mean that $P(B$ wins race 2$) = \frac{1}{5}$, and odds of 29 to 1 on the double mean that $P(A$ and B both win $) = \frac{1}{30}$. Hence assuming the races are independent:

$$P(A \text{ wins race 1 } and \text{ } B \text{ wins race 2}) = P(A \text{ wins race 1}) \cdot P(B \text{ wins race 2}),$$

$$\frac{1}{30} = \frac{1}{5} \cdot \frac{1}{6}.$$

This motivates our definition of independent events below. Independence depends on the probabilities assigned to the events, and this mathematical definition allows us to establish independence in cases where the probabilities are assigned, as in Chapter 2 and the previous section, in a non-intuitive fashion.

Definition 5.8. *If* $(\Omega, \mathcal{F}, P)$ *is a probability space, then* $A \in \mathcal{F}$ *and* $B \in \mathcal{F}$ *are independent events if*

$$P(A \cap B) = P(A) \cdot P(B).$$

Since $A \cap B = B \cap A$ we see that A is independent of B if and only if B is independent of A.

Example 5.9. In this example we see that independence depends on the probabilities assigned to events. Suppose experiment $\mathfrak{E}$ consists of throwing a die with all outcomes equally likely. Then $\Omega = \{1, 2, 3, 4, 5, 6\}$, $\mathcal{F} = 2^\Omega$ and $P(\{i\}) = 1/6$ for all i. Let $A = \{2, 3\}, B = \{2, 4, 6\}$ and $C = \{2, 4, 5\}$. Then $P(A) = 1/3, P(B) = 1/2$ and $P(C) = 1/2$. Since $A \cap B = \{2\}$ and $B \cap C = \{2, 4\}$, we have $P(A \cap B) = 1/6$ and $P(B \cap C) = 1/3$, and as $P(A \cap B) = 1/6 = P(A) \cdot P(B)$, events A and B are independent. On the other hand, $P(B \cap C) = 1/3 \neq 1/4 = P(B) \cdot P(C)$, and events B and C are not independent.

We keep the *same* measurable space and consider the *same* three sets, A, B, and C, but *change* the probabilities. Let $P_1(\{1\}) = P_1(\{2\}) = 1/12, P_1(\{3\}) = P_1(\{4\}) = 1/6$ and $P_1(\{5\}) = P_1(\{6\}) = 1/4$. Since $P_1(\Omega) = 1$ the triple $(\Omega, \mathcal{F}, P_1)$ is a probability space. Since $P_1(A) = 1/4, P_1(B) = 1/2, P_1(C) =$

$1/2, P_1(A \cap B) = 1/12$ and $P_1(B \cap C) = 1/4$, we have

$$P_1(A \cap B) = 1/12 \neq 1/8 = P_1(A) \cdot P_1(B)$$

and

$$P_1(B \cap C) = 1/4 = P_1(B) \cdot P_1(C).$$

In contrast to the equally likely case, events A and B are not independent, while B and C are independent.

When $P(A) > 0$ we interpret independence by means of conditional probabilities. If $(\Omega, \mathcal{F}, P)$ is a probability space, $A \in \mathcal{F}$ and $P(A) > 0$, let

$$P(B|A) = \frac{P(A \cap B)}{P(A)}$$

for all $B \in \mathcal{F}$.

Proposition 5.10. *If $(\Omega, \mathcal{F}, P)$ is a probability space, $A \in \mathcal{F}$ and $P(A) > 0$, then $(\Omega, \mathcal{F}, P(\cdot|A))$ is a probability space.*

Proof. If $B \in \mathcal{F}$, then $A \cap B \in \mathcal{F}$ and $A \cap B \subset A$. Hence $P(A \cap B) \leq P(A)$, $0 \leq P(B|A) \leq 1$ and $P(\cdot|A)$ maps $\mathcal{F}$ into $[0, 1]$. Since $\Omega \cap A = A, P(\Omega \cap A) = P(A)$ and $P(\Omega|A) = \frac{P(\Omega \cap A)}{P(A)} = 1$.

If $(A_n)_{n=1}^{\infty}$ is a pairwise disjoint sequence in $\mathcal{F}$, then $(A_n \cap A)_{n=1}^{\infty}$ is also a pairwise disjoint sequence of $\mathcal{F}$ measurable sets. Hence

$$
\begin{aligned}
P(\bigcup_{n=1}^{\infty} A_n | A) &= \frac{P((\bigcup_{n=1}^{\infty} A_n) \cap A)}{P(A)} = \frac{P(\bigcup_{n=1}^{\infty}(A_n \cap A))}{P(A)} \\
&= \frac{\sum_{n=1}^{\infty} P(A_n \cap A)}{P(A)} = \sum_{n=1}^{\infty} \frac{P(A_n \cap A)}{P(A)} \\
&= \sum_{n=1}^{\infty} P(A_n | A)
\end{aligned}
$$

and $P(\cdot|A)$ satisfies axioms (5.3) and (5.4). This completes the proof. $\square$

We now interpret $P(B|A)$ intuitively. Suppose an experiment is performed a large number of times, k. Let n denote the number of times that A occurs and let m denote the number of times that both A and B occur. Then $\frac{P(A \cap B)}{P(A)} \approx (\frac{m}{k})/(\frac{n}{k}) = \frac{m}{n}$. Since $\frac{m}{n}$ is also the proportion of times B occurs when we consider only outcomes in which A has already occurred, we may thus consider $P(B|A)$ as the probability that B will occur given that we already know that A has occurred. For this reason $P(B|A)$ is called the *conditional probability* of B given A. Part (a) of the following lemma says that if $P(A) > 0$, then the events A and B are independent *if and only if* the probability that B occurs is unchanged by *information* about A.

Lemma 5.11. *Let* $(\Omega, \mathcal{F}, P)$ *denote a probability space and let* A, B, *and* C *belong to* $\mathcal{F}$.

(a) *If* $P(A) > 0$, *then* A *and* B *are independent if and only if* $P(B|A) = P(B)$.

(b) *If* A *and* B *are independent, then* A *and* B^c *are independent.*

(c) *If* A *and* B *are disjoint and both are independent of* C, *then* $A \cup B$ *is independent of* C.

(d) *If* $P(A) = 0$ *or* 1, *then* A *and* B *are independent.*

Proof. (a) If A and B are independent, then

$$P(B|A) = \frac{P(A \cap B)}{P(A)} = \frac{P(A) \cdot P(B)}{P(A)} = P(B).$$

Conversely, if $P(B|A) = P(B)$, $\frac{P(A \cap B)}{P(A)} = P(B)$ and $P(A \cap B) = P(A) \cdot P(B)$. Hence A and B are independent and this proves (a).

(b) Since $B \cap A$ and $B^c \cap A$ are disjoint, independence implies

$$P(A) = P(B \cap A) + P(B^c \cap A) = P(B) \cdot P(A) + P(B^c \cap A).$$

Hence

$$P(B^c \cap A) = P(A)(1 - P(B)) = P(A) \cdot P(B^c),$$

and A and B^c are independent. This proves (b).

(c) Since A and B are disjoint, $P(A \cup B) = P(A) + P(B)$. Moreover, $A \cap C$ and $B \cap C$ are also disjoint with union $(A \cup B) \cap C$. Hence

$$\begin{aligned} P((A \cup B) \cap C) &= P((A \cap C) \cup (B \cap C)), \\ &= P(A \cap C) + P(B \cap C), \text{ disjoint events}, \\ &= P(A) \cdot P(C) + P(B) \cdot P(C), \text{ independence}, \\ &= (P(A) + P(B))P(C), \\ &= P(A \cup B) \cdot P(C), \text{ disjoint events}. \end{aligned}$$

(d) If $P(A) = 0$, then $A \cap B \subset A$ and $0 \leq P(A \cap B) \leq P(A) = 0$. Hence $P(A \cap B) = P(A) \cdot P(B) = 0$ and A and B are independent events. If $P(A) = 1$, apply this result and (b). This completes the proof.   □

We next introduce a collective form of independence.

Definition 5.12. *Let* $(\Omega, \mathcal{F}, P)$ *denote a probability space and let* $\mathcal{F}_1$ *and* $\mathcal{F}_2$ *denote* σ-*fields on* Ω *with* $\mathcal{F}_1 \subset \mathcal{F}$ *and* $\mathcal{F}_2 \subset \mathcal{F}$. *We say that* $\mathcal{F}_1$ *and* $\mathcal{F}_2$ *are independent* σ-*fields if every* $A \in \mathcal{F}_1$ *is independent of every* $B \in \mathcal{F}_2$. *If* $\mathcal{F}_1$ *and* $\mathcal{F}_2$ *are independent* σ-*fields, we write* $\mathcal{F}_1 \perp \mathcal{F}_2$.

Example 5.13. Let $\Omega = \{1,2,3,4,5,6\}$, $\mathcal{F} = 2^\Omega$, $P(\{1\}) = P(\{4\}) = P(\{5\})$ $= 1/6$, $P(\{2\}) = P(\{3\}) = 1/12$ and $P(\{6\}) = 1/3$. Let $\mathcal{F}_1$ and $\mathcal{F}_2$ denote the σ-fields on Ω generated, respectively, by $(\{1,2\},\{3,5\})$ and $\{2,3,4\}$. The σ-fields are displayed in Figure 5.4 with certain events labelled.

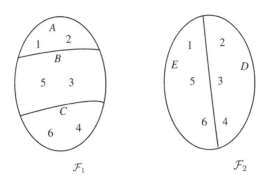

Figure 5.4

We will show that $\mathcal{F}_1$ and $\mathcal{F}_2$ are independent σ-fields. By Lemma 5.11(b) and (d) it suffices to show that any $\mathcal{F}_1$ measurable set with positive measure is independent of D, and by Lemma 5.11(b) and (c), it suffices to show that A and B are independent of D. We first show that A and D are independent. We have $P(A) = P(\{1,2\}) = \frac{1}{6} + \frac{1}{12} = \frac{1}{4}$, $P(D) = P(\{2,3,4\}) = \frac{1}{12} + \frac{1}{12} + \frac{1}{6} = \frac{1}{3}$ and $P(A \cap D) = P(\{2\}) = \frac{1}{12}$. Hence $P(A \cap D) = P(A) \cdot P(D)$ and A and D are independent events. We next see that $P(B) = P(\{3,5\}) = \frac{1}{4}$, $P(B \cap D) = P(\{3\}) = \frac{1}{12}$, and hence $P(B \cap D) = \frac{1}{12} = \frac{1}{4} \cdot \frac{1}{3} = P(B) \cdot P(D)$ and B and D are independent. This shows that the σ-fields $\mathcal{F}_1$ and $\mathcal{F}_2$ are independent.

The ideas used in the previous example can be employed in a straightforward manner to prove the following result.

Proposition 5.14. *Let $(\Omega, \mathcal{F}, P)$ denote a probability space. Let $\mathcal{F}_1$ and $\mathcal{F}_2$ denote σ-fields on Ω with $\mathcal{F}_1 \subset \mathcal{F}$ and $\mathcal{F}_2 \subset \mathcal{F}$. Suppose $\mathcal{F}_1$ is generated by the countable partition $(A_n)_{n=1}^\infty$ and $\mathcal{F}_2$ is generated by the countable partition $(B_n)_{n=1}^\infty$. Then $\mathcal{F}_1 \perp \mathcal{F}_2$ if and only if*

$$P(A_n \cap B_m) = P(A_n) \cdot P(B_m)$$

for all n and m.

The two relationships that we consider between σ-fields, $\mathcal{G} \subset \mathcal{F}$ and $\mathcal{G} \perp \mathcal{F}$, are the extreme cases. When $\mathcal{G} \subset \mathcal{F}$, $\mathcal{F}$ contains complete information about $\mathcal{G}$, while $\mathcal{G} \perp \mathcal{F}$ if and only if $\mathcal{G}$ and $\mathcal{F}$ contain no information about one another. If both $\mathcal{G}$ and $\mathcal{F}$ are generated by countable partitions of the sample space Ω, then

$\mathcal{G} \subset \mathcal{F}$ if and only if every $\mathcal{F}$-set is obtained by combining $\mathcal{G}$-sets, while $\mathcal{G} \perp \mathcal{F}$ roughly says that the partitions cut across one another (see Example 5.13).

Our final task is to show that Definition 5.8 conforms with our intuition. That is, given two events known to be independent in the *real world,* can we place them in the mathematical world so that they are mathematically independent? To even consider this question, both events must, by Definition 5.8, belong to the *same* probability space. Real world independent events, as for instance those connected with tossing a coin and throwing a die, are usually connected with different spaces. We need to construct a new probability space and transfer all information about both events to it. We discuss this in our next example, which contains simple but important ideas that will be further developed in Chapters 7, 9 and 10.

Example 5.15. Consider two unconnected experiments $\mathfrak{E}_1$ and $\mathfrak{E}_2$. For simplicity suppose $\mathfrak{E}_1$ has sample space $\Omega_1 = \{x_1, x_2, x_3\}$ and $\mathfrak{E}_2$ has sample space $\Omega_2 = \{y_1, y_2\}$. We use a tree diagram (Figure 5.5) to display the combined outcomes of both experiments.

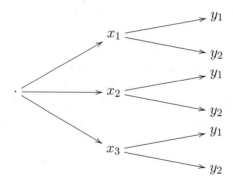

Figure 5.5

Tree diagrams are a good starting point but become crowded rapidly as the number of outcomes increases; e.g. a tree diagram for two experiments, each with 10 outcomes, would contain over 100 lines. Nevertheless, even in such cases, it is helpful to keep such a mental image in mind. A more mathematical representation is obtained by listing the set of all pairs:

$$\{(x_i, y_j) : i = 1, 2, 3, j = 1, 2\}.$$

This is the product space $\Omega := \Omega_1 \times \Omega_2$. We suppose that the probability spaces associated with $\mathfrak{E}_i$ are $(\Omega_i, \mathcal{F}_i, P_i), i = 1, 2$, where $\mathcal{F}_i$ is the set of all subsets of Ω_i. We next establish a relationship between the $\mathcal{F}_1$ measurable subsets of Ω_1 and certain subsets of Ω. If both experiments are performed, then the events

$$\{\mathfrak{E}_1 \text{ resulted in } x_1\}$$

and

$$\{(\mathfrak{E}_1, \mathfrak{E}_2) \text{ resulted in } (x_1, y_1) \text{ or } (x_1, y_2)\}$$

contain *precisely* the same information, and it is natural to identify the subset $\{x_1\}$ of Ω_1 with the subset $\{(x_1, y_1), (x_1, y_2)\}$ of Ω. The same argument suggests that we identify $A \subset \Omega_1$ with $A \times \Omega_2 \subset \Omega$ and $B \subset \Omega_2$ with $\Omega_1 \times B \subset \Omega$. We express this in a more precise way by using the *projections* π_1 and π_2. Let

$$\pi_1 : \Omega \longrightarrow \Omega_1, \pi_1(x_i, y_j) = x_i$$

and

$$\pi_2 : \Omega \longrightarrow \Omega_2, \pi_2(x_i, y_j) = y_j$$

for all $(x_i, y_j) \in \Omega_1 \times \Omega_2 = \Omega$. If $A \subset \Omega_1$, then

$$\begin{aligned} \pi_1^{-1}(A) &= \{(x_i, y_j) \in \Omega : \pi_1(x_i, y_j) = x_i \in A\} \\ &= \{(x_i, y_j) \in \Omega : x_i \in A, y_j \in \Omega_2\} \\ &= A \times \Omega_2; \end{aligned}$$

and similarly if $B \subset \Omega_2$, then

$$\pi_2^{-1}(B) = \Omega_1 \times B.$$

An obvious modification to the proof of Proposition 4.4 shows that $\pi_i^{-1}(\mathcal{F}_i)$ $:= \{\pi_i^{-1}(A) : A \in \mathcal{F}_i\}, i = 1, 2$, are σ-fields on Ω. The sets $\{\pi_1^{-1}(A), \pi_2^{-1}(B)\}$, $A \in \mathcal{F}_1, B \in \mathcal{F}_2$ do not always form[17] a σ-field on Ω, and we let $\mathcal{F}$ denote the σ-field they generate. We display in Figure 5.6 the σ-fields $\pi_1^{-1}(\mathcal{F}_1), \pi_2^{-1}(\mathcal{F}_2)$ and $\mathcal{F}$.

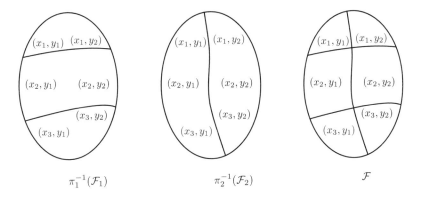

Figure 5.6

---

[17]See Exercise 5.15.

Since $\pi_i^{-1}(\mathcal{F}_i) \subset \mathcal{F}$ for $i = 1, 2$, the events in $\mathcal{F}_1$ and $\mathcal{F}_2$ are now both associated with events in the *same* σ-field $\mathcal{F}$. If $A \subset \Omega_1$ and $B \subset \Omega_2$, then

$$(x_i, y_j) \in \pi_1^{-1}(A) \cap \pi_2^{-1}(B) \quad \Leftrightarrow \quad (x_i, y_j) \in \pi_1^{-1}(A) \text{ and } (x_i, y_j) \in \pi_2^{-1}(B)$$
$$\Leftrightarrow \quad x_i \in A \text{ and } y_j \in B$$
$$\Leftrightarrow \quad (x_i, y_j) \in A \times B.$$

Hence

$$(5.12) \qquad\qquad \pi_1^{-1}(A) \cap \pi_2^{-1}(B) = A \times B$$

for $A \subset \Omega_1$ and $B \subset \Omega_2$, and if $A \in \mathcal{F}_1$ and $B \in \mathcal{F}_2$, then $A \times B \in \mathcal{F}$.

It remains to construct a probability measure P on the measurable space $(\Omega, \mathcal{F})$. This measure must satisfy two conditions. To represent $(\Omega_i, \mathcal{F}_i, P_i)$ faithfully, we require

$$(5.13) \qquad\qquad P(\pi_i^{-1}(A_i)) = P_i(A_i)$$

for $A_i \in \mathcal{F}_i, i = 1, 2$. To obtain independence between $\mathcal{F}_1$ and $\mathcal{F}_2$ events, we need

$$
\begin{aligned}
P(A \times B) &= P(\pi_1^{-1}(A) \cap \pi_2^{-1}(B)) \\
&= P(\pi_1^{-1}(A)) \cdot P(\pi_2^{-1}(B)) \\
(5.14) \qquad\qquad &= P_1(A) \cdot P_2(B)
\end{aligned}
$$

for all $A \in \mathcal{F}_1$ and $B \in \mathcal{F}_2$. By using, in turn, $A = \Omega_1$ and $B = \Omega_2$ in (5.14), we see that (5.13) is a special case of (5.14). In particular

$$P\{(x_i, y_j)\} = P_1(\{x_i\}) P_2(\{y_j\})$$

for $x_i \in \Omega_1$ and $y_j \in \Omega_2$. Let $p_i = P_1(\{x_i\})$ and $q_j = P_2(\{y_j\})$ for all i and j. We use a tree diagram (Figure 5.7) to display this information.

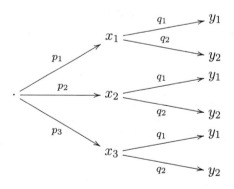

Figure 5.7

Since

$$\Sigma_{i=1}^3 \Sigma_{j=1}^2 p_i q_j = (p_1 + p_2 + p_3)(q_1 + q_2) = 1$$

we obtain the required probability measure by letting $P(C) = \Sigma_{(x_i, y_j) \in C} p_i q_j$ for all $C \subset \mathcal{F}$ (for details see the proof of Proposition 5.16.). This probability measure is easily seen to satisfy (5.14). The σ-field $\mathcal{F}$ (respectively the measure P) is called the product of $\mathcal{F}_1$ and $\mathcal{F}_2$ (respectively P_1 and P_2) and is written $\mathcal{F}_1 \times \mathcal{F}_2$ (respectively $P_1 \times P_2$).

We have achieved our objective and successfully transferred all information regarding experiments $\mathfrak{E}_1$ and $\mathfrak{E}_2$ to one probability space. By (5.14) every event from $\mathfrak{E}_1$ is independent of every event from $\mathfrak{E}_2$.

This example also shows that *more than one* probability space can be used to analyze the same experiment. For example, $(\Omega_1, \mathcal{F}_1, P_1)$ and $(\Omega_1 \times \Omega_2, \mathcal{F}_1 \times \mathcal{F}_2, P_1 \times P_2)$ both fully describe the results of experiment $\mathfrak{E}_1$. The first space is simpler to deal with and would be used if our attention were focused solely on $\mathfrak{E}_1$, but the second allows us to discuss the relationship between events from $\mathfrak{E}_1$ and $\mathfrak{E}_2$.

Our next result generalizes the result in Example 5.15 to σ-fields generated by *countable partitions*. The proof develops abstractly concrete ideas from the previous example, and in this, it is typical of how proofs and results evolve. The next level of generality is considerably more involved and is covered in Section 7.7. We include the full details for the product of two probability spaces. The products of countable and uncountable probability spaces are necessary for the complete development of the stochastic processes required here. We use, but do not prove, the existence of such measures in later chapters.

Proposition 5.16. *Let $(\Omega_i, \mathcal{F}_i, P_i), i = 1, 2$, denote probability spaces where $\mathcal{F}_1$ is generated by the countable partition $(A_n)_{n=1}^\infty$ of Ω_1 and $\mathcal{F}_2$ is generated by the countable partition $(B_m)_{m=1}^\infty$ of Ω_2.*

The σ-field $\mathcal{F}_1 \times \mathcal{F}_2$ on $\Omega_1 \times \Omega_2$ generated by $\{\pi_1^{-1}(\mathcal{F}_1), \pi_2^{-1}(\mathcal{F}_2)\}$ coincides with the σ-field generated by the partition $\mathcal{P} := (A_n \times B_m)_{n,m=1}^\infty$ of $\Omega_1 \times \Omega_2$, and there exists a probability measure $P_1 \times P_2$ on $(\Omega_1 \times \Omega_2, \mathcal{F}_1 \times \mathcal{F}_2)$ such that

$$(5.15) \qquad P_1 \times P_2(A \times B) = P_1(A) \cdot P_2(B)$$

for all $A \in \mathcal{F}_1$ and all $B \in \mathcal{F}_2$.

Proof. Since $\pi_1^{-1}(A_n) \cap \pi_2^{-1}(B_m) = A_n \times B_m$, $\mathcal{P} \subset \mathcal{F}_1 \times \mathcal{F}_2$. Hence $\mathcal{F}(\mathcal{P}) \subset \mathcal{F}_1 \times \mathcal{F}_2$. On the other hand, since $\pi_1^{-1}(A_n) = A_n \times \Omega_2 = \bigcup_{m=1}^\infty A_n \times B_m \in \mathcal{F}(\mathcal{P})$ and $\pi_2^{-1}(B_m) = \Omega_1 \times B_m = \bigcup_{n=1}^\infty A_n \times B_m \in \mathcal{F}(\mathcal{P})$, we have $\mathcal{F}_1 \times \mathcal{F}_2 \subset \mathcal{F}(\mathcal{P})$ and $\mathcal{F}(\mathcal{P}) = \mathcal{F}_1 \times \mathcal{F}_2$.

If C is an $\mathcal{F}_1 \times \mathcal{F}_2$ measurable subset of $\Omega_1 \times \Omega_2$, then $C = \bigcup_{(n,m) \in M} A_n \times B_m$ for some $M \subset \mathbf{N} \times \mathbf{N}$. Let

$$P_1 \times P_2(C) := P(C) = \sum_{(n,m) \in M} P_1(A_n) \cdot P_2(B_m).$$

We have

$$P(\Omega_1 \times \Omega_2) = \sum_{n,m=1}^{\infty} P_1(A_n) \cdot P_2(B_m)$$

$$= \sum_{n=1}^{\infty} P_1(A_n) \cdot \sum_{m=1}^{\infty} P_2(B_m)$$

$$= P_1(\Omega_1) \cdot P_2(\Omega_2) = 1.$$

If $(C_n)_{n=1}^{\infty}$ is a pairwise disjoint sequence of $\mathcal{F}$ measurable sets, then for each n, $C_n = \bigcup_{(j,k)\in M_n} A_j \times B_k$ and the sequence of sets $(M_n)_{n=1}^{\infty}$ is pairwise disjoint. If $M = \bigcup_{n=1}^{\infty} M_n$, then $\bigcup_{n=1}^{\infty} C_n = \bigcup_{(j,k)\in M} A_j \times B_k$ and

$$P(\bigcup_{n=1}^{\infty} C_n) = \sum_{(j,k)\in M} P_1(A_j) \cdot P_2(B_k)$$

$$= \sum_{n=1}^{\infty} \Big\{ \sum_{(j,k)\in M_n} P_1(A_j) \cdot P_2(B_k) \Big\}$$

$$= \sum_{n=1}^{\infty} P(C_n).$$

This proves that $(\Omega_1 \times \Omega_2, \mathcal{F}_1 \times \mathcal{F}_2, P_1 \times P_2)$ is a probability space. Our definition of $P_1 \times P_2$ shows that (5.15) is satisfied. This completes the proof. $\square$

5.4. Random Variables

In this section we bring together probability spaces and measurable functions to define random variables.

Definition 5.17. *If $(\Omega, \mathcal{F}, P)$ is a probability space and $X : \Omega \to \mathbf{R}$ is measurable, we call X a random variable[18] on $(\Omega, \mathcal{F}, P)$.*

Since random variables are nothing more than measurable functions on a space with some additional structure, it follows that the results in this and previous chapters immediately transfer to random variables. For example, the sum of random variables is a random variable (Proposition 4.9), the pointwise limit of a sequence of random variables is a random variable (Proposition 4.22), and the composition of a random variable and a Borel measurable function is again a random variable (Example 4.15).

---

[18]The terminology is standard but somewhat inappropriate, as a random variable is not really a "variable" but a function. It is consistent with the convention, dating back to the seventeenth century, of using the letters at the end of the alphabet for variables and the letters at the beginning for known quantities.

In Proposition 4.4 we saw that a measurable function generates a σ-field on the sample space. Here we go a step further and show that a random variable generates a probability space with sample space $(\mathbf{R}, \mathcal{B}(\mathbf{R}))$. Let $(\Omega, \mathcal{F}, P)$ denote a probability space and let $X : \Omega \to \mathbf{R}$ denote a random variable. For each Borel set $B \subset \mathbf{R}$, $X^{-1}(B) \in \mathcal{F}$, and we define P_X by letting $P_X(B) = P(X^{-1}(B))$. Since $0 \leq P(A) \leq 1$ for all $A \in \mathcal{F}$, we have $0 \leq P_X(B) \leq 1$ for every Borel set B and

$$P_X : \mathcal{B}(\mathbf{R}) \longrightarrow [0, 1].$$

We now verify the axioms in Definition 5.1. Since $X^{-1}(\mathbf{R}) = \Omega$ and $P(\Omega) = 1$, $P_X(\mathbf{R}) = 1$. If $(B_n)_{n=1}^{\infty}$ is a pairwise disjoint sequence of Borel sets, then $(X^{-1}(B_n))_{n=1}^{\infty}$ is a pairwise disjoint sequence of Borel sets. If not, then we can find $n \neq m$ such that $X^{-1}(B_n) \cap X^{-1}(B_m)$ is non-empty. If $\omega \in X^{-1}(B_n) \cap X^{-1}(B_m)$, then $X(\omega) \in B_n$ and $X(\omega) \in B_m$ and B_n and B_m are not disjoint. This contradiction establishes our claim. By (4.2)

$$P_X(\bigcup_{n=1}^{\infty} B_n) = P(X^{-1}(\bigcup_{n=1}^{\infty} B_n)) = P(\bigcup_{n=1}^{\infty} X^{-1}(B_n))$$

$$= \sum_{n=1}^{\infty} P(X^{-1}(B_n)) = \sum_{n=1}^{\infty} P_X(B_n)$$

and $(\mathbf{R}, \mathcal{B}(\mathbf{R}), P_X)$ is a probability space. This space contains all essential[19] information about the random variable X. In our studies we sometimes use P and sometimes P_X; it depends on which is more convenient. We are now in a position to compare, from a probabilistic point of view, random variables on possibly *unrelated* probability spaces. If $X : (\Omega, \mathcal{F}, P) \to \mathbf{R}$ and $Y : (\widetilde{\Omega}, \widetilde{\mathcal{F}}, \widetilde{P}) \to \mathbf{R}$ are random variables, we say that X and Y are *identically distributed* if $P_X = P_Y$.

If X is a random variable on $(\Omega, \mathcal{F}, P)$, let $\widetilde{X} : \mathbf{R} \to \mathbf{R}$ denote the identity mapping; that is $\widetilde{X}(x) = x$ for all $x \in \mathbf{R}$. Since $\widetilde{X}^{-1}(B) = B$ for all Borel sets B, $\widetilde{X}$ is a random variable on the probability space $(\mathbf{R}, \mathcal{B}(\mathbf{R}), P_X)$. Moreover, $P_{\widetilde{X}}(B) = P_X(\widetilde{X}^{-1}(B)) = P_X(B)$ and X and $\widetilde{X}$ are *identically distributed* random variables. For many purposes we may regard X and $\widetilde{X}$ as identical and transfer the study of the random variable X to the study of $\widetilde{X}$.

Certain probability measures occur frequently in practice and as a result occupy a special place in the theory. Random variables associated with the more important measures are often bestowed with special names. This simplifies the presentation and allows us to refer to certain random variables without

---

[19]However, it is not sufficient if we wish to discuss the relationship between two or more random variables. In such cases we require, as suggested by Example 5.14, measures on $\mathbf{R}^n$ where $n > 1$ and even where n is infinite. This is related to our need for special measures, such as Wiener measure, in Chapter 10.

specifying the precise probability space on which they are defined. A random variable X is called Poisson with parameter $\alpha > 0$ or is said to have a Poisson distribution with parameter $\alpha > 0$, if $P_X(\{n\}) = e^{-\alpha}\alpha^n/n!$ for all $n \in \mathbf{N}^*$. Such a statement implies that there is a probability space $(\Omega, \mathcal{F}, P)$ such that $X : \Omega \longrightarrow \mathbf{R}$ is a random variable and $P(\{\omega \in \Omega : X(\omega) = n\}) = e^{-\alpha}\alpha^n/n!$.

We now define independent random variables.

Definition 5.18. *We say that random variables X and Y on the probability space $(\Omega, \mathcal{F}, P)$ are independent if the σ-fields they generate, $\mathcal{F}_X$ and $\mathcal{F}_Y$, are independent. If $\mathcal{G}$ is a σ-field on Ω, then X and $\mathcal{G}$ are independent if the σ-fields $\mathcal{F}_X$ and $\mathcal{G}$ are independent.*

If X and Y are independent random variables on $(\Omega, \mathcal{F}, P)$ and A and B are Borel sets, then $X^{-1}(A)$ and $Y^{-1}(B)$ are independent events. Hence

$$P(X^{-1}(A) \cap Y^{-1}(B)) = P(X^{-1}(A)) \cdot P(Y^{-1}(B)) = P_X(A) \cdot P_Y(B).$$

Proposition 5.19. *The following conditions are equivalent for random variables X and Y on the probability space $(\Omega, \mathcal{F}, P)$;*

(a) *X and Y are independent random variables,*

(b) *$f(X)$ and $g(Y)$ are independent random variables for any pair of Borel measurable functions f and g,*

(c) *$f(X)$ and $g(Y)$ are independent random variables for any pair of bounded Borel measurable functions f and g.*

Proof. If f and g are Borel measurable functions, then, by Example 4.15, $\mathcal{F}_{f(X)} \subset \mathcal{F}_X$ and $\mathcal{F}_{g(Y)} \subset \mathcal{F}_Y$. Hence $\mathcal{F}_X \perp \mathcal{F}_Y$ implies $\mathcal{F}_{f(X)} \perp \mathcal{F}_{g(Y)}$ and $f(X)$ and $g(Y)$ are independent. This shows that (a) implies (b), and (b) implies (c) trivially.

Suppose (c) holds. We are required to show that $A \in \mathcal{F}_X$ and $B \in \mathcal{F}_Y$, chosen arbitrarily, are independent. By the definition of $\mathcal{F}_X$ and $\mathcal{F}_Y$ there exist Borel subsets of $\mathbf{R}$, A_1 and B_1, such that $A = X^{-1}(A_1)$ and $B = Y^{-1}(B_1)$. Let $f = \mathbf{1}_{A_1}$ and $g = \mathbf{1}_{B_1}$. Since f and g are indicator functions,[20] they are bounded. If $\omega \in \Omega$, then

$$f(X)(\omega) = f(X(\omega)) = \begin{cases} 1 & \text{if } X(\omega) \in A_1 \\ 0 & \text{if } X(\omega) \notin A_1 \end{cases} = \begin{cases} 1 & \text{if } \omega \in X^{-1}(A_1) \\ 0 & \text{if } \omega \notin X^{-1}(A_1) \end{cases}$$

$$= \mathbf{1}_{X^{-1}(A_1)}(\omega) = \mathbf{1}_A(\omega).$$

Hence $f(X) = \mathbf{1}_A$ and $A = f(X)^{-1}(\{1\}) \in \mathcal{F}_{f(X)}$. Similarly $g(Y) = \mathbf{1}_B$ and $B = g(Y)^{-1}(\{1\}) \in \mathcal{F}_{g(Y)}$. Since $f(X)$ and $g(Y)$ are independent random

---

[20]The construction which shows that $\mathbf{1}_A$, $A \in \mathcal{F}_X$, can be presented as a function of X is very useful and will be used again.

variables, A and B are independent events. This shows that (c) implies (a) and completes the proof. $\square$

5.5. Stochastic Processes

A random variable models the outcome of a single experiment. To study collections of random variables we introduce stochastic processes, that is processes which develop with time in a random fashion.

Definition 5.20. *A stochastic process X is a collection of random variables $(X_t)_{t \in T}$ on a probability space $(\Omega, \mathcal{F}, P)$, indexed by a subset T of the real numbers.*

If the indexing set is countable, for instance the positive integers, we call X a *discrete stochastic process* and generally write $(X_n)_{n=1}^{\infty}$ in such cases. The indexing set T may also be an interval in $\mathbf{R}, [a, b]$ or $[0, \infty)$. In both cases it is useful to consider the indexing set as *time*.

A stochastic process involves *two* variables, $t \in T$ and $\omega \in \Omega$. For each *fixed* t the mapping

$$\omega \in \Omega \longmapsto X_t(\omega) \in \mathbf{R}$$

is a random variable, and for each *fixed* ω the mapping

$$t \in T \longmapsto X_t(\omega) \in \mathbf{R}$$

is *one realization* or *sample* of the process over the full period of time. It is called a *sample path* or just a *path* and is not a random variable.

Definition 5.21. *If $X = (X_t)_{t \in T}$ is a stochastic process on $(\Omega, \mathcal{F}, P)$ and $(\mathcal{F}_t)_{t \in T}$ is a filtration on $(\Omega, \mathcal{F}, P)$, then X is adapted to the filtration if X_t is $\mathcal{F}_t$ measurable for all $t \in T$.*

A stochastic process $(X_t)_{t \in T}$ on $(\Omega, \mathcal{F}, P)$ has a natural filtration associated with it. We let $\mathcal{F}_t$ denote the σ-field generated by $(X_s)_{s \leq t}$ for all $t \in T$. Then $(\mathcal{F}_t)_{t \in T}$ is a filtration on $(\Omega, \mathcal{F}, P)$ and $(X_t)_{t \in T}$ is adapted to $(\mathcal{F}_t)_{t \in T}$.

A typical example, of interest to us, is the following: let X_0 denote the share price of a certain stock at flotation and let X_t denote the share price at time t. Then $\mathcal{F}_t$ is the *history* of the share price up to time t and $(X_t)_{t \geq 0}$ is adapted to the filtration $(\mathcal{F}_t)_{t \geq 0}$. At this stage we can ask questions such as: what is the probability that $[X_{15} \geq 100]$? Answers such as $1/4$ or $2/3$ are now meaningful. However, to make such statements precise we need a probability space $(\Omega, \mathcal{F}, P)$ on which each X_t is a random variable. Before considering such situations mathematically we discuss expected values.

5.6. Exercises

(5.1) If $(A_n)_{n=1}^{\infty}$ is a decreasing sequence of subsets of Ω and each A_n is $\mathcal{F}$ measurable where $(\Omega, \mathcal{F}, P)$ is a probability space, show that $\lim_{n \to \infty} P(A_n) = P(A)$, where $A = \bigcap_{n=1}^{\infty} A_n$.

(5.2) If $(\Omega, \mathcal{F}, P)$ is a probability space and $(A_n)_{n=1}^{\infty}$ is a sequence of measurable sets, show that $P(\bigcup_{n=1}^{\infty} A_n) \leq \sum_{n=1}^{\infty} P(A_n)$. Show, by example, that we may have strict inequality.

(5.3) Let $(\Omega, \mathcal{F}, P)$ denote a probability space and suppose $\{\omega\} \in \mathcal{F}$ for all $\omega \in \Omega$. If $A_n = \{\omega \in \Omega : P(\{\omega\}) \geq 1/n\}$, show that A_n contains at most n elements. Hence show that the set $A = \{\omega \in \Omega : P(\{\omega\}) > 0\}$ is countable.

(5.4) Let $\Omega = \{1, 2, 3, 4, 5, 6\}$ and let $\mathcal{F}$ denote the σ-field generated by $\{2, 3, 4\}$ and $\{4, 5, 6\}$. If $P(\{1\}) = \frac{1}{6}, P(\{2, 3\}) = \frac{1}{4}$ and $P(\{4\}) = P(\{5, 6\})$, find $P(\{4\})$. Let $X = \mathbf{1}_{\{2\}} - \mathbf{1}_{\{3,4\}} + 3\mathbf{1}_{\{5,6\}}$. Is X $\mathcal{F}$ measurable? Is X^2 $\mathcal{F}$ measurable? Find $P[X^4 \leq 2]$.

(5.5) Let $\mathcal{R}$ denote the set of random variables on $(\Omega, \mathcal{F}, P)$. If $X, Y \in \mathcal{R}$, let $X \sim Y$ if $P(\{\omega \in \Omega : X(\omega) = Y(\omega)\}) = 1$. Show that $\sim$ is an equivalence relationship on $\mathcal{R}$. If $X_n \sim Y_n$ for all n and $X \in \mathcal{R}$, show that $P(\{\omega \in \Omega : X_n(\omega) \longrightarrow X(\omega)\}) = P(\{\omega \in \Omega : Y_n(\omega) \longrightarrow X(\omega)\})$.

(5.6) If $(\Omega, \mathcal{F}, P)$ is a probability space and $\mathcal{G} = \{A \in \mathcal{F} : P(A) = 0 \text{ or } 1\}$, show that $\mathcal{G}$ is a σ-field.

(5.7) If $\Omega = \mathbf{N}^*$, the non-negative integers, $\mathcal{F} = 2^{\mathbf{N}^*}$, and $P(\{n\}) = \frac{e^{(.2)n}(.2)^n}{n!}$ for all n, find $P([.5, 3.5])$.

(5.8) If $(\Omega, \mathcal{F})$ is a measurable space and $P : \mathcal{F} \mapsto [0, 1]$ satisfies $P(\Omega) = 1, P(A^c) = 1 - P(A)$, for $A \in \mathcal{F}$ and $P(\bigcup_{j=1}^{n} A_j) = \sum_{j=1}^{n} P(A_j)$ for any *finite* pairwise disjoint sequence in $\mathcal{F}$, show that the following are equivalent: (a) P is a probability measure; (b) if $(A_n)_{n=1}^{\infty}$ is a convergent sequence in $\mathcal{F}$, then $\lim_{n \to \infty} P(A_n) = P(\lim_{n \to \infty} A_n)$; (c) if $(A_n)_{n=1}^{\infty}$ is a decreasing sequence of sets in $\mathcal{F}$ and $\lim_{n \to \infty} A_n = \emptyset$, then $\lim_{n \to \infty} P(A_n) = 0$; (d) if $(A_n)_{n=1}^{\infty}$ is a decreasing sequence of sets in $\mathcal{F}$ and there exist $\epsilon > 0$ such that $P(A_n) \geq \epsilon$ for all n, then $\bigcap_{n=1}^{\infty} A_n \neq \emptyset$.

(5.9) Let X denote a random variable on $(\Omega, \mathcal{F}, P)$ and let λ and α be strictly positive numbers. If $P[\omega : X(\omega) \leq c] = \int_0^c \alpha \exp(-\lambda x) dx$ for all positive c, find the relationship between α and λ.

(5.10) Let $(\Omega, \mathcal{F}, P)$ denote a probability space and let $A, B \in \mathcal{F}$. Show that A and B are independent events if and only if $\mathbf{1}_A$ and $\mathbf{1}_B$ are independent random variables.

(5.11) Let $\Omega = \{1, 2, 3, 4, 5, 6\}, \mathcal{F} = 2^\Omega$ and let P denote a probability measure on $(\Omega, \mathcal{F})$ with $P(\{1\}) = P(\{2\}) = 1/12$, $P(\{3\}) = P(\{4\}) = 1/4$. Find $P(\{5\})$ and $P(\{6\})$ if the events $\{1, 3, 4\}$ and $\{1, 2, 3, 5\}$ are independent.

(5.12) Let $\Omega = \{1, 2, 3, 4, 5, 6\}, \mathcal{F} = 2^\Omega$ and suppose P is a probability measure on $(\Omega, \mathcal{F})$ with $P(\{i\}) = i/12$ for $i = 1, 2, 3, 4$. If the events $\{1, 2, 5\}$ and $\{2, 3, 6\}$ are independent, find $P(\{5\})$ and $P(\{6\})$.

(5.13) Let X and Y be independent random variables on the probability space $(\Omega = \{1, 2, \ldots, n\}, 2^\Omega, P)$. If $P[X = i] = P[Y = i] = 1/n$ for all i, show that $P[\max(X, Y) = i] = (2i - 1)/n^2$ for all i.

(5.14) Let X and Y denote independent random variables on $(\Omega, \mathcal{F}, P)$. If $P[X = n] = P[Y = n] = q^{n-1}p$ for all n, where $0 < p < 1$ and $p + q = 1$, find $P[X = Y]$ and $P[X \geq Y]$.

(5.15) Let $(\Omega_i, \mathcal{F}_i), i = 1, 2$, denote measurable spaces. Show that $C \subset \Omega_1 \times \Omega_2$ equals $\pi_1^{-1}(A)$ for some subset A of Ω_1 if and only if C has the following property: if $(x, y) \in C$, then $(x, z) \in C$ for all $z \in \Omega_2$. Show that the collection of sets $\pi_1^{-1}(\mathcal{F}_1)$ and $\pi_2^{-1}(\mathcal{F}_2)$ is a σ-field if and only if $\mathcal{F}_i = \mathcal{F}_\emptyset$ for at least one i.

(5.16) Let $\Omega = \{1, 2, \ldots, 6\}, X = 4 \cdot \mathbf{1}_{\{1,3\}} + 2 \cdot \mathbf{1}_{\{2,4,6\}}$ and $Y = 3 \cdot \mathbf{1}_{\{3,5\}} - 3 \cdot \mathbf{1}_{\{2,6\}}$. Express in canonical form X^2 and XY. Display the σ-fields generated by $(X - 3)^+$ and $(Y - 2)^+$. If $\mathcal{F} = 2^\Omega, P(\{1\}) = P(\{2\}) = 1/6$, $P(\{3\}) = P(\{4\}), P(\{5\}) = P(\{6\})$, and $(X - 3)^+$ and $(Y - 2)^+$ are independent, find $P(\{3\})$ and $P(\{6\})$.

(5.17) Let $\Omega = \{1, 2, 3, 4, 5, 6\}, \mathcal{F} = 2^\Omega$ and $P(\{1\}) = P(\{2\}) = P(\{3\}) > 0$, $P(\{4\}) = P(\{5\})$ and $P(\{6\}) = 1/12$. If $X = \mathbf{1}_{\{1,2\}} - \mathbf{1}_{\{3,4\}}$ and $Y = 2 \cdot \mathbf{1}_{\{1,3,5\}} + 3 \cdot \mathbf{1}_{\{2,4,6\}}$ are independent random variables, find $P(\{1\})$ and $P(\{4\})$.

(5.18) Suppose a share price at time $t = 0$ is 8 and that it is known that the share price will be 12 or 6 in one year's time. If the interest rate is 8%, find the cost per share of a call option with strike price 9 in one year's time, assuming no commission is charged. What is the change in price of the option if (a) the interest rate is raised by 2%, (b) the strike price is raised to 10, (c) both (a) and (b) apply? Find (d) the price of a put option, (e) a contract to buy and (f) a contract to sell at the original strike price. Construct hedging portfolios for all of the above.

(5.19) Verify the call-put parity for the data given in Example 5.5.

(5.20) A share is priced $15 today and will go to $20 or $12 in six months' time. If the interest rate is 10%, no commission is charged, and the price of a call option maturing in six months is $1.788, find the strike price. Find the price of a put option under the same conditions.

(5.21) Explain why it is reasonable to suppose $e^{rT} < u$ in Proposition 5.6.

(5.22) Show that the prices for a call option and a put option in Proposition 5.6 are arbitrage-free prices and construct a portfolio of shares and bonds to hedge a put option.

(5.23) A share with price \$15 today will move to \$6 or \$20 in two months' time. An investor who has \$7,500 in shares wishes to sell some of his shares and buy a put option to hedge the remaining shares. If the interest rate is 4%, the strike price is \$11, and no commission is charged, how many shares should he sell? If the share price goes down, how much will he lose if he follows this strategy? How much will he lose if he holds on to all his shares and the price goes down?

(5.24) If the interest rate is r and a stock has share price S today, show that the price C_T of a call option at time T with strike price k satisfies $S - ke^{-rT} \leq C_T$. If it is known that the share price will either be Su or Sd at time T where $d < 1 < e^{rT} < u$ and $Sd < k < Su$, show that $C_T \leq (Su - k)e^{-rT}$.

(5.25) Show that any rearrangement of a convergent series $\sum_{n=1}^{\infty} a_n$ with positive entries is also convergent and all rearrangements converge to the same sum.

(5.26) If $(a_n)_{n=1}^{\infty}$ is a decreasing sequence of positive real numbers, show that $\sum_{n=1}^{\infty} a_n$ converges, if and only if, $\sum_{n=1}^{\infty} 2^n a_{2^n}$ converges. Hence show that $\sum_{n=1}^{\infty} n^{-p}$ converges if and only if $p > 1$.

(5.27) Let $(\Omega, \mathcal{F}, P)$ denote a probability space. Let $\mathcal{G} = \{(A \backslash B) \cup C : B \subset B_1, C \subset C_1$ where $A, B_1, C_1 \in \mathcal{F}, P(B_1) = P(C_1) = 0\}$ and let $Q((A \backslash B) \cup C) = P(A)$. Show that $(\Omega, \mathcal{G}, Q)$ is a probability space.

Chapter 6

Expected Values

The expectations of life depend on diligence; the mechanic that would perfect his work must first sharpen his tools.

Confucius

Summary

To study expected values we develop the Lebesgue integral[1] with respect to a probability measure. This is defined successively for four collections of functions: simple random variables, positive bounded random variables, positive random variables and arbitrary random variables. At each stage a new technique is introduced, results from the previous collection refined and the scope of the integral extended. We prove the *Monotone Convergence Theorem* and the *Dominated Convergence Theorem*.

6.1. Simple Random Variables

Expected values, lengths and areas are measurements which share a common mathematical background. We sketch rapidly the development of length and, by analogy, motivate the definition of expected value. This provides a brief guide to the directions we follow in successive sections of this chapter.

To measure *length* we begin by defining some straight object to have *unit* length. This is our chosen standard, and all subsequent measurements are

---

[1]Also known as the *Abstract Lebesgue Integral.*

105

expressed as multiples of this unit. On identifying the object of unit length with the interval $[0,1] \subset \mathbf{R}$, we can measure the length of any finite straight line by placing it on an interval $[a,b]$, in which case it will have length $b - a$. Next we measure the length of objects, such as perimeters of triangles and rectangles, which can be *partitioned* into a *finite* number of straight lines of finite length. Each line is measured and the total length obtained by adding these measurements together. At this stage basic properties begin to emerge, but the length of more interesting objects, such as circles, cannot yet be calculated. To cover such examples we *approximate* using a finite number of straight lines and take limits. For instance, to measure the length of the perimeter of a circle with radius 1 we draw a polygon with n sides (see Figure 6.1), and on letting n tend to infinity[2] we obtain 2π.

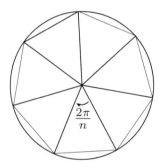

Figure 6.1

Many interesting mathematical questions need to be addressed and solved in this final stage, for example: how to approximate, what type of limits are allowed, whether different approximations lead to the same limit, and which objects have an unambiguously defined length. Before discussing these questions for expected values, we look at the historical development[3] of the Lebesgue integral.

During the final decade of the 19th century mathematicians in Paris began investigating which sets in Euclidean space, $\mathbf{R}^n$, were capable of being measured, that is whether or not they had length, area, volume, etc. Emile Borel made the fundamental observation that all figures used in science, at that time, could be obtained from simple figures such as line segments, squares and cubes by forming countable unions and taking complements. This led to his introducing σ-fields in 1898. To measure subsets of $\mathbf{R}^n$ that could be obtained in this way, he proposed rules similar to (5.2) and (5.4) from the previous chapter and the use *alternatively* of countable disjoint unions and complements. In this way

---

[2]Viète used a polygon with 39,216 sides to calculate π to 10 decimal places in 1593.

[3]For a discussion of the period up to the middle of the 19th century, we refer to Section 7.4.

a measurement was obtained at each step, and his intention was to define the measure of the set under consideration as the limit of these measurements. He did not succeed, as he could not show that the resulting measure of a set was independent of the way it was built up from simple sets.

Henri Lebesgue used Borel's ideas on countability and complements but proceeded in a different way. In his 1902 thesis he defined a set A in $\mathbf{R}^n$ to be measurable if for any positive number ϵ, *no matter how small*, the set A could be transformed into a finite disjoint union of simple figures A_ϵ by adding and removing sets, B_ϵ and C_ϵ, each of which could be covered by a *countable* disjoint union of simple figures $(B_n)_{n=1}^\infty$ and $(C_n)_{n=1}^\infty$, such that[4]

$$\sum_{n=1}^\infty m(B_n) + \sum_{n=1}^\infty m(C_n) < \epsilon.$$

The measure of A was defined to be the limit of the measure of A_ϵ as ϵ tended to 0. In this way he constructed what we now call *Lebesgue Measure* on $\mathbf{R}^n$ and developed the theory of integration with respect to this measure. We state but do not prove his fundamental existence result, when $n = 1$, as Proposition 7.15. Without Lebesgue's key example of a measure on $\mathbf{R}^n$ *which agreed* with and extended the classical notions of length, area and volume, the abstract integrals that we shortly construct would have very limited applications. The extension of Lebesgue's theory of integration, based on measurable subsets of $\mathbf{R}^n$ and Lebesgue[5] measure, to σ-fields on abstract spaces is due to Maurice Fréchet[6] in 1915.

We use two basic integrals, the *Lebesgue Integral* and the *Itô Integral*, and discuss two special examples, the *Riemann Integral* and *Summation of Series*. We first construct the Lebesgue integral and, in the process, establish two powerful convergence results. In Section 7.1, we show that Lebesgue integration with respect to a probability measure on a countable set or with respect to

---

[4]We use m to denote length, area, volume, depending on the dimension.

[5]Henri Lebesgue (1875-1941), a French mathematician, published his first results in 1901 on what we now call the Lebesgue integral. In his thesis, which appeared in 1902, and subsequent papers he developed and applied this integral so that today it is one of the most used, useful and indispensable tools available to mathematicians. Lebesgue's penetrating analysis of major themes from the past and the presence of two other interested and gifted mathematicians in Paris at that time, Rene Baire and Emile Borel, led him to his remarkable discoveries. He devoted half his working life to mathematical education and promoted passionately an integrated approach to learning, based on motivation, physical interpretation and rigor. His extensive writings on mathematical education, and in particular *Measure and the Integral*, Holden-Day, 1966, provide the layman, the student and the professional mathematician with the *rare opportunity* of observing a renowned expert examining how to explain fundamental ideas to students.

[6]Maurice René Fréchet (1878-1973) was a professor of mathematics at Poiters, Strasbourg and Paris. He defined and developed many *abstract* concepts which are now standard within mathematics, e.g. metric spaces, compact sets, abstract spaces, and made major contributions in the extension of the differential calculus from finite to infinite dimensions.

the probability measure generated by a random variable with countable range reduces to the study of convergent series. The countable setting is not sufficient in order to deal with several important random variables, for example normal random variables. We discuss, in Section 7.4, the Riemann integral, which played an important role in the development of probability theory, and show that the Lebesgue integral with respect to Lebesgue measure generalizes the Riemann integral. Riemann sums are used to construct the Riemann integral and play an important role in defining the Itô integral.

We return to the mathematical development of expected values. We fix once and for all an experiment $\mathfrak{E}$ and an associated probability space $(\Omega, \mathcal{F}, P)$. Expected values are averages, and by fixing $\mathcal{F}$ and P we have fixed our *standards*. Our definition of P implies that we *expect*, for $A \in \mathcal{F}$, that $P(A)$ will be close to the fraction of times that A occurs in a large number of experiments. The indicator function plays a role in making this mathematically precise. If we perform the experiment $\mathfrak{E}$, then $\mathbf{1}_A$ will register 1 when A occurs and will register 0 otherwise. Hence $\mathbf{1}_A$ *counts* the number of occurrences of A, and the average[7] value of $\mathbf{1}_A$ in a large number of experiments should be approximately $P(A)$. We are led naturally to the following definition.

Definition 6.1. *If $(\Omega, \mathcal{F}, P)$ is a probability space and $A \in \mathcal{F}$, then*

$$\mathbb{E}[\mathbf{1}_A] := P(A).$$

We call $\mathbb{E}[\mathbf{1}_A]$ the *expected value* of the random variable $\mathbf{1}_A$.

We have now established our system of units. Our next step is to extend by linearity the definition of expected value to random variables which are finite combinations of indicator functions.

A *simple random variable* is a simple measurable function (see Example 4.11) defined on a probability space. Our results in Chapter 4 show that these are precisely the random variables with finite range. Any simple random variable X on the probability space $(\Omega, \mathcal{F}, P)$ has a unique canonical representation:

$$(6.1) \qquad\qquad X = \sum_{i=1}^{n} c_i \mathbf{1}_{A_i}$$

where $c_i \neq c_j$ for $i \neq j$, $A_i = X^{-1}(\{c_i\}) \in \mathcal{F}$ for each i and $(A_i)_{i=1}^{n}$ is a finite partition of Ω. The range of X is the set $\{c_i\}_{i=1}^{n}$.

---

[7]Conceptually *averages* and *expected values* are identical. At times we use the word "average" because of its suggestive connotations and reserve "expected values" for the mathematically defined concept.

Definition 6.2. *The expected value,* $\mathbb{E}[X]$, *of the simple random variable* X *on the probability space* $(\Omega, \mathcal{F}, P)$ *with canonical representation* (6.1) *is given by*

$$(6.2) \qquad \mathbb{E}[X] = \sum_{i=1}^{n} c_i P(A_i).$$

The remainder of this section is devoted to examining basic properties of the expected value. Definition 6.2 is unambiguous because the canonical representation is *unique*. However, it is often inconvenient to check that a simple function is written in its canonical form. Our next result shows that we need only pairwise disjoint measurable sets in order to obtain a similar formula and it is not necessary to require $c_i \neq c_j$ for $i \neq j$.

Lemma 6.3. *If* $(\Omega, \mathcal{F}, P)$ *is a probability space and* $X = \sum_{i=1}^{n} c_i \mathbf{1}_{A_i}$, *where* $(A_i)_{i=1}^{n}$ *is a pairwise disjoint finite collection of* $\mathcal{F}$ *measurable subsets of* Ω, *then*

$$(6.3) \qquad \mathbb{E}[X] = \sum_{i=1}^{n} c_i P(A_i).$$

Proof. If $A_0 := X^{-1}(\{0\}) = (\bigcup_{i=1}^{n} A_i)^c$ and $c_0 = 0$, then $(A_i)_{i=0}^{n}$ is a partition of Ω and $X = \sum_{i=0}^{n} c_i \mathbf{1}_{A_i}$. If $(x_j)_{j=1}^{m}$ denotes the range of X, then $(c_i)_{i=0}^{n} = (x_j)_{j=1}^{m}$. For each $j, 1 \leq j \leq m$, let $N_j = \{i : 0 \leq i \leq n, c_i = x_j\}$. Then $(N_j)_{j=1}^{m}$ is a partition of $\{0, 1, \ldots, n\}$ and $\bigcup_{i \in N_j} A_i = X^{-1}(\{x_j\})$. Since $(A_i)_{i=0}^{n}$ is a partition of Ω, $(A_i)_{i \in N_j}$ is a partition of $X^{-1}(\{x_j\})$. Hence $P(X^{-1}(\{x_j\})) = \sum_{i \in N_j} P(A_i)$. Since $c_i = x_j$ for all $i \in N_j$, we have $x_j P(X^{-1}(\{x_j\})) = \sum_{i \in N_j} c_i P(A_i)$. Hence

$$\mathbb{E}[X] = \sum_{j=1}^{m} x_j P(X^{-1}(\{x_j\})) = \sum_{j=1}^{m} (\sum_{i \in N_j} c_i P(A_i)) = \sum_{i=1}^{n} c_i P(A_i).$$

This completes the proof. $\qquad\qquad\qquad\qquad\qquad\qquad\qquad\qquad\qquad\quad$ $\square$

Example 6.4. If X is a random variable on the probability space $(\Omega, \mathcal{F}, P)$, where Ω is finite and $\mathcal{F} = 2^{\Omega}$, then $X = \sum_{\omega \in \Omega} X(\omega) \mathbf{1}_{\{\omega\}}$. Hence

$$\mathbb{E}[X] = \sum_{\omega \in \text{ domain of } X} X(\omega) P(\{\omega\}) = \sum_{x \in \text{ range of } X} x P_X(\{x\}).$$

Our next result is an immediate consequence of the different ways we can write the level sets of a simple random variable.

Proposition 6.5. *Let X denote a simple random variable on the probability space $(\Omega, \mathcal{F}, P)$. If X has range $(x_i)_{i=1}^n$ and $\omega_i \in X^{-1}(\{x_i\})$ for all i, then*

$$
\begin{aligned}
\mathbb{E}[X] &= \sum_{i=1}^n x_i P[\omega \in \Omega : X(\omega) = x_i] = \sum_{i=1}^n x_i P[X^{-1}(\{x_i\})] \\
&= \sum_{i=1}^n x_i P_X(\{x_i\}) = \sum_{i=1}^n X(\omega_i) P_X(\{X(\omega_i)\}).
\end{aligned}
$$

We collect, in the following proposition, fundamental properties of the expectation of simple random variables. Even though (a) appears elementary we will require some time later to show that it holds for all integrable random variables.

Proposition 6.6. *Let $(\Omega, \mathcal{F}, P)$ denote a probability space, let X, Y be simple random variables on $(\Omega, \mathcal{F}, P)$ and let $c \in \mathbf{R}$ and $A \in \mathcal{F}$. Then*

(a) $\mathbb{E}[X \pm Y] = \mathbb{E}[X] \pm \mathbb{E}[Y]$;

(b) *if X and Y are independent, then* $\mathbb{E}[X \cdot Y] = \mathbb{E}[X] \cdot \mathbb{E}[Y]$;

(c) $\mathbb{E}[cX] = c\mathbb{E}[X]$;

(d) *if $X \geq 0$, then* $\mathbb{E}[X] \geq 0$;

(e) *if $X \geq Y$, then*[8] $\mathbb{E}[X] \geq \mathbb{E}[Y]$;

(f) *if $|X| \leq M$ on $A \in \mathcal{F}$, then* $|\mathbb{E}[X \cdot \mathbf{1}_A]| \leq M \cdot P(A)$.

Proof. Let $X = \sum_{i=1}^n x_i \mathbf{1}_{A_i}$ and $Y = \sum_{j=1}^m y_j \mathbf{1}_{B_i}$ denote canonical representations. Then $(A_i)_{i=1}^n$ and $(B_j)_{j=1}^m$ are partitions of Ω into non-empty $\mathcal{F}$ measurable sets. For $1 \leq i \leq n, 1 \leq j \leq m$, let $C_{ij} = A_i \cap B_j$. Then $(C_{ij})_{i=1,j=1}^{n,m}$ is also a partition of Ω into $\mathcal{F}$ measurable sets (see Figure 6.2).

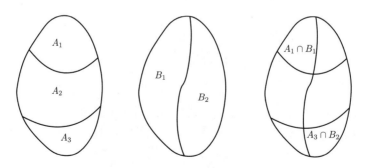

Figure 6.2

---

[8]We write $Y \leq X$ and $X \geq Y$ if $X - Y \geq 0$ and $|X| \leq M$ if $|X(\omega)| \leq M$ for all $\omega \in \Omega$, see Definition 4.12.

Let $c_{ij}^{\pm} = x_i \pm y_j$ and $d_{ij} = x_i \cdot y_j$ for $1 \leq i \leq n, 1 \leq j \leq m$. Since X and Y are constant on A_i and B_j, respectively, and $\mathbf{1}_{A_i} \cdot \mathbf{1}_{B_j} = \mathbf{1}_{C_{ij}}$, we have $X \pm Y = \sum_{i,j=1}^{n,m} c_{ij}^{\pm} \mathbf{1}_{C_{ij}}$ and $X \cdot Y = \sum_{i,j=1}^{n,m} d_{ij}\mathbf{1}_{C_{ij}}$. For each i, $(A_i \cap B_j)_{j=1}^{m}$ is a pairwise disjoint finite sequence and

$$\bigcup_{j=1}^{m} C_{ij} = \bigcup_{j=1}^{m} A_i \cap B_j = A_i \cap (\bigcup_{j=1}^{m} B_j) = A_i \cap \Omega = A_i.$$

Similarly for each j, $\bigcup_{i=1}^{n} C_{ij} = B_j$. Hence, for each i,

$$P(\bigcup_{j=1}^{m} C_{ij}) = \sum_{j=1}^{m} P(C_{ij}) = P(A_i)$$

and, for each j,

$$P(\bigcup_{i=1}^{n} C_{ij}) = \sum_{i=1}^{n} P(C_{ij}) = P(B_j).$$

Combining these equalities we obtain, by Lemma 6.3,

$$
\begin{aligned}
\mathbb{E}[X \pm Y] &= \sum_{i=1}^{n}\sum_{j=1}^{m} c_{ij}^{\pm} P(C_{ij}) = \sum_{i=1}^{n}\sum_{j=1}^{m}(x_i \pm y_j)P(C_{ij}) \\
&= \sum_{i=1}^{n} x_i \Big\{ \sum_{j=1}^{m} P(C_{ij}) \Big\} \pm \sum_{j=1}^{m} y_i \Big\{ \sum_{i=1}^{n} P(C_{ij}) \Big\} \\
&= \sum_{i=1}^{n} x_i P(A_i) \pm \sum_{j=1}^{m} y_j P(B_j) \\
&= \mathbb{E}[X] \pm \mathbb{E}[Y]
\end{aligned}
$$

and this proves (a).

If X and Y are independent, then $P(C_{ij}) = P(A_i \cap B_j) = P(A_i) \cdot P(B_j)$ and

$$
\begin{aligned}
\mathbb{E}[X \cdot Y] &= \sum_{i=1}^{n}\sum_{j=1}^{m} d_{ij} P(A_i) \cdot P(B_j) \\
&= \{ \sum_{i=1}^{n} x_i P(A_i) \} \cdot \{ \sum_{j=1}^{m} y_j P(B_j) \} \\
&= \mathbb{E}[X] \cdot \mathbb{E}[Y].
\end{aligned}
$$

This proves (b). Since $c \cdot X = \sum_{i=1}^{n} c \cdot x_i \mathbf{1}_{A_i}$ we immediately have (c) and, as $X \geq 0$ if and only if $x_i \geq 0$ for all i, $\mathbb{E}[X] \geq 0$ if $X \geq 0$ and (d) holds.

If $X \geq Y$, then $X - Y \geq 0$ and (d) implies $\mathbb{E}[X - Y] \geq 0$. By (a), $\mathbb{E}[X] = \mathbb{E}[Y] + \mathbb{E}[X - Y] \geq 0$ and (e) holds.

If $A \in \mathcal{F}$, then $X \cdot \mathbf{1}_A = \sum_{i=1}^{n} x_i \mathbf{1}_{A_i \cap A}$ and $(A \cap A_i)_{i=1}^{n}$ is a pairwise disjoint sequence of $\mathcal{F}$ measurable sets. If $A_i \cap A \neq \emptyset$, $|x_i| \leq M$ and

$$
\begin{aligned}
|\mathbb{E}[X \cdot \mathbf{1}_A]| &= |\sum_{i=1}^{n} x_i P(A_i \cap A)| \leq \sum_{i=1}^{n} |x_i| P(A_i \cap A) \\
&\leq M \sum_{i, A_i \cap A \neq \emptyset} P(A_i \cap A) = M \cdot P(A).
\end{aligned}
$$

This completes the proof. $\qquad\qquad\qquad\qquad\qquad\qquad\qquad\qquad\qquad$ $\square$

Example 6.7. Let $\Omega = \{1, 2, \ldots, 10\}$ and let $\mathcal{F}$ denote the partition of Ω generated by the sets $\{1, 2, 3\}, \{4, 5\}, \{6\}$ and $\{7, 8, 9, 10\}$. Let $P(\{1, 2, 3\}) = P(\{4, 5\}) = P(\{6\}) = 1/6$ and $P(\{7, 8, 9, 10\}) = 1/2$ and suppose $X : \Omega \longrightarrow \mathbf{R}$ is given by $X(i) = 1$ if $i \leq 5$ and $X(i) = 2$ if $i > 5$. The partitions of Ω given by $\mathcal{F}$ and $\mathcal{F}_X$ are displayed in Figure 6.3.

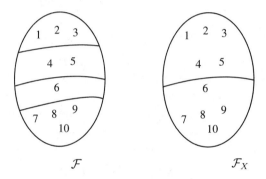

Figure 6.3

Since $\mathcal{F}_X \subset \mathcal{F}, X$ is a random variable on $(\Omega, \mathcal{F}, P)$. By inspection

$$
X = \mathbf{1}_{\{1,2,3,4,5\}} + 2 \cdot \mathbf{1}_{\{6,7,8,9,10\}}.
$$

Hence

$$
\begin{aligned}
\mathbb{E}[X] &= 1 \cdot P(\{1, 2, 3, 4, 5\}) + 2 \cdot P(\{6, 7, 8, 9, 10\}) \\
&= 1 \cdot (P(\{1, 2, 3\}) + P(\{4, 5\})) + 2 \cdot (P(\{6\}) + P(\{7, 8, 9, 10\})) \\
&= (\frac{1}{6} + \frac{1}{6}) + 2(\frac{1}{6} + \frac{1}{2}) \\
&= \frac{5}{3}.
\end{aligned}
$$

The notation $\mathbb{E}[X]$ is compact, but to display the different components in the construction we introduce new notation and let

$$
(6.4) \qquad\qquad\qquad \int_{\Omega} X dP := \mathbb{E}[X].
$$

The law of survival of the fittest applies to mathematical notation and generally results in the most efficient notation being widely adopted. This usually leads to *unique* notation, but in this particular case we see an exception to the general rule. The $\mathbb{E}[\cdot]$ notation is extremely useful in dealing with conditional expectation and martingales, while the integral notation, introduced in (6.4), applies to a wider set of situations and almost invariably leads to further insight. For probability measures we will have two interchangeable ways of expressing many results. The advantages become apparent as we proceed.

Many different integrals have been constructed, and we encounter several in this book. For orientation purposes we spend some time examining the thinking behind the integral notation. All integrals are limits of finite sums. The notation for sum is $\sum$ and the symbol $\int$ is a corruption of $\sum$. Thus the presence of the symbol $\int$ will generally indicate the existence of a finite sum or a limit of finite sums. Traditionally Δ has been used to denote a *small portion* with limiting symbol[9] d. The combination dP with d placed in front of P indicates that each term in the finite sum contains a *small portion* of P. It is helpful to consider P as a physical substance spread over Ω and that the small portions are the amounts of P deposited above the sets in a partition of Ω. Hence P is *not* evaluated at points of Ω but on some collection of subsets of Ω. The set being partitioned, in our case Ω, is always placed below the integral sign, and the limit being taken involves finer and finer partitions of this set. The position of X indicates that it is a function with domain Ω, while the combination XdP suggests that a typical term in the finite sums has the form $X(\omega)P(A)$ where A is a typical set in the partition and ω is a typical point in A. Thus the complete symbol $\int_{\Omega} XdP$ is an efficient reminder of the underlying process. Naturally each integral has its own special features, and these have to be borne in mind in particular cases.

In the only case of integration considered so far we do not require a limiting process since the partition of Ω is finite. Rewriting our integral when $X = \sum_{i=1}^{n} x_i \mathbf{1}_{A_i}$, $(A_i)_{i=1}^{n}$ is a partition of Ω into $\mathcal{F}$ measurable sets and $x_i = X(\omega_i)$ for any $\omega_i \in A_i$, we obtain from (6.3) and (6.4),

$$(6.5) \qquad \mathbb{E}[X] = \sum_{i=1}^{n} X(\omega_i)P(A_i) = \int_{\Omega} XdP.$$

If $(\Omega, \mathcal{F}, P)$ is a probability space, X is a random variable on Ω and $A \in \mathcal{F}$, we let,[10] whenever the right-hand side is defined,

$$(6.6) \qquad \int_{A} XdP = \int_{\Omega} \mathbf{1}_A \cdot XdP.$$

---

[9]In one variable calculus we use $\Delta y/\Delta x$ with limit dy/dx.

[10]This applies to all integrals we define.

As expected values and integrals are now inter-changeable we may rewrite Proposition 6.6 using integral notation. For example (a) is equivalent to the following:

$$\int_\Omega (X \pm Y)dP = \int_\Omega XdP \pm \int_\Omega YdP.$$

Certain formulae are more suggestive when written in integral notation. For instance, given a probability space $(\Omega, \mathcal{F}, P)$, A and B disjoint $\mathcal{F}$ measurable sets and X a simple random variable on Ω, then by Proposition 6.6(a) and (f),

$$\int_{A \cup B} XdP = \int_A XdP + \int_B XdP$$

and

(6.7) $$\left| \int_A XdP \right| \leq \|X\|_A \cdot P(A)$$

where $\|X\|_A = \sup\{|X(\omega)| : \omega \in A\}$.

Example 6.8. Let $\Omega = \{1, \ldots, 6\}$, $\mathcal{F} = 2^\Omega$, $P(\{i\}) = 1/8, i = 1, 2, P(\{i\}) = 3/16$ for $i > 2$. Let $X(i) = i^2$ for $i \leq 3$, $X(i) = 5$ for $i > 3$, and let $A = \{1, 2, 4, 6\}$. Then

$$
\begin{aligned}
\int_A XdP &= \int_{\{1,2,4,6\}} XdP = \sum_{i \in \{1,2,4,6\}} X(i)P(\{i\}) \\
&= X(1)P(\{1\}) + X(2)P(\{2\}) + X(4)P(\{4\}) + X(6)P(\{6\}) \\
&= 1 \times \frac{1}{8} + 4 \times \frac{1}{8} + 5 \times \frac{3}{16} + 5 \times \frac{3}{16} \\
&= \frac{5}{2}.
\end{aligned}
$$

Our final result in this section is the key technical result required in later sections. It is worth noting the control we obtain because of the *order* in which we let n and m tend to infinity.

Proposition 6.9. *If $(X_n)_{n=1}^\infty$ and $(Y_n)_{n=1}^\infty$ are increasing sequences of simple positive random variables on the probability space $(\Omega, \mathcal{F}, P)$ and*

$$\lim_{n \to \infty} X_n(\omega) = \lim_{n \to \infty} Y_n(\omega)$$

for all $\omega \in \Omega$, then[11]

(6.8) $$\lim_{n \to \infty} \mathbb{E}[X_n] = \lim_{n \to \infty} \mathbb{E}[Y_n].$$

---

[11]Note that we may have $\lim_{n \to \infty} X_n(\omega) = +\infty$ for some ω and that we are proving only that the limits *coincide*. These may be finite or infinite. The same remark applies to Propositions 6.14 and 6.22.

Proof. Fix a positive integer m and let $A_n = \{\omega \in \Omega : X_n(\omega) \geq Y_m(\omega) - \frac{1}{m}\}$ for each positive integer n. Since

$$X_n \geq X_n \cdot \mathbf{1}_{A_n} \geq Y_m \cdot \mathbf{1}_{A_n} - \frac{1}{m}$$

Proposition 6.6(e) implies

$$
\begin{aligned}
\mathbb{E}[X_n] = \int_\Omega X_n dP &\geq \int_\Omega (X_n \cdot \mathbf{1}_{A_n}) dP \\
&\geq \int_\Omega (Y_m \cdot \mathbf{1}_{A_n}) dP - \int_\Omega \frac{1}{m} dP \\
&= \int_\Omega Y_m dP - \int_{A_n^c} Y_m dP - \frac{1}{m} \\
&\geq \mathbb{E}[Y_m] - \|Y_m\| \cdot P(A_n^c) - \frac{1}{m}.
\end{aligned}
$$

Since $(X_n)_{n=1}^\infty$ is an increasing sequence $A_n \subset A_{n+1}$ for all n and, as $(X_n)_{n=1}^\infty$ and $(Y_n)_{n=1}^\infty$ converge pointwise to the same limit, $\lim_{n\to\infty} A_n = \Omega$. By Proposition 5.3, $\lim_{n\to\infty} P(A_n^c) = P(\emptyset) = 0$. By Proposition 6.6(e), $(\mathbb{E}[X_n])_{n=1}^\infty$ is an increasing sequence of positive real numbers and hence $\lim_{n\to\infty} \mathbb{E}[X_n]$ exists.[12] Hence

$$
\begin{aligned}
\lim_{n\to\infty} \mathbb{E}[X_n] &\geq \lim_{n\to\infty} \{\mathbb{E}[Y_m] - \|Y_m\| \cdot P(A_n^c)\} - \frac{1}{m} \\
&= \mathbb{E}[Y_m] - \frac{1}{m}.
\end{aligned}
$$

Since this holds for all m and $(Y_m)_{m=1}^\infty$ is an increasing sequence, we have

$$\lim_{n\to\infty} \mathbb{E}[X_n] \geq \lim_{m\to\infty} \mathbb{E}[Y_m].$$

Reversing the roles of X_n and Y_m and combining the two estimates, we obtain

$$\lim_{n\to\infty} \mathbb{E}[X_n] = \lim_{m\to\infty} \mathbb{E}[Y_m].$$

This completes the proof. $\qquad\square$

6.2. Positive Bounded Random Variables

The remainder of this chapter, where we extend the domain of the integral, is technically demanding. We suggest that the reader, on a first reading, concentrate on the details in this section, which show how limits are applied, and note the important definitions and results in the next two sections. These are Definitions 6.12, 6.17 and 6.20 and Propositions 6.23, 6.25 and 6.30. We strongly urge

---

[12]Either as a real number, by the upper bound principle, if the sequence is bounded above or as + infinity if the sequence is unbounded.

the reader to read these sections carefully later, as the methods used, although technical, lead to insight and useful basic skills.

In this section we use approximations and convergence to extend Definition 6.2 to positive bounded measurable functions. All convergence will be reduced to convergence of sequences of real numbers, at which point we apply the upper bound principle.

Consider a *positive bounded* random variable X on the probability space $(\Omega, \mathcal{F}, P)$. Let m denote a positive *integer* such that $0 \leq X < m$. We first partition Ω into a finite number of $\mathcal{F}$ measurable sets on each of which X varies very little. Let n denote a positive integer. For positive integers $j, 0 \leq j < 2^n$, and $k, 0 \leq k < m$, let

$$(6.9) \qquad I_{j,k}^n = \{x \in \mathbf{R} : k + \frac{j}{2^n} \leq x < k + \frac{j+1}{2^n}\}.$$

The finite sequence $(I_{j,k}^n)_{0 \leq j < 2^n, 0 \leq k < m}$ partitions $[0, m)$ into adjacent intervals[13] each of length $1/2^n$ (see Figure 6.4). Since intervals are Borel sets and X is measurable

$$X^{-1}(I_{j,k}^n) = \{\omega \in \Omega : X(\omega) \in I_{j,k}^n\} = \{\omega \in \Omega : k + \frac{j}{2^n} \leq X(\omega) < k + \frac{j+1}{2^n}\}$$

lies in $\mathcal{F}$. By (4.2), $(X^{-1}(I_{j,k}^n))_{0 \leq j < 2^n, 0 \leq k < m}$ is a partition of Ω. If ω_1 and ω_2 belong to $I_{j,k}^n$, then $k + \frac{j}{2^n} \leq X(\omega_i) < k + \frac{j+1}{2^n}$ for $i = 1, 2$ and $|X(\omega_1) - X(\omega_2)| < 1/2^n$. Hence X varies very little on each $X^{-1}(I_{j,k}^n)$ when n is large.

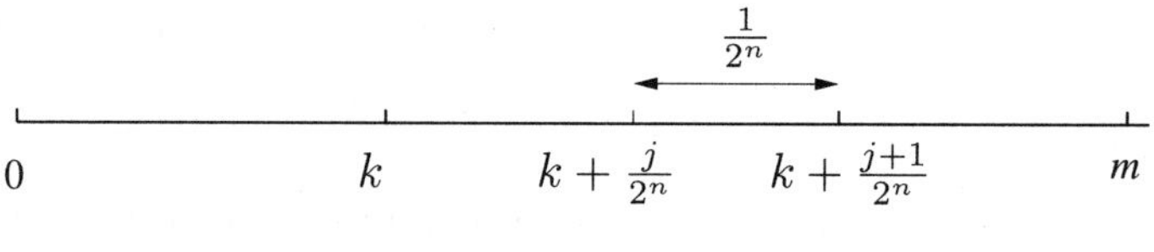

Figure 6.4

If $\omega \in X^{-1}(I_{j,k}^n) = X^{-1}([k + \frac{j}{2^n}, k + \frac{j+1}{2^n}))$, let $X_n(\omega) = k + \frac{j}{2^n}$. Then

$$(6.10) \qquad X_n = \sum_{k=0}^{m-1} \sum_{j=0}^{2^n-1} (k + \frac{j}{2^n}) \mathbf{1}_{X^{-1}(I_{j,k}^n)}$$

---

[13]To use the axioms for a probability space we need a countable partition containing the range of X. Partitions into intervals are tidy. If we use adjacent *open* intervals, we miss some points, and if we use *closed* intervals, we cover some points twice. Neither leads to a partition. By using *half open* intervals, $[a, b) := \{x \in \mathbf{R} : a \leq x < b\}$, we avoid overlaps and cover $[0, m)$. Minor technical matters of this kind frequently arise in mathematics and must be included for mathematical correctness even though they can distract the student from the more essential points in an argument. They are minor, but this becomes apparent only when the main ideas are understood.

is a simple positive random variable on $(\Omega, \mathcal{F}, P)$. We call $(X_n)_{n=1}^{\infty}$ the *canonical sequence* associated with the positive bounded random variable X. Our next lemma gathers together simple properties of canonical sequences.

Lemma 6.10. *If X is a positive bounded random variable on a probability space $(\Omega, \mathcal{F}, P)$ with canonical sequence $(X_n)_{n=1}^{\infty}$, then*

   (a) *for all $\omega \in \Omega$ and all n, $|X_n(\omega) - X(\omega)| \leq 1/2^n$;*
   (b) *$(X_n)_{n=1}^{\infty}$ is increasing and $X_n \longrightarrow X$ pointwise as $n \longrightarrow \infty$;*
   (c) *for all n, $0 \leq X_n \leq X$ and $|\mathbb{E}[X_n] - \mathbb{E}[X_{n+1}]| \leq 1/2^{n+1}$;*
   (d) *$(\mathbb{E}[X_n])_{n=1}^{\infty}$ is a convergent sequence of positive numbers;*
   (e) *if X is a simple random variable, then $\mathbb{E}[X_n]$ converges to $\mathbb{E}[X]$, as n tends to infinity.*

Proof. If $\omega \in X^{-1}(I_{j,k}^n)$, then $k + \frac{j}{2^n} = X_n(\omega) \leq X(\omega) < k + \frac{j+1}{2^n}$ and

$$|X_n(\omega) - X(\omega)| < 1/2^n.$$

This proves (a) and shows that $X_n \longrightarrow X$ pointwise as $n \longrightarrow \infty$. Since

$$[k + \frac{j}{2^n}, k + \frac{j+1}{2^n}) = [k + \frac{2j}{2^{n+1}}, k + \frac{2j+1}{2^{n+1}}) \cup [k + \frac{2j+1}{2^{n+1}}, k + \frac{2j+2}{2^{n+1}})$$

we have $I_{j,k}^n = I_{2j,k}^{n+1} \cup I_{2j+1,k}^{2n+1}$ and

$$X_{n+1}(\omega) = \begin{cases} k + \frac{2j}{2^{n+1}} = X_n(\omega) & \text{if } k + \frac{2j}{2^{n+1}} \leq X(\omega) < k + \frac{2j+1}{2^{n+1}}, \\ k + \frac{2j+1}{2^{n+1}} = X_n(\omega) + \frac{1}{2^{n+1}} & \text{if } k + \frac{2j+1}{2^{n+1}} \leq X(\omega) < k + \frac{2j+2}{2^{n+1}}. \end{cases}$$

Hence $0 \leq X_n(\omega) \leq X_{n+1}(\omega) \leq X(\omega)$ and $(X_n)_{n=1}^{\infty}$ is an increasing sequence. This proves (b). Since $|X_n(\omega) - X_{n+1}(\omega)| \leq 1/2^{n+1}$ for all ω, (c) follows from Proposition 6.6(a) and (f).

Since $X(\omega) < m$ for all $\omega \in \Omega$, Proposition 6.6(e) implies $\mathbb{E}[X_n] \leq \mathbb{E}[X_{n+1}] < m$ and, by the upper bound principle, $(\mathbb{E}[X_n])_{n=1}^{\infty}$ is a convergent sequence. This proves (d).

To prove (e) we apply Proposition 6.9 and (b) to the canonical sequence for X, $(X_n)_{n=1}^{\infty}$, and the sequence $(Y_n)_{n=1}^{\infty}$ where $Y_n = X$ for all n. This completes the proof. $\square$

Example 6.11. In this example we illustrate some of the above constructions. Let $m = 1; \Omega = [0, 1]; \mathcal{F} = \mathcal{B}([0, 1])$, the Borel field generated by the intervals in $[0, 1]$; and $n = 2$. In this case we have 4 intervals (see Figure 6.5). For instance

$$I_{2,0}^2 = \{x \in [0, 1] : 0 + \frac{2}{2^2} \leq x < 0 + \frac{3}{2^2}\}.$$

Using the graph of X, $\{(\omega, X(\omega)) : \omega \in \Omega\}$, we see how to locate $X^{-1}(I_{1,0}^2)$. Since $I_{1,0}^2 = \{x \in \mathbf{R} : \frac{1}{4} \leq x < \frac{1}{2}\}$, $X^{-1}(I_{1,0}^2)$ consists of all ω satisfying

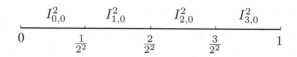

Figure 6.5

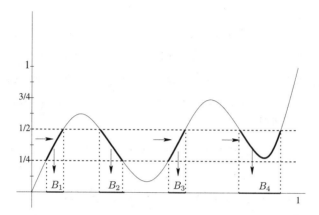

Figure 6.6

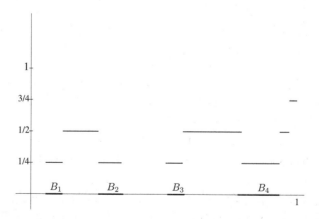

Figure 6.7

$1/4 \leq X(\omega) < 1/2$. We locate the interval $[1/4, 1/2)$ in the range of X, that is on the vertical axis (Figure 6.6). Horizontal lines through $[1/4, 1/2)$ intersect the graph at points $(\omega, X(\omega))$ where $X(\omega) \in I_{1,0}^2$. Projecting these points onto the horizontal axis gives $X^{-1}(I_{1,0}^2)$. Following this recipe we obtain

$$X^{-1}(I_{1,0}^2) = B_1 \cup B_2 \cup B_3 \cup B_4.$$

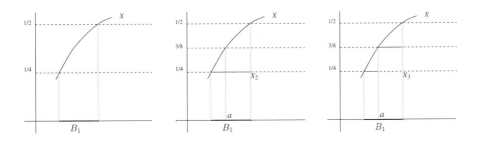

Figure 6.8

Since $X_2(\omega) = 1/4$ on $I_{1,0}^2$ we can modify the graph of X over $X^{-1}(I_{1,0}^2)$, and afterwards over all $X^{-1}(I_{i,k}^2)$, and sketch the graph of X_2. The graph of X_2 is shown in Figure 6.7.

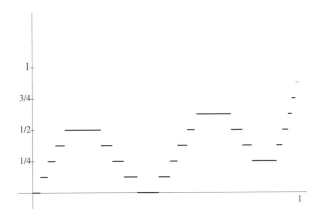

Figure 6.9

In Figure 6.8 we show parts of X and X_2 and the changes needed to obtain the corresponding part of X_3, and in Figure 6.9 we sketch the graph of X_3.

In view of Proposition 6.10(e) the following definition reduces to Definition 6.2 when X is a simple positive random variable.

Definition 6.12. *If X is a positive bounded random variable defined on the probability space $(\Omega, \mathcal{F}, P)$, then the expected value of X, $\mathbb{E}[X]$, is defined by*

$$\mathbb{E}[X] = \lim_{n \longrightarrow \infty} \mathbb{E}[X_n]$$

where $(X_n)_{n=1}^{\infty}$ is the canonical sequence for X.

By Proposition 6.9 the canonical sequence can be replaced by any increasing sequence of *simple* positive random variables which converges pointwise to X. Our next result, which extends Proposition 6.10, shows the degree of approximation present in the above definition.

Lemma 6.13. *If $(X_n)_{n=1}^{\infty}$ is the canonical sequence for the positive bounded random variable X on the probability space $(\Omega, \mathcal{F}, P)$, then*

(6.11) $$|\mathbb{E}[X] - \mathbb{E}[X_n]| \leq 1/2^n$$

for all n.

Proof. By Proposition 6.10(c), $|\mathbb{E}[X_{n+1}] - \mathbb{E}[X_n]| \leq 1/2^{n+1}$. Hence

$$
\begin{aligned}
|\mathbb{E}[X] - \mathbb{E}[X_n]| &= \lim_{m \to \infty} |\mathbb{E}[X_m] - \mathbb{E}[X_n]| \\
&= \lim_{m \to \infty} | \sum_{j=n}^{m-1} (\mathbb{E}[X_{j+1}] - \mathbb{E}[X_j])| \\
&\leq \lim_{m \to \infty} \sum_{j=n}^{m-1} |\mathbb{E}[X_{j+1}] - \mathbb{E}[X_j]| \\
&\leq \sum_{j=n}^{\infty} 1/2^{j+1} = 1/2^n.
\end{aligned}
$$

$\square$

We now upgrade Proposition 6.9. This implies that the canonical sequence in Definition 6.12 can be replaced by *any* increasing sequence of positive bounded random variables which converges pointwise to X.

Proposition 6.14. *If $(X_n)_{n=1}^{\infty}$ and $(Y_n)_{n=1}^{\infty}$ are increasing sequences of positive bounded random variables on the probability space $(\Omega, \mathcal{F}, P)$ and*

$$\lim_{n \to \infty} X_n(\omega) = \lim_{n \to \infty} Y_n(\omega)$$

for all $\omega \in \Omega$, then

(6.12) $$\lim_{n \to \infty} \mathbb{E}[X_n] = \lim_{n \to \infty} \mathbb{E}[Y_n].$$

Proof. For each n let $(X_n^m)_{m=1}^{\infty}$ denote the canonical sequence for X_n. Since $X_n \leq X_{n+1}$ we have $X_n^n \leq X_n^{n+1} \leq X_{n+1}^{n+1}$ and the sequence $(X_n^n)_{n=1}^{\infty}$ is an increasing sequence of simple positive random variables. If $\omega \in \Omega$, Proposition 6.10(a) implies $|X_n^n(\omega) - X_n(\omega)| \leq 1/2^n$ for all n. Hence

$$\lim_{n \to \infty} X_n^n(\omega) = \lim_{n \to \infty} X_n(\omega) + \lim_{n \to \infty} (X_n^n(\omega) - X_n(\omega)) = \lim_{n \to \infty} X_n(\omega).$$

By Lemma 6.13, $|\mathbb{E}[X_n^n] - \mathbb{E}[X_n]| \leq 1/2^n$ for all n. Hence

$$\lim_{n \to \infty} \mathbb{E}[X_n^n] = \lim_{n \to \infty} \mathbb{E}[X_n] + \lim_{n \to \infty} (\mathbb{E}[X_n^n] - \mathbb{E}[X_n]) = \lim_{n \to \infty} \mathbb{E}[X_n].$$

If $(Y_n^n)_{n=1}^\infty$ is the corresponding sequence for $(Y_n)_{n=1}^\infty$, then we have two increasing sequences of *simple* positive random variables which converge pointwise to the same limit. An application of Proposition 6.9 completes the proof. □

Our next step is to adjust the above definition of expected value so that it may be interpreted as an integral. Let X denote a random variable with $X(\Omega) \subset [0, m)$ where m is a positive integer. By Definition 6.12, Lemma 6.3 and (6.10)

$$\mathbb{E}[X] = \lim_{n \longrightarrow \infty} \mathbb{E}[X_n] = \lim_{n \longrightarrow \infty} \sum_{k=0}^{m-1} \sum_{j=0}^{2^n-1} (k + \frac{j}{2^n}) P(X^{-1}(I_{j,k}^n))$$

where $(X_n)_{n=1}^\infty$ is the canonical sequence for X. If $\omega_{j,k} \in X^{-1}(I_{j,k}^n)$, then $X_n(\omega_{j,k}) = k + \frac{j}{2^n}$ and $|X(\omega_{j,k}) - (k + \frac{j}{2^n})| \leq \frac{1}{2^n}$. Since $(X^{-1}(I_{j,k}^n))_{j,k}$ is a partition of Ω, this implies

$$|\sum_{k=0}^{m-1} \sum_{j=0}^{2^n-1} (k + \frac{j}{2^n}) P(X^{-1}(I_{j,k}^n)) - \sum_{k=0}^{m-1} \sum_{j=0}^{2^n-1} X(\omega_{j,k}) P(X^{-1}(I_{j,k}^n))|$$

$$\leq \sum_{k=0}^{m-1} \sum_{j=0}^{2^n-1} |k + \frac{j}{2^n} - X(\omega_{j,k})| P(X^{-1}(I_{j,k}^n))$$

$$\leq \frac{1}{2^n} \sum_{k=0}^{m-1} \sum_{j=0}^{2^n-1} P(X^{-1}(I_{j,k}^n)) = \frac{1}{2^n} P(\Omega) = \frac{1}{2^n}.$$

and

(6.13) $$\mathbb{E}[X] = \lim_{n \to \infty} \sum_{k=0}^{m-1} \sum_{j=0}^{2^n-1} X(\omega_{j,k}) P(X^{-1}(I_{j,k}^n)).$$

If $x_{j,k} = X(\omega_{j,k})$, then, since $P_X(B) = P(X^{-1}(B))$ for B a Borel subset of $\mathbf{R}$, we may rewrite (6.13) as

(6.14) $$\mathbb{E}[X] = \lim_{n \to \infty} \sum_{k=0}^{m-1} \sum_{j=0}^{2^n-1} x_{j,k} P_X(I_{j,k}^n).$$

In view of our previous informal remarks on integrals, we use (6.13) and (6.14) *as the definition* of the Lebesgue integrals of $X : \Omega \longrightarrow \mathbf{R}$ with respect to P and of the identity mapping[14] $x : \mathbf{R} \longrightarrow \mathbf{R}$ with respect to P_X.

---

[14]The functions $\mathbf{1_R}$ and $\mathbf{i_R}$ where $\mathbf{1_R}(x) = 1$ and $\mathbf{i_R}(x) = x$ for $x \in \mathbf{R}$ are two of the most frequently used functions in mathematics. Their traditional notation in integration theory may cause confusion, and, as we use both, we clarify the situation. Our normal notation is $\int_B g \, dP$ for the integral of g over the Borel set B with respect to a probability measure P on $(\mathbf{R}, \mathcal{B}(\mathbf{R}))$. However, if $g = \mathbf{1_R}$, we drop the function and write $\int_B dP$; and if $g = \mathbf{i_R}$, we write $\int_B x \, dP$.

Definition 6.15. *If X is a positive bounded random variable defined on the probability space $(\Omega, \mathcal{F}, P)$, let*

$$\int_\Omega X \, dP := \int_{\mathbf{R}} x \, dP_X := \mathbb{E}[X].$$

We require the analogue of Proposition 6.6 for positive bounded random variables later.

Proposition 6.16. *Let $(\Omega, \mathcal{F}, P)$ denote a probability space, let X and Y be positive bounded random variables on $(\Omega, \mathcal{F}, P)$ and let $A \in \mathcal{F}$. Then*

(a) $\mathbb{E}[X] \geq 0$;

(b) $\mathbb{E}[X + Y] = \mathbb{E}[X] + \mathbb{E}[Y]$;

(c) *if $X \geq Y$, then $\mathbb{E}[X] \geq \mathbb{E}[Y]$;*

(d) *if $|X| \leq M$, then $|\mathbb{E}[X]| \leq M$;*

(e) *if $|X(\omega)| \leq M$ for all $\omega \in A$, then $\mathbb{E}[X \cdot \mathbf{1}_A] \leq M \cdot P(A)$.*

Proof. Let $(X_n)_{n=1}^\infty$ and $(Y_n)_{n=1}^\infty$ denote the canonical sequences for X and Y respectively. By Proposition 6.6(d), $\mathbb{E}[X_n] \geq 0$ and hence $\mathbb{E}[X] \geq 0$. This proves (a). The sequence $(X_n + Y_n)_{n=1}^\infty$ is an increasing sequence of simple positive random variables which converges pointwise to $X + Y$. By Proposition 6.14, $\lim_{n\to\infty} \mathbb{E}[X_n] = \mathbb{E}[X]$, $\lim_{n\to\infty} \mathbb{E}[Y_n] = \mathbb{E}[Y]$ and $\lim_{n\to\infty} \mathbb{E}[X_n + Y_n] = \mathbb{E}[X + Y]$. By Proposition 6.6(a), $\mathbb{E}[X_n + Y_n] = \mathbb{E}[X_n] + \mathbb{E}[Y_n]$. Hence

$$\mathbb{E}[X + Y] = \lim_{n\to\infty} \mathbb{E}[X_n] + \lim_{n\to\infty} \mathbb{E}[Y_n] = \mathbb{E}[X] + \mathbb{E}[Y].$$

This proves (b). For part (c) we note that $X \geq Y$ implies $X_n \geq Y_n$ for all n and hence $\mathbb{E}[X] = \lim_{n\to\infty} \mathbb{E}[X_n] \geq \lim_{n\to\infty} \mathbb{E}[Y_n] = \mathbb{E}[Y]$. Parts (d) and (e) are immediate from our construction. $\qquad\square$

6.3. Positive Random Variables

In this section we discuss *positive* random variables using *positive bounded* random variables as our approximating sequence and encounter random variables which *do not* have expected values. In the previous sections we required limits of increasing sequences of *real numbers*, for instance in Propositions 6.9 and 6.16, but in this section we need[15] limits of increasing sequences of *positive bounded random variables*.

---

[15]There are a number of different approaches to the material discussed in this and the following sections. Most involve a revision of the definition of random variable, either by allowing the range to include $\pm\infty$ or by considering random variables as equivalence classes of functions (see Exercise 5.17). All approaches involve similar set theoretic calculations and all lead to the same final set of results.

If X is a positive random variable on the probability space $(\Omega, \mathcal{F}, P)$, let

$$X^{[m]}(\omega) = \begin{cases} X(\omega) & \text{if } X(\omega) < m, \\ m & \text{if } X(\omega) \geq m. \end{cases}$$

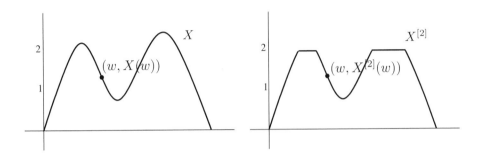

Figure 6.10

We have $0 \leq X^{[m]} \leq X$ for all m (see Figure 6.10) and $(X^{[m]})_{m=1}^{\infty}$ is an increasing sequence of positive bounded random variables which converges pointwise to X as m tends to infinity. By Proposition 6.16(c), $(\mathbb{E}[X^{[m]}])_{m=1}^{\infty}$ is an increasing sequence of positive real numbers. By the upper bound principle this sequence either converges to a positive real number or tends to $+$ infinity.

Definition 6.17. *Let X denote a positive random variable on the probability space $(\Omega, \mathcal{F}, P)$. If $\lim_{m \to \infty} \mathbb{E}[X^{[m]}] < \infty$, we call X an integrable random variable. If X is integrable, we let*

$$(6.15) \qquad \mathbb{E}[X] = \lim_{m \to \infty} \mathbb{E}[X^{[m]}].$$

Proposition 6.18. *Let X and Y denote positive random variables on the probability space $(\Omega, \mathcal{F}, P)$.*

(a) *If X is integrable and $(X_n)_{n=1}^{\infty}$ is an increasing sequence of positive bounded random variables converging pointwise to X, then $\mathbb{E}[X_n] \longrightarrow \mathbb{E}[X]$ as $n \to \infty$.*

(b) *If X and Y are integrable, then $X + Y$ is integrable and $\mathbb{E}[X + Y] = \mathbb{E}[X] + \mathbb{E}[Y]$.*

(c) *If X is integrable and $0 \leq Y \leq X$, then Y and $X - Y$ are integrable, $0 \leq \mathbb{E}[Y] \leq \mathbb{E}[X]$ and $\mathbb{E}[X - Y] = \mathbb{E}[X] - \mathbb{E}[Y]$.*

Proof. (a) The sequences $(X_n)_{n=1}^{\infty}$ and $(X^{[n]})_{n=1}^{\infty}$ are increasing, positive and bounded, and converge pointwise to X. By Proposition 6.14 and Definition 6.17

$$\lim_{n \to \infty} \mathbb{E}[X_n] = \lim_{n \to \infty} \mathbb{E}[X^{[n]}] = \mathbb{E}[X].$$

(b) The sequence $(X^{[n]} + Y^{[n]})_{n=1}^{\infty}$ is an increasing sequence of positive bounded random variables which converges pointwise to $X + Y$. An application of (a) and Proposition 6.16(b) prove (b).

(c) If $Y \leq X$, then $Y^{[n]} \leq X^{[n]}$ for all n, and hence $\lim_{n\to\infty} \mathbb{E}[Y^{[n]}] < \infty$. This implies that Y is integrable and clearly $\mathbb{E}[Y] \leq \mathbb{E}[X]$. Since $0 \leq X - Y \leq X$, $X - Y$ is integrable and as $X = Y + (X - Y)$ and both Y and $X - Y$ are positive, (b) implies $\mathbb{E}[X] = \mathbb{E}[Y] + \mathbb{E}[X - Y]$. This proves (c). $\qquad\square$

Sets of probability zero will play an important role from now on in our investigations. An event with probability zero may occur but only rarely, and it is plausible to suppose that a small number of such events will not influence the average or expected value. We say that two random variables X and Y on a probability space $(\Omega, \mathcal{F}, P)$ are *almost surely* equal[16] if

$$P(\{\omega \in \Omega : X(\omega) = Y(\omega)\}) = 1.$$

Lemma 6.19. *Let X and Y denote positive random variables on the probability space $(\Omega, \mathcal{F}, P)$. If X is integrable and $X = Y$ almost surely, then Y is integrable and $\mathbb{E}[X] = \mathbb{E}[Y]$.*

Proof. Let $A = \{\omega \in \Omega : X(\omega) = Y(\omega)\}$. By our hypothesis $P(A^c) = 0$. We have $X = X \cdot \mathbf{1}_A + X \cdot \mathbf{1}_{A^c}$ and $Y = X \cdot \mathbf{1}_A + Y \cdot \mathbf{1}_{A^c}$. Since $0 \leq (X \cdot \mathbf{1}_{A^c})^{[m]} \leq m \mathbf{1}_{A^c}$ for all m, $0 \leq \mathbb{E}[(X \cdot \mathbf{1}_{A^c})^{[m]}] \leq m\mathbb{E}[\mathbf{1}_{A^c}] = mP(\mathbf{1}_{A^c}) = 0$. Hence $X \cdot \mathbf{1}_{A^c}$ is integrable and $\mathbb{E}[X \cdot \mathbf{1}_{A^c}] = 0$. Similarly $Y \cdot \mathbf{1}_{A^c}$ is integrable and $\mathbb{E}[Y \cdot \mathbf{1}_{A^c}] = 0$. Since $0 \leq X \cdot \mathbf{1}_A \leq X$, Proposition 6.18(c) implies that $X \cdot \mathbf{1}_A$ is integrable. Hence $Y = X \cdot \mathbf{1}_A + Y \cdot \mathbf{1}_{A^c}$ is integrable and

$$\mathbb{E}[Y] = \mathbb{E}[X \cdot \mathbf{1}_A] + \mathbb{E}[Y \cdot \mathbf{1}_{A^c}] = \mathbb{E}[X \cdot \mathbf{1}_A] + \mathbb{E}[X \cdot \mathbf{1}_{A^c}] = \mathbb{E}[X].$$

$\qquad\square$

To obtain a flexible version of the Monotone Convergence Theorem we introduce a refinement of the notion of pointwise convergence involving sets of probability zero.

Definition 6.20. *A sequence of random variables $(X_n)_{n=1}^{\infty}$ on the probability space $(\Omega, \mathcal{F}, P)$ converges almost surely if there exists a random variable X and a set $A \in \mathcal{F}$ with $P(A) = 1$ such that $\lim_{n\to\infty} X_n(\omega) = X(\omega)$ for all $\omega \in A$. We call X an almost sure limit of the sequence $(X_n)_{n=1}^{\infty}$ and write $X = \lim_{n\to\infty} X_n$ almost surely.*

By Proposition 4.22 a sequence which converges pointwise converges almost surely, and it may appear that we are replacing a straightforward type of convergence by a weaker and more complicated version. Almost sure convergence

---

[16]Since $X - Y$ is a random variable, $(X - Y)^{-1}(\{0\}) = \{\omega \in \Omega : X(\omega) = Y(\omega)\} \in \mathcal{F}$.

makes use of the underlying probability space while pointwise convergence does not, and it is often possible to show almost sure convergence where it may be difficult or impossible to verify pointwise convergence.

There are a number of subtle points connected with almost sure convergence due, mainly, to the fact that an almost sure limit of a sequence of random variables is not in general[17] *unique*. For example, if $(\Omega, \mathcal{F}, P)$ is a probability space and there exists an $\omega_1 \in \Omega$ such that $\{\omega_1\} \in \mathcal{F}$ and $P(\{\omega_1\}) = 0$, then the sequence $(X_n)_{n=1}^{\infty}, X_n(\omega) = 0$ for all n and ω converges almost surely to the random variables $\mathbf{1}_{\{\omega_1\}}$ and $\mathbf{1}_{\emptyset}$. On the other hand, if $X_n \longrightarrow X$ and $X_n \longrightarrow Y$ almost surely as $n \longrightarrow \infty$, then there are $A, B \in \mathcal{F}$ with $P(A) = P(B) = 1$ such that $X_n(\omega) \longrightarrow X(\omega)$ for all $\omega \in A$ and $X_n(\omega) \longrightarrow Y(\omega)$ for all $\omega \in B$ as $n \longrightarrow \infty$. Hence $X(\omega) = Y(\omega)$ for all $\omega \in A \cap B$. Since

$$1 \geq P(A \cap B) = P(A) + P(B) - P(A \cup B) \geq 2 - P(A \cup B) \geq 1,$$

$X = Y$ almost surely and any two limits of an almost surely convergent sequence are equal almost surely.

In many areas of mathematics, for instance the differential calculus, non-uniqueness of limits would cause problems. We avoid such problems by being careful in our *interpretations* of what such limits mean by either specifying that we are talking only about a particular limit or using only properties *shared* by *all* limits. When the sequence $(X_n)_{n=1}^{\infty}$ on $(\Omega, \mathcal{F}, P)$ converges almost surely, the expression $(\lim_{n \to \infty} X_n)(\omega)$ for $\omega \in \Omega$ on its own is *not* defined, since if X and Y are almost sure limits of the sequence, we may very well have $X(\omega) \neq Y(\omega)$ for some ω and there is no way of choosing between them. Thus when we write $(\lim_{n \to \infty} X_n)(\omega)$ we are *assuming* we have chosen one of the almost sure limits of the sequence. As long as the result proved *does not depend* on the actual limit chosen, it can be interpreted as a result about $\lim_{n \to \infty} X_n$. When working with conditional expectation[18] and the Itô integral, most people treat almost sure limits as if they were unique and hence random variables and, having obtained results in this way, examine their proofs in order to see that they apply to all almost sure limits. We recommend this approach.

To prove our next main result, a version of the Monotone Convergence Theorem, we need the following lemma. The main technique in the proof, already used in Proposition 4.19, consists of expressing convergence statements in the language of set theory.

---

[17]This lack of uniqueness is also a feature of other modes of convergence introduced later: convergence in distribution, convergence in measure, $\mathbf{L}^1$ and $\mathbf{L}^2$ convergence. See Exercise 6.6 for examples where pointwise and almost sure convergence coincide.

[18]The general concept of conditional expectation is only defined almost surely. We establish existence in a special case which avoids this ambiguity. The Itô integral is defined using convergence in measure, which is itself defined using almost sure convergence.

Lemma 6.21. Let $(X_n)_{n=1}^{\infty}$ and $(Y_n)_{n=1}^{\infty}$ denote increasing sequences of positive random variables on the probability space $(\Omega, \mathcal{F}, P)$. Then

$$A := \{\omega \in \Omega : \lim_{n \longrightarrow \infty} X_n(\omega) = \lim_{n \longrightarrow \infty} Y_n(\omega)\} \in \mathcal{F}.$$

Proof. Since

$$A = \{\omega : \lim_{n \longrightarrow \infty} X_n(\omega) \geq \lim_{n \longrightarrow \infty} Y_n(\omega)\} \cap \{\omega : \lim_{n \longrightarrow \infty} X_n(\omega) \leq \lim_{n \longrightarrow \infty} Y_n(\omega)\}$$

it suffices, by symmetry, to show that

$$B := \{\omega \in \Omega : \lim_{n \longrightarrow \infty} X_n(\omega) \geq \lim_{n \longrightarrow \infty} Y_n(\omega)\} \in \mathcal{F}.$$

As $(Y_n)_{n=1}^{\infty}$ is increasing

$$B = \bigcap_{m=1}^{\infty} \{\omega \in \Omega : \lim_{n \longrightarrow \infty} X_n(\omega) \geq Y_m(\omega)\},$$

and it suffices to show

$$B_m = \{\omega \in \Omega : \lim_{n \longrightarrow \infty} X_n(\omega) \geq Y_m(\omega)\} \in \mathcal{F}$$

for all positive integers m. Since $\omega \in B_m$ if and only if

$$\lim_{n \longrightarrow \infty} X_n(\omega) > Y_m(\omega) - \frac{1}{k}$$

for all positive integers k

$$B_m = \bigcap_{k=1}^{\infty} \{\omega \in \Omega : \lim_{n \longrightarrow \infty} X_n(\omega) > Y_m(\omega) - \frac{1}{k}\},$$

and it suffices to show

$$B_{m,k} := \{\omega \in \Omega : \lim_{n \longrightarrow \infty} X_n(\omega) > Y_m(\omega) - \frac{1}{k}\} \in \mathcal{F}$$

for all m and k. Since $(X_n)_{n=1}^{\infty}$ is an increasing sequence

$$B_{m,k} = \bigcup_{n=1}^{\infty} \{\omega \in \Omega : X_n(\omega) > Y_m(\omega) - \frac{1}{k}\}$$

and as $\{\omega \in \Omega : X_n(\omega) > Y_m(\omega) - \frac{1}{k}\} = (X_n - Y_m)^{-1}((-\frac{1}{k}, \infty))$ and $X_n - Y_m$ is a random variable, each $B_{m,k} \in \mathcal{F}$. This completes the proof. $\square$

Our next result upgrades Proposition 6.14 and is our final extension of Proposition 6.9.

Proposition 6.22. If $(X_n)_{n=1}^{\infty}$ and $(Y_n)_{n=1}^{\infty}$ are increasing sequences of positive integrable random variables on the probability space $(\Omega, \mathcal{F}, P)$ and

$$\lim_{n \to \infty} X_n = \lim_{n \to \infty} Y_n$$

almost surely, then

(6.16)
$$\lim_{n\longrightarrow\infty} \mathbb{E}[X_n] = \lim_{n\longrightarrow\infty} \mathbb{E}[Y_n].$$

Proof. By Proposition 6.21,

$$A := \{\omega \in \Omega : \lim_{n\to\infty} X_n(\omega) = \lim_{n\to\infty} Y_n(\omega)\}$$

belongs to $\mathcal{F}$ and, by our hypothesis, $P(A) = 1$. Since $\lim_{n\to\infty} X_n(\omega) \cdot \mathbf{1}_A(\omega) = \lim_{n\to\infty} Y_n(\omega) \cdot \mathbf{1}_A(\omega)$ for all $\omega \in \Omega$, the sequences of random variables $(X_n \cdot \mathbf{1}_A)_{n=1}^{\infty}$ and $(Y_n \cdot \mathbf{1}_A)_{n=1}^{\infty}$ are increasing and converge *pointwise* to the same limit. By Lemma 6.19, $\mathbb{E}[X_n] = \mathbb{E}[X_n \cdot \mathbf{1}_A]$ and $\mathbb{E}[Y_n] = \mathbb{E}[Y_n \cdot \mathbf{1}_A]$ for all n, and we may suppose for the remainder of the proof that the sequences $(X_n)_{n=1}^{\infty}$ and $(Y_n)_{n=1}^{\infty}$ converge pointwise to the same limit.

Choose j_1 such that $\mathbb{E}[X_1] - \mathbb{E}[X_1^{[j_1]}] \leq 1/2$; then choose $j_2 > j_1$ such that $\mathbb{E}[X_2] - \mathbb{E}[X_2^{[j_2]}] \leq 1/2^2$ and inductively choose $j_{n+1} > j_n$ such that $\mathbb{E}[X_{n+1}] - \mathbb{E}[X_{n+1}^{[j_{n+1}]}] \leq 1/2^{n+1}$. Such choices are possible since each X_n is positive and integrable. Since $X_n^{[j_n]}(\omega) \leq X_n^{[j_{n+1}]}(\omega) \leq X_{n+1}^{[j_{n+1}]}(\omega)$ for all $\omega \in \Omega$, the sequence $(X_n^{[j_n]})_{n=1}^{\infty}$ is an increasing sequence of positive bounded random variables. We have

$$\lim_{n\longrightarrow\infty} \mathbb{E}[X_n] = \lim_{n\longrightarrow\infty} \mathbb{E}[X_n^{[j_n]}] + \lim_{n\longrightarrow\infty} (\mathbb{E}[X_n] - \mathbb{E}[X_n^{[j_n]}]) = \lim_{n\longrightarrow\infty} \mathbb{E}[X_n^{[j_n]}].$$

If $\lim_{n\to\infty} X_n(\omega) < \infty$, then $X_n(\omega) < j_n$ for all n sufficiently large, and hence $X_n(\omega) = X_n^{[j_n]}(\omega)$ for all n sufficiently large. If $\lim_{n\to\infty} X_n(\omega) = \infty$, then for all n we have either $X_n(\omega) - X_n^{[j_n]}(\omega) \leq 1/2^{j_n}$ or $X_n^{[j_n]}(\omega) = j_n$. Since $j_n \geq n$ we have, in either case, $\lim_{n\to\infty} X_n^{[j_n]}(\omega) = \infty$. Hence $\lim_{n\to\infty} X_n^{[j_n]}(\omega) = \lim_{n\to\infty} X_n(\omega)$ for all $\omega \in \Omega$.

Similarly we can find a strictly increasing sequence of positive integers $(k_n)_{n=1}^{\infty}$ such that $\lim_{n\to\infty} \mathbb{E}[Y_n^{[k_n]}] = \lim_{n\to\infty} \mathbb{E}[Y_n]$ and $\lim_{n\to\infty} Y_n^{[k_n]}(\omega) = \lim_{n\to\infty} Y_n(\omega)$ for all $\omega \in \Omega$. Hence $\lim_{n\to\infty} X_n^{[j_n]}(\omega) = \lim_{n\to\infty} Y_n^{[k_n]}(\omega)$ for all $\omega \in \Omega$, and as both sequences are increasing sequences of *positive bounded* random variables, an application of Proposition 6.14 completes the proof. $\square$

The following proposition will shortly be rewritten as the *Monotone Convergence Theorem.*

Proposition 6.23. *Let $(X_n)_{n=1}^{\infty}$ denote an increasing sequence of positive integrable random variables on the probability space $(\Omega, \mathcal{F}, P)$. There exists an integrable random variable X on Ω such that $X_n \longrightarrow X$ almost surely as $n \longrightarrow \infty$ if and only if $\lim_{n\to\infty} \mathbb{E}[X_n] < \infty$. When the limit is finite we have*

$$\mathbb{E}[X] = \lim_{n\to\infty} \mathbb{E}[X_n].$$

Proof. Let $A = \{\omega \in \Omega : \lim_{n\to\infty} X_n(\omega) = +\infty\}$. Application of Lemma 6.21 with $Y_n(\omega) = n$ for all n and ω and X_n as above shows that $A \in \mathcal{F}$. If n and m are positive integers, let $A_{n,m} = \{\omega \in \Omega : X_n(\omega) \geq m\}$. Since $(X_n)_{n=1}^\infty$ is increasing, the sequence $(A_{n,m})_{n=1}^\infty$ is an increasing sequence of $\mathcal{F}$ measurable sets and $A \subset \lim_{n\to\infty} A_{n,m}$. By Proposition 5.3, $\lim_{n\to\infty} P(A_{n,m}) \geq P(A)$. For all n, $X_n \geq X_n \cdot \mathbf{1}_{A_{n,m}} \geq m\mathbf{1}_{A_{n,m}}$. By Proposition 6.18(c),

$$(6.17) \qquad \lim_{n\to\infty} \mathbb{E}[X_n] \geq \lim_{n\to\infty} \mathbb{E}[m\mathbf{1}_{A_{n,m}}] \geq mP(A).$$

First suppose $P(A) > 0$. Since m was arbitrary (6.17) implies $\lim_{n\to\infty} \mathbb{E}[X_n] = \infty$. If $\lim_{n\to\infty} X_n(\omega) = X(\omega)$ for all $\omega \in B$, where B is an $\mathcal{F}$ measurable set with $P(B) = 1$, then $P(A) = P(A \cap B) + P(A \cap B^c) = P(A \cap B) > 0$ since $0 \leq P(A \cap B^c) \leq P(B^c) = 0$. Hence $X \geq m\mathbf{1}_{A \cap B}$ for any positive integer m. Since $X(\omega) \geq m$ for $\omega \in A \cap B$ and every positive integer m, the sequence $(X_n)_{n=1}^\infty$ does not converge almost surely to any (real-valued) random variable.[19] This completes the proof when $P(A) > 0$.

If $P(A) = 0$, the sequence $(X_n)_{n=1}^\infty$ converges almost surely to a random variable that we denote by X. The increasing sequences of positive random variables, $(X_n)_{n=1}^\infty$ and $(X^{[n]})_{n=1}^\infty$, converge almost surely to the same limit X. By Proposition 6.22

$$(6.18) \qquad \lim_{n\to\infty} \mathbb{E}[X_n] = \lim_{n\to\infty} \mathbb{E}[X^{[n]}].$$

By definition X is integrable if and only if the right-hand side of (6.18) is finite while the finiteness of the left-hand side is our hypothesis. Since the limit on the right-hand side is $\mathbb{E}[X]$ this completes the proof. $\qquad\square$

It is interesting to compare the *upper bound principle* and the Monotone Convergence Theorem. Both state that an increasing sequence converges if and only if it is bounded, and both imply the *existence* of a limit under very weak assumptions. We now interpret the above results using integral notation. Let X denote a positive random variable on the probability space $(\Omega, \mathcal{F}, P)$. Let Y_n denote the nth term in the canonical sequence for $X^{[n]}$. If $\omega \in \Omega$, then, since $X(\omega) < \infty$, we have $X^{[n]}(\omega) = X(\omega)$ for all n sufficiently large. By Lemma 6.10(a), $|X^{[n]}(\omega) - Y_n(\omega)| \leq 1/2^n$. Hence $(Y_n)_{n=1}^\infty$ converges pointwise to X. Moreover, since $X^{[n]} \leq X^{[n+1]}$ we have $Y_n \leq Y_{n+1}$, and by (6.10) or (6.19) below each Y_n is $\mathcal{F}_X$ measurable. We have proved the following result.

Proposition 6.24. *If X is a positive random variable on the probability space $(\Omega, \mathcal{F}, P)$, then X is the pointwise limit of an increasing sequence of simple positive $\mathcal{F}_X$ measurable random variables.*

---

[19]Even if the sequence converged to a random variable, the limit would not be integrable since we would have $\mathbb{E}[X] \geq mP(A \cap B)$ for all $m > 0$.

We keep the above notation but now suppose that X is integrable. Then $(\mathbb{E}[Y_n])_{n=1}^{\infty}$ is an increasing sequence that converges to $\mathbb{E}[X]$. If $I_{j,k}^n$ is defined by (6.9) and $J_n = \{\omega \in \Omega : X(\omega) \geq n\}$, then (6.10) implies

$$(6.19) \qquad Y_n = \sum_{k=0}^{n} \sum_{j=0}^{2^n-1} (k + \frac{j}{2^n}) \mathbf{1}_{X^{-1}(I_{j,k}^n)} + n \mathbf{1}_{J_n}.$$

The analysis used to derive (6.13) is still valid and shows that

$$(6.20) \qquad \mathbb{E}[X] = \lim_{n \to \infty} \sum_{k=0}^{n} \sum_{j=0}^{2^n-1} X(\omega_{j,k}) P(X^{-1}(I_{j,k}^n)) + n P(J_n).$$

In view of (6.19) and (6.20) we *define* for any positive integrable random variable X on $(\Omega, \mathcal{F}, P)$

$$\int_{\Omega} X \, dP =: \mathbb{E}[X].$$

The following is a restatement of Proposition 6.23.

Proposition 6.25. (*Monotone Convergence Theorem*) *If $(X_n)_{n=1}^{\infty}$ is an increasing sequence of positive integrable random variables on the probability space $(\Omega, \mathcal{F}, P)$, then there exists an integrable random variable X such that $X_n \longrightarrow X$ almost surely as $n \longrightarrow \infty$ if and only if $\lim_{n \to \infty} \int_{\Omega} X_n dP < \infty$. When this limit is finite we have*[20]

$$(6.21) \qquad \int_{\Omega} (\lim_{n \to \infty} X_n) dP = \int_{\Omega} X \, dP = \lim_{n \to \infty} \int_{\Omega} X_n dP.$$

Our final result in this section shows how positive integrable random variables can be used to construct new probability measures. The converse, the Radon-Nikodým Theorem (Proposition 8.6), is much deeper.

Proposition 6.26. *Let X denote a positive integrable random variable on the probability space $(\Omega, \mathcal{F}, P)$ and suppose $\mathbb{E}[X] = 1$. If for each $A \in \mathcal{F}$ we let $Q(A) = \int_A X \, dP = \int_{\Omega} (X \cdot \mathbf{1}_A) dP$, then $(\Omega, \mathcal{F}, Q)$ is a probability space. If Y is a positive*[21] *integrable random variable on $(\Omega, \mathcal{F}, Q)$, then*

$$\int_A Y \, dQ = \int_A X \cdot Y \, dP$$

---

[20]It is possible and useful to interpret (6.21) even when the limit on the right-hand side is $+\infty$. In this case, see the proof of Proposition 6.23, the left-hand side is interpreted as follows: either $(X_n)_{n=1}^{\infty}$ converges to $+\infty$ on a set of positive measure (and thus cannot converge almost surely to any random variable) or converges almost surely to a non-integrable random variable. A similar interpretation holds for Fatou's Lemma (see Proposition 6.30). It is convenient to let $\mathbb{E}[X] = \int_{\Omega} X \, dP = +\infty$ if $X \geq 0$ and X is non-integrable.

[21]The representation of positive Q integrable random variables given here, extends easily using results in the next section, to *arbitrary integrable random variables*.

for all $A \in \mathcal{F}$. Moreover, if $A \in \mathcal{F}$ and $P(A) = 0$, then $Q(A) = 0$.[22]

Proof. We are required to verify the axioms in Definition 5.2. If $A \in \mathcal{F}$, then $0 \leq X \cdot \mathbf{1}_A \leq X$. By Proposition 6.18(c), $0 \leq Q(A) = \int_\Omega X \cdot \mathbf{1}_A dP \leq \int_\Omega X dP = Q(\Omega) = \mathbb{E}[X] = 1$. Hence $0 \leq Q(A) \leq 1$ for all $A \in \mathcal{F}$ and $Q(\Omega) = 1$. If $(A_n)_{n=1}^\infty$ is a sequence of pairwise disjoint $\mathcal{F}$ measurable sets in Ω, let $X_m = X \cdot \mathbf{1}_{\cup_{n=1}^m A_n} = \sum_{n=1}^m X \cdot \mathbf{1}_{A_n}$ for any positive integer m. Then $(X_m)_{m=1}^\infty$ is an increasing sequence of positive integrable random variables which converges pointwise to $X \cdot \mathbf{1}_{\cup_{n=1}^\infty A_n}$. By the Monotone Convergence Theorem

$$Q(\bigcup_{n=1}^\infty A_n) = \int_\Omega (X \cdot \mathbf{1}_{\cup_{n=1}^\infty A_n}) dP = \lim_{m \to \infty} \int_\Omega (X \cdot \mathbf{1}_{\cup_{n=1}^m A_n}) dP$$

$$= \lim_{m \to \infty} \int_\Omega \left(\sum_{n=1}^m X \cdot \mathbf{1}_{A_n} \right) dP = \lim_{m \to \infty} \sum_{n=1}^m \left(\int_\Omega X \cdot \mathbf{1}_{A_n} dP \right)$$

$$= \lim_{m \to \infty} \sum_{n=1}^m Q(A_n) = \sum_{n=1}^\infty Q(A_n)$$

and (5.4) holds. Hence Q is a probability measure.

If $Y := \sum_{i=1}^n c_i \mathbf{1}_{A_i}$ is a simple random variable, then

$$\int_\Omega Y dQ = \sum_{i=1}^n c_i Q(A_i) = \sum_{i=1}^n c_i \int_{A_i} X dP$$

$$= \int_\Omega \left(\sum_{i=1}^n c_i \mathbf{1}_{A_i} \right) \cdot X dP = \int_\Omega Y \cdot X dP.$$

The Monotone Convergence Theorem can now be employed to prove the same result for (positive) integrable random variables.

If $P(A) = 0$, the sequence $(Y_n)_{n=1}^\infty$ of random variables, with $Y_n(\omega) = 0$ for all n and ω, is positive, increasing and converges almost surely to $X \cdot \mathbf{1}_A$. By the Monotone Convergence Theorem, $Q(A) = \int_\Omega X \cdot \mathbf{1}_A dP = \lim_{n \to \infty} \int_\Omega Y_n dP = 0$. This completes the proof. $\qquad\square$

6.4. Integrable Random Variables

In this section we define arbitrary integrable random variables and prove the *Dominated Convergence Theorem*.

---

[22]If $Q(A) = 0$ whenever $P(A) = 0$ for probability measures P and Q, Q is said to be *absolutely continuous* with respect to P and we write $Q \ll P$. We call X the *Radon–Nikodým derivative* of Q with respect to P and write $X = \frac{dQ}{dP}$.

Definition 6.27. *A random variable X on a probability space $(\Omega, \mathcal{F}, P)$ is integrable if its positive and negative parts, X^+ and X^-, are both integrable. If X is integrable we let*

$$\mathbb{E}[X] := \mathbb{E}[X^+] - \mathbb{E}[X^-] = \int_\Omega X^+ dP - \int_\Omega X^- dP = \int_\Omega X\, dP.$$

We call $\int_\Omega X\, dP$ the Lebesgue integral of X over Ω with respect to P and let $\mathbf{L}^1(\Omega, \mathcal{F}, P)$ denote the set of all integrable random variables on $(\Omega, \mathcal{F}, P)$.

The following proposition is an easy consequence of earlier results.

Proposition 6.28. *Let X and Y denote random variables on the probability space $(\Omega, \mathcal{F}, P)$.*

(a) *X is the pointwise limit of a sequence of $\mathcal{F}_X$ measurable simple random variables $(X_n)_{n=1}^\infty$ such that $|X_n| \leq |X|$ for all n.*

(b) *X is integrable if and only if $|X|$ is integrable.*

(c) *If X is integrable, then $|\mathbb{E}[X]| \leq \mathbb{E}[|X|]$.*

(d) *If $|Y| \leq |X|$ and X is integrable, then Y is integrable.*

(e) *If X and Y are integrable random variables and c is a real number, then $X \pm Y$ and cX are integrable.[23]*

Proof. (a) follows from applying Proposition 6.24 to X^+ and X^-. By (6.10), the simple random variables used to approximate X^+ and X^- are $\mathcal{F}_X$ measurable. If X is integrable, then X^+ and X^- are positive integrable random variables. By Proposition 6.18(b), $|X| = X^+ + X^-$ is integrable. If $|X|$ is integrable, then, since $0 \leq X^+ \leq |X|$ and $0 \leq X^- \leq |X|$, Proposition 6.18(c) implies that X^+ and X^- and hence X, are integrable. We also have $|\mathbb{E}[X]| = |\mathbb{E}[X^+] - \mathbb{E}[X^-]| \leq \mathbb{E}[X^+] + \mathbb{E}[X^-] = \mathbb{E}[|X|]$. This proves (b) and (c).

If $|Y| \leq |X|$, then $|Y^+| \leq |X|$ and $|Y^-| \leq |X|$. By Proposition 6.18(c), Y^+ and Y^- are integrable and hence Y is integrable. This proves (d).

If X and Y are integrable, then (b) shows that $|X|$ and $|Y|$ are positive integrable random variables. By Proposition 6.18(b), $|X| + |Y|$ is integrable. Since $|X \pm Y| \leq |X| + |Y|$, (d) shows that $X \pm Y$ is integrable. The remaining assertion is a simple exercise. □

Increasing sequences of real numbers and the upper bound principle were our two main tools in the development of positive integrable random variables. For arbitrary integrable random variables we require arbitrary sequences of real numbers. By Definition 4.16, convergence of a sequence of real numbers

---

[23]This shows that the integrable random variables form a vector space. Note that we have not yet shown that $\mathbb{E}[\cdot]$ is a linear operator and, in particular, that $\mathbb{E}[X + Y] = \mathbb{E}[X] + \mathbb{E}[Y]$.

is equivalent to the convergence of two sequences of real numbers, one *increasing* and one *decreasing*. To obtain our main convergence result for integrable random variables, *The Dominated Convergence Theorem*, we need to refine this equivalence.

Let $(a_n)_{n=1}^{\infty}$ denote a sequence of real numbers that is bounded above by M. If the sequence contains an element a_{n_0} such that $a_n \le a_{n_0}$ for all n, then clearly a_{n_0} is a least upper bound for the sequence. If no such n_0 exists, we consider the interval $(a_1, M]$ and divide it into two non-overlapping intervals J_1 and J_2 of equal length (see Figure 6.11):

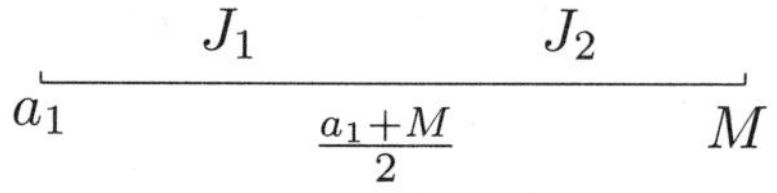

$$\underset{a_1 \qquad\qquad\qquad \frac{a_1+M}{2} \qquad\qquad M}{\underbrace{\qquad\overset{J_1}{\qquad\qquad}\qquad}\overbrace{\qquad\overset{J_2}{\qquad\qquad}\qquad}}$$

Figure 6.11

One of these intervals must contain a point from the sequence. If both intervals contain points from the sequence, we choose a point a_{n_1} from the interval on the right. Next consider the interval $(a_{n_1}, M] \cap J_i$ where $a_{n_1} \in J_i$ and again divide it in two. One of these intervals must contain a point a_{n_2} from the sequence with $n_2 > n_1$, as otherwise we would have $a_n \le a_{n_1}$ for all $n \ge n_1$, and then the least upper bound of the sequence would be one of the finite set $\{a_1, \ldots, a_{n_1}\}$. Choose such an n_2, with a_{n_2} from the right-hand interval if available. Continuing in this way we generate an increasing subsequence $(a_{n_j})_{j=1}^{\infty}$ of $(a_n)_{n=1}^{\infty}$ which is bounded above by M. By the upper bound principle this sequence converges to a real number m. By our construction $a_n \le a_{n_j} + \frac{l}{2^j}$ for all n and j where $l = M - a_1$. Hence $a_n \le \lim_{j\to\infty} a_{n_j} + \lim_{j\to\infty} 1/2^j = m$. This shows that m is an upper bound and, as $\lim_{j\to\infty} a_{n_j} = m$, it is a least upper bound. We have shown that any sequence with an upper bound has a least upper bound. Similarly any sequence $(a_n)_{n=1}^{\infty}$ which has a lower bound has a *greatest lower bound*. Hence any bounded sequence has a least upper bound and a greatest lower bound.

We now fix a bounded sequence of real numbers $(a_n)_{n=1}^{\infty}$, and for each positive integer n we let $u_n := \sup_{m \ge n} a_m$ denote the least upper bound and let $l_n := \inf_{m \ge n} a_m$ denote the greatest lower bound of the sequence $(a_m)_{m \ge n}$. Clearly

(6.22) $$l_n \le l_m \le a_m \le u_m \le u_n$$

for all positive integers n and $m, n \le m$. The sequence $(l_n)_{n=1}^{\infty}$ is an increasing bounded sequence and $(u_n)_{n=1}^{\infty}$ is a decreasing bounded sequence. By the upper bound principle both sequences converge.[24] We denote the limit of the

---

[24]Apply the upper bound principle to the sequence $(-u_n)_{n=1}^{\infty}$ to obtain convergence.

sequence $(l_n)_{n=1}^{\infty}$ by $\liminf_{n\to\infty} a_n$ and the limit of the sequence $(u_n)_{n=1}^{\infty}$ by $\limsup_{n\to\infty} a_n$. By Definition 4.16 and (6.22), the sequence $(a_n)_{n=1}^{\infty}$ converges if $\limsup_{n\to\infty} a_n = \liminf_{n\to\infty} a_n$. Conversely, if the sequence $(a_n)_{n=1}^{\infty}$ converges to a real number a, then given any positive number ϵ there exists, by Lemma 4.17, a positive integer n_0 such that $a_n \in [a - \epsilon, a + \epsilon]$ for all $n \geq n_0$. Hence $a - \epsilon \leq l_n \leq a_n \leq u_n \leq a + \epsilon$ for all $n \geq n_0$. Since ϵ was arbitrary this implies $\limsup_{n\to\infty} a_n = \liminf_{n\to\infty} a_n$. This proves part (a) of the following proposition. Part (b) will be used in Chapter 7 to show that continuous functions on a closed interval have a maximum and a minimum and are uniformly continuous.

Proposition 6.29. (a) *A bounded sequence of real numbers $(a_n)_{n=1}^{\infty}$ converges if and only if*

$$\liminf_{n\to\infty} a_n = \limsup_{n\longrightarrow\infty} a_n.$$

When the sequence converges we have

$$\liminf_{n\longrightarrow\infty} a_n = \lim_{n\longrightarrow\infty} a_n = \limsup_{n\longrightarrow\infty} a_n.$$

(b) *Every bounded sequence of real numbers has a convergent subsequence.*

Proof. (b) We use the above notation. For each positive integer n there exists a positive integer $j_n \geq n$ such that $u_n - (1/n) < a_{j_n} \leq u_n$. By taking a subsequence, if necessary, we may suppose that the sequence $(j_n)_{n=1}^{\infty}$ is strictly increasing. Since the sequence $(u_n)_{n=1}^{\infty}$ converges the sequence $(a_{j_n})_{n=1}^{\infty}$ also converges and $(a_{j_n})_{n=1}^{\infty}$ is a subsequence of $(a_n)_{n=1}^{\infty}$. This completes the proof. $\square$

The upper bound principle enabled us to determine if the limit of an *increasing* (or decreasing) sequence *exists* without prior knowledge of the actual limit. Using Proposition 6.29 we obtain a similar rule for *arbitrary* sequences. A sequence of real numbers $(a_n)_{n=1}^{\infty}$ is called a *Cauchy sequence* if $\lim_{n,m\to\infty} |a_n - a_m| = 0$; that is, given any $\epsilon > 0$ there exists a positive integer n_0 such that $|a_n - a_m| < \epsilon$ for all $n \geq n_0$ and all $m \geq n_0$. Clearly every convergent sequence is a Cauchy sequence. Conversely suppose $(a_n)_{n=1}^{\infty}$ is a Cauchy sequence. Then, given $\epsilon > 0$ choose n_0 as above. Since $|a_n - a_{n_0}| < \epsilon$ for all $n \geq n_0$ we have $a_{n_0} - \epsilon < a_n < a_{n_0} + \epsilon$ for all $n \geq n_0$. Hence

$$a_{n_0} - \epsilon \leq \inf_{n\geq n_0} a_n \leq \liminf_{n\longrightarrow\infty} a_n \leq \limsup_{n\longrightarrow\infty} a_n \leq \sup_{n\geq n_0} a_n \leq a_{n_0} + \epsilon$$

and

$$|\liminf_{n\longrightarrow\infty} a_n - \limsup_{n\longrightarrow\infty} a_n| \leq 2\epsilon.$$

Since ϵ was arbitrary this implies $\liminf_{n\to\infty} a_n = \limsup_{n\to\infty} a_n$ and, by Proposition 6.29, the sequence converges. We have proved the *Cauchy Convergence Criterion*: every Cauchy sequence of real numbers converges.

We now prove one of the main results in Lebesgue Integration Theory.

Proposition 6.30. (*Dominated Convergence Theorem*)[25] *Let* $(X_n)_{n=1}^{\infty}$ *denote a sequence of random variables on the probability space* $(\Omega, \mathcal{F}, P)$ *and suppose* $(X_n)_{n=1}^{\infty}$ *converges almost surely to the random variable* X. *If there exists an integrable random variable* Y *such that for all* n, $|X_n| \leq Y$ *almost surely, then* X *and each* X_n *are integrable and*

$$\lim_{n\to\infty} \int_{\Omega} X_n dP = \int_{\Omega} X dP.$$

Proof. First suppose that each X_n is positive. Let $Z_n = \inf_{m \geq n} X_m$ for any positive integer n. If $a \in \mathbf{R}$ and $\omega \in \Omega$, then $Z_n(\omega) < a$ if and only if $X_m(\omega) < a$ for *at least* one $m \geq n$. Hence

$$Z_n^{-1}((-\infty, a)) = \bigcup_{m \geq n} X_m^{-1}((-\infty, a)).$$

By Exercise 4.1 and Proposition 4.7, Z_n is measurable. Since $0 \leq Z_n \leq X_n$ for all n, Proposition 6.18(c) implies that Z_n is integrable. The sequence $(Z_n)_{n=1}^{\infty}$ is an increasing sequence of positive integrable random variables which converges almost surely to $\liminf_{n\to\infty} X_n$. By the Monotone Convergence Theorem

$$\lim_{n\to\infty} \int_{\Omega} Z_n dP = \int_{\Omega} (\liminf_{n\to\infty} X_n) dP.$$

Since $X_n \geq Z_n$, Proposition 6.18(c) implies $\int_{\Omega} X_n dP \geq \int_{\Omega} Z_n dP$ and hence[26]

$$(6.23) \quad \liminf_{n\to\infty} \int_{\Omega} X_n dP \geq \lim_{n\to\infty} \int_{\Omega} Z_n dP = \int_{\Omega} (\liminf_{n\to\infty} X_n) dP.$$

---

[25]If

$$f_n(x) = \begin{cases} n^2 x & \text{if } 0 \leq x \leq 1/n, \\ -n^2(x - \frac{2}{n}) & \text{if } 1/n \leq x \leq 2/n, \\ 0 & \text{if } 2/n \leq 1, \end{cases}$$

then $(f_n)_{n=1}^{\infty}$ is a sequence of continuous functions which converges pointwise to 0 on $[0, 1]$. However, $\lim_{n\to\infty} \int_0^1 f_n(x) d\mathbf{m} = 1 \neq \int_0^1 (\lim_{n\to\infty} f_n) d\mathbf{m}$ where $\mathbf{m}$ is Lebesgue measure on $[0, 1]$ (see Propositions 7.15 and 7.16). This shows that the *dominated* hypothesis is necessary in Proposition 6.30.

[26]Inequality (6.23) is an important result known as *Fatou's Lemma*. In proving it we assumed only that each X_n was a positive integrable random variable. If the left-hand side of (6.23) equals $+\infty$, we interpret it as saying that either (a) $\liminf_{n\to\infty} X_n(\omega) = +\infty$ on a set of positive measure or (b) $\liminf_{n\to\infty} X_n(\omega)$ is almost surely equal to a non-integrable random variable (see Proposition 6.23). Pierre Joseph Fatou (1878-1929) was a French mathematician and astronomer who worked in harmonic and complex analysis and measure theory.

If $(X_n)_{n=1}^{\infty}$ converges almost surely to the random variable X, then $\liminf\limits_{n \to \infty} X_n$ $= X$ almost surely, and by (6.23),

$$(6.24) \qquad \liminf_{n \to \infty} \int_{\Omega} X_n dP \geq \int_{\Omega} X dP.$$

Let $W_n = \sup_{m \geq n} X_n$. Then, as for Z_n, W_n is a random variable on $(\Omega, \mathcal{F}, P)$ and $(W_n)_{n=1}^{\infty}$ is a decreasing sequence of random variables which converges almost surely to X. Hence $(Y - W_n)_{n=1}^{\infty}$ is an increasing sequence of positive random variables which converges almost surely to $Y - X$ as $n \longrightarrow \infty$. By the Monotone Convergence Theorem

$$\int_{\Omega} (Y - X) dP = \lim_{n \to \infty} \int_{\Omega} (Y - W_n) dP.$$

Since $0 \leq X \leq Y$ and $0 \leq W_n \leq Y$ almost surely, Proposition 6.18(c) implies $\int_{\Omega} (Y - X) dP = \int_{\Omega} Y dP - \int_{\Omega} X dP$ and $\int_{\Omega} (Y - W_n) dP = \int_{\Omega} Y dP - \int_{\Omega} W_n dP$ for all n. Hence

$$\int_{\Omega} X dP = \lim_{n \to \infty} \int_{\Omega} W_n dP.$$

Since $W_n \geq X_n$ we have $\int_{\Omega} W_n dP \geq \int_{\Omega} X_n dP$ and

$$(6.25) \qquad \int_{\Omega} X dP = \lim_{n \to \infty} \int_{\Omega} W_n dP \geq \limsup_{n \to \infty} \int_{\Omega} X_n dP.$$

Combining (6.24) and (6.25) we obtain

$$\liminf_{n \to \infty} \int_{\Omega} X_n dP \geq \limsup_{n \to \infty} \int_{\Omega} X_n dP.$$

Since we always have

$$\liminf_{n \to \infty} \int_{\Omega} X_n dP \leq \limsup_{n \to \infty} \int_{\Omega} X_n dP$$

this implies

$$\liminf_{n \to \infty} \int_{\Omega} X_n dP = \limsup_{n \to \infty} \int_{\Omega} X_n dP.$$

By Proposition 6.29(a), (6.24) and (6.25)

$$\lim_{n \to \infty} \int_{\Omega} X_n dP = \int_{\Omega} X dP.$$

This completes the proof when each X_n is positive.

If X_n is arbitrary we apply the above result to the positive sequences $(X_n^+)_{n=1}^{\infty}$ and $(X_n^-)_{n=1}^{\infty}$. Since X_n^+ and X_n^- converge almost surely to X^+ and

X^-, respectively, as $n \longrightarrow \infty$, we obtain $\lim_{n \to \infty} \int_\Omega X_n^+ dP = \int_\Omega X^+ dP$ and $\lim_{n \to \infty} \int_\Omega X_n^- dP = \int_\Omega X^- dP$. Hence

$$
\begin{aligned}
\lim_{n \longrightarrow \infty} \int_\Omega X_n dP &= \lim_{n \longrightarrow \infty} \left(\int_\Omega X_n^+ dP - \int_\Omega X_n^- dP \right) \\
&= \left(\lim_{n \longrightarrow \infty} \int_\Omega X_n^+ dP \right) - \left(\lim_{n \longrightarrow \infty} \int_\Omega X_n^- dP \right) \\
&= \int_\Omega X^+ dP - \int_\Omega X^- dP \\
&= \int_\Omega X dP.
\end{aligned}
$$

This completes the proof. □

Proposition 6.31. *If X and Y are integrable random variables on $(\Omega, \mathcal{F}, P)$, then $\mathbb{E}[X + Y] = \mathbb{E}[X] + \mathbb{E}[Y]$.*

Proof. By Proposition 6.28(e) $X + Y$ is integrable, and by Proposition 6.24, there exist increasing sequences, $(U_n)_{n=1}^\infty, (V_n)_{n=1}^\infty, (W_n)_{n=1}^\infty$, and $(Z_n)_{n=1}^\infty$, of simple positive random variables which converge pointwise to X^+, X^-, Y^+ and Y^-, respectively. The sequences $(U_n - V_n)_{n=1}^\infty, (W_n - Z_n)_{n=1}^\infty$ and $(U_n - V_n + W_n - Z_n)_{n=1}^\infty$ converge pointwise to X, Y and $X + Y$, respectively, as $n \longrightarrow \infty$. Since $|U_n - V_n| \leq |X|, |W_n - Z_n| \leq |Y|$ and $|U_n - V_n + W_n - Z_n| \leq |X| + |Y|$ for all n, the Dominated Convergence Theorem implies that $\mathbb{E}[U_n - V_n], \mathbb{E}[W_n - Z_n]$ and $\mathbb{E}[U_n - V_n + W_n - Z_n]$ tend to $\mathbb{E}[X], \mathbb{E}[Y]$ and $\mathbb{E}[X + Y]$, respectively, as $n \longrightarrow \infty$. By Proposition 6.6(a), $\mathbb{E}[U_n - V_n + W_n - Z_n] = \mathbb{E}[U_n - V_n] + \mathbb{E}[W_n - Z_n]$. Hence

$$
\begin{aligned}
\mathbb{E}[X + Y] &= \lim_{n \longrightarrow \infty} \mathbb{E}[U_n - V_n + W_n - Z_n] \\
&= \lim_{n \longrightarrow \infty} \mathbb{E}[U_n - V_n] + \mathbb{E}[W_n - Z_n] \\
&= \mathbb{E}[X] + \mathbb{E}[Y].
\end{aligned}
$$

This completes the proof. □

Similar arguments shows that cX is integrable for $c \in \mathbf{R}$. This shows that the operator $\mathbb{E}[\cdot]$ is a linear[27] operator on the vector space of integrable random variables. We have a choice of notation for expected values and any statement

---

[27]Linearity is at the heart of any measuring process and is the point of departure for the P.J. Daniell (1889-1946)-F. Riesz (1880-1956) approach to integration theory. If T is a real-valued linear operator on $\mathcal{C}([a,b])$, the continuous real-valued functions on $[a, b]$, such that $T(\mathbf{1}_{[a,b]}) = 1$ and $T(f) \geq 0$ whenever $f \geq 0$, then there exists a unique Borel probability measure P on $[a, b]$ such that $T(f) = \int_{[a,b]} f dP$ for all $f \in \mathcal{C}([a,b])$. Stefan Banach (1892-1945) in an appendix to *Theory of the Integral* by Stanislaw Saks, Dover Edition, 1964, showed that the abstract Lebesgue Integral is the unique linear operator that satisfies abstract Monotone Convergence and Dominated Convergence Theorems. This partially explains the importance of linearity and why proving it is non-trivial.

involving $\mathbb{E}[\cdot]$ can be rewritten using integral notation. For example, the above proposition says the following: if X and Y are integrable functions on the probability space $(\Omega, \mathcal{F}, P)$, then

$$\int_\Omega (X+Y)dP = \int_\Omega X dP + \int_\Omega Y dP.$$

We complete this section by noting that the construction used in Proposition 6.26 and the Dominated Convergence Theorem can be combined to prove the following result. If X is an integrable random variable on the probability space $(\Omega, \mathcal{F}, P)$ and $(A_n)_{n=1}^\infty$ is a sequence of pairwise disjoint $\mathcal{F}$ measurable subsets of Ω, then

$$\int_{\cup_{n=1}^\infty A_n} X dP = \sum_{n=1}^\infty \int_{A_n} X dP.$$

This reduces to axiom (5.4) for a probability space when $X = \mathbf{1}_\Omega$.

6.5. Exercises

(6.1) Give a simple example, say on a set with two elements, of a random variable X such that $\mathbb{E}[X^2] \neq \mathbb{E}[X]^2$.

(6.2) Let $X : [0,1) \longrightarrow \mathbf{R}, X(x) = x^2$. Sketch X and the approximations X_1 and X_2 to X. Write, in canonical form, X_1 and X_2.

(6.3) Let $\Omega = \{1,2,3,4,5,6\}, \mathcal{F} = 2^\Omega$, $P(\{i\}) = 1/12$ for $i \leq 3$ and $P(\{i\}) = a/i$ for $i > 3$. Let $X(i) = i^2$ for $i \leq 4$ and $X(5) = X(6) = 2$. If $A = \{1,2,5\}$ and $g(x) = x^3, x \in \mathbf{R}$, evaluate $\int_A g(X)dP$ and $\int_{-10}^{3.5} g dP_X$. Find $\mathbb{E}[g(X)]$.

(6.4) If X is an integrable random variable on $(\Omega, \mathcal{F}, P)$ and $\mathbb{E}[|X|] = 0$, show that $X = 0$ almost surely.

(6.5) If X and Y are random variables on $(\Omega, \mathcal{F}, P)$, with X integrable and $|Y| \leq M$ almost surely, show that $X \cdot Y$ is integrable and that $|\mathbb{E}[X \cdot Y]| \leq M \cdot \mathbb{E}[|X|]$.

(6.6) Let $\Omega = \{\omega_n\}_{n=1}^\infty$, $\mathcal{F} = 2^\Omega$ and let P denote a probability measure on $(\Omega, \mathcal{F})$. If $P(\{\omega_n\}) > 0$ for all n, show that pointwise and almost sure convergence for *sequences* of random variables coincide.

(6.7) Give an example of an integrable random variable X such that X^2 is not integrable. Hint: consider $P(\{n\}) = 1/2^n$ and $X(n) = r^n$.

(6.8) Let X denote a random variable on $(\Omega, \mathcal{F}, P)$. If $n \in \mathbf{N}$, let $A_n = \{\omega \in \Omega : 2^n \leq |X(\omega)| < 2^{n+1}\}$. Show that X is integrable if and only if $\sum_{n=1}^\infty 2^n P(A_n) < \infty$.

(6.9) Let $\Omega = \mathbf{N}, \mathcal{F} = 2^{\mathbf{N}}$, $P(\{n\}) = a2^{-n}$ and $Q(\{n\}) = b3^{-n}$ for all n. If $(\Omega, \mathcal{F}, P)$ and $(\Omega, \mathcal{F}, Q)$ are probability spaces, find a and b. Find $\frac{dP}{dQ}(n)$ and $\frac{dQ}{dP}(n)$ and the relationship between them.

(6.10) If the random variable X has a Poisson distribution with parameter α, calculate $\mathbb{E}[X^2]$ and $\mathbb{E}[e^X]$.

(6.11) If $\Omega = [0,1], \mathcal{F}$ is the set of Borel subsets of $[0,1]$, $P([a,b]) = b - a$ for any interval $[a,b] \in [0,1]$ and $\mathbf{Q}([0,1]) := (q_n)_{n=1}^{\infty}$ is the sets of non-zero rational numbers in $[0,1]$, find $\mathbb{E}[\mathbf{1}_{\mathbf{Q}([0,1])}]$ and $\mathbb{E}[\sum_{n=1}^{\infty} \frac{1}{q_n} \mathbf{1}_{\{q_n\}}]$.

(6.12) Use the Dominated Convergence Theorem to prove the following. Let $(A_m)_{m=1}^{\infty}$ denote a *sequence* of sequences where $A_m = (a_{n,m})_{n=1}^{\infty}$ for all m. Suppose $\lim_{m \to \infty} a_{n,m}$ exists for all n and there exists convergent sequences of strictly positive real numbers $(a_n)_{n=1}^{\infty}$ and $(b_n)_{n=1}^{\infty}$ such that $\sum_{n=1}^{\infty} a_n b_n < \infty$ and $|a_{n,m}| \leq a_n$ for all n and m. Show that

$$\lim_{m \to \infty} \left(\sum_{n=1}^{\infty} a_{n,m} b_n \right) = \sum_{n=1}^{\infty} \left(\lim_{m \to \infty} a_{n,m} \right) b_n.$$

(6.13) Show that $(a_n)_{n=1}^{\infty}$ is a Cauchy sequence of real numbers if and only if $\lim_{j \to \infty}(a_{n_{j+1}} - a_{n_j}) = 0$ for every strictly increasing sequence of positive integers $(n_j)_{j=1}^{\infty}$.

(6.14) Let X denote a random variable on $(\Omega, \mathcal{F}, P)$ and let $f : \mathbf{R} \mapsto [0,1]$ be Borel measurable. If $A, B \in \mathcal{F}$, $f(A) = 1$ and $f(B) = 0$, show that $P(A) \leq \mathbb{E}[f(X)] \leq 1 - P(B)$.

Chapter 7

Continuity and Integrability

Every measure of a quantity is a real number.

René Descartes, 1596-1650

Summary

We prove fundamental results about continuous and convex real-valued functions and construct the Lebesgue integral on product spaces. The relationship between the Lebesgue integral, the Riemann integral and absolute convergence of series is discussed; independent random variables are characterized using expected values; and we state without proof the Central Limit Theorem.

7.1. Summation of Series

We consider the simplest example of the Lebesgue integral involving limits. Let $\Omega = (\omega_n)_{n=1}^{\infty}, \mathcal{F} = 2^{\Omega}$ and let P denote a probability measure on $(\Omega, \mathcal{F})$. In this case *every* real-valued function X on Ω is a random variable,

$$X = \sum_{n=1}^{\infty} X(\omega_n) \mathbf{1}_{\{\omega_n\}} \quad , \quad |X| = \sum_{n=1}^{\infty} |X(\omega_n)| \mathbf{1}_{\{\omega_n\}},$$

and

$$X^{+} = \sum_{\{n:X(\omega_n)\geq 0\}} X(\omega_n) \mathbf{1}_{\{\omega_n\}} \quad , \quad X^{-} = \sum_{\{n:X(\omega_n)\leq 0\}} (-X(\omega_n)) \mathbf{1}_{\{\omega_n\}}.$$

For each positive integer m let

$$X_m^+ = \sum_{\{n:X(\omega_n)\geq 0, n\leq m\}} X(\omega_n)\mathbf{1}_{\omega_n}.$$

Then X_m^+ is a simple positive random variable, and the increasing sequence $(X_m^+)_{m=1}^\infty$ converges pointwise to X^+. By Definition 6.2,

$$\int_\Omega X_m^+ dP = \sum_{\{n:X(\omega_n)\geq 0, n\leq m\}} X(\omega_n)P(\{\omega_n\})$$

and, by the Monotone Convergence Theorem, X^+ is integrable if and only if

$$\lim_{m\to\infty} \sum_{\{n:X(\omega_n)\geq 0, n\leq m\}} X(\omega_n)P(\{\omega_n\}) = \sum_{\{n:X(\omega_n)\geq 0\}} X(\omega_n)P(\{\omega_n\}) < \infty.$$

If X^+ is integrable, then

$$\int_\Omega X^+ dP = \sum_{\{n:X(\omega_n)\geq 0\}} X(\omega_n)P(\{\omega_n\}).$$

Similarly X^- is integrable if and only if $\sum_{\{n:X(\omega_n)\leq 0\}}(-X(\omega_n))P(\{\omega_n\}) < \infty$ and, when X^- is integrable, $\int_\Omega X^- dP = \sum_{\{n:X(\omega_n)\leq 0\}}(-X(\omega_n))P(\{\omega_n\})$. Since X is integrable if and only X^+ and X^- are both integrable, we obtain on combining the above results the following proposition.

Proposition 7.1. *If $(\Omega, \mathcal{F}, P)$ is a probability space with $\Omega = (\omega_n)_{n=1}^\infty$ and $\mathcal{F} = 2^\Omega$, then $X : \Omega \longrightarrow \mathbf{R}$ is integrable if and only if*

$$\sum_{n=1}^\infty |X(\omega_n)|P(\{\omega_n\}) < \infty.$$

If X is integrable

$$\mathbb{E}[X] = \int_\Omega X dP = \sum_{n=1}^\infty X(\omega)P(\{\omega_n\}).$$

Thus existence and evaluation of the above integral reduces to convergence of series of real numbers. Familiar facts about convergent series can be obtained using the methods we have developed, and a re-examination of known facts from this new point of view helps understand both our construction of the integral and convergence of series. We pause to look at an example. Suppose we are given an absolutely convergent[1] series of real numbers $\sum_{n=1}^\infty a_n$. Let $b_n = |a_n|/M$ for all n where $M = \sum_{n=1}^\infty |a_n|$. Then $b_n \geq 0$ for all n and $\sum_{n=1}^\infty b_n = 1$. If $\Omega = \{1, 2, \ldots\}$, $\mathcal{F} = 2^\Omega$ and $P(\{n\}) = b_n$ for all n, then $(\Omega, \mathcal{F}, P)$ is a probability space. Let $X(n) = M$ if $a_n \geq 0$ and $X(n) = -M$ if $a_n < 0$.

---

[1]A series of real numbers is *absolutely convergent* if $\sum_{n=1}^\infty |a_n| < \infty$.

With this choice we have $X(n)P(\{n\}) = a_n$ and $|X(n)|P(\{n\}) = Mb_n = |a_n|$ for all n. Since X is bounded, or alternatively since $\sum_{n=1}^{\infty} |X(n)|P(\{n\}) = \sum_{n=1}^{\infty} |a_n| < \infty$, X is integrable and $\int_{\Omega} X dP = \sum_{n=1}^{\infty} X(n)P(\{n\}) = \sum_{n=1}^{\infty} a_n$. In particular, we see that any absolutely convergent series of real numbers is convergent (see also Exercise 7.1).

Now suppose we rearrange the terms in the series $\sum_{n=1}^{\infty} a_n$. This amounts to rearranging the indexing set Ω and thus is derived from a bijective mapping $\theta : \Omega \longrightarrow \Omega$. Hence any rearrangement of the series $\sum_{n=1}^{\infty} a_n$ has the form $\sum_{n=1}^{\infty} a_{\theta(n)}$. If $C_m = \{\theta(1), \ldots, \theta(m)\}$ and $Y_m = X \cdot \mathbf{1}_{C_m}$, then $|Y_m| \le |X|$ for all m and $Y_m \longrightarrow X$ pointwise as $m \longrightarrow \infty$. By the Dominated Convergence Theorem $\int_{\Omega} Y_m dP \longrightarrow \int_{\Omega} X dP$ as $m \longrightarrow \infty$. Since $\int_{\Omega} Y_m dP = \sum_{n=1}^{m} a_{\theta(n)}$ this shows that $\sum_{n=1}^{\infty} a_{\theta(n)} < \infty$ and $\sum_{n=1}^{\infty} a_n = \sum_{n=1}^{\infty} a_{\theta(n)} < \infty$ and proves that any rearrangement of an absolutely convergent series of real numbers converges and has the same sum as the original series.

On multiplying term by term the absolutely convergent series $\sum_{n=1}^{\infty} a_n$ and $\sum_{n=1}^{\infty} b_n$, we obtain $\sum_{n=1}^{\infty} \sum_{m=1}^{\infty} a_n b_m$. This is *not* a series, but since $\mathbf{N} \times \mathbf{N}$ is countable we can arrange the entries to obtain a series. If $\phi : \mathbf{N} \longrightarrow \mathbf{N} \times \mathbf{N}$ is bijective and $c_n = a_i \cdot b_j$ when $\phi(n) = (i, j)$, we obtain the series $\sum_{n=1}^{\infty} c_n$. Any other bijective mapping gives a rearrangement of this series and hence all bijective mappings give rise to convergent series with the same sum if one arrangement is absolutely convergent. Let $\sum_{n=1}^{\infty} |a_n| = s$ and $\sum_{m=1}^{\infty} |b_m| = s'$. If $J := \{\phi(n)\}_{n=1}^{j}$ is a finite subset of $\mathbf{N} \times \mathbf{N}$, then there exists a positive integer n_0 such that $J \subset \{1, 2, \ldots, n_0\} \times \{1, 2, \ldots, n_0\}$. Hence

$$\sum_{n=1}^{j} |c_n| = \sum_{(n,m) \in J} |a_n| \cdot |b_m| \le \sum_{n=1}^{n_0} |a_n| \cdot \sum_{m=1}^{n_0} |b_m| \le s \cdot s'.$$

This implies $\sum_{n=1}^{\infty} |c_n| < \infty$ for any bijective mapping $\phi : \mathbf{N} \longrightarrow \mathbf{N} \times \mathbf{N}$, and there is no ambiguity if we write $\sum_{n=1}^{\infty} \sum_{m=1}^{\infty} a_n \cdot b_m$ in place of $\sum_{n=1}^{\infty} c_n$. Moreover, we may sum the double series in *any* order we wish. Hence

$$\sum_{n=1}^{\infty} \sum_{m=1}^{\infty} a_n \cdot b_m = \lim_{n,m \longrightarrow \infty} \sum_{j=1}^{n} \sum_{k=1}^{m} a_j \cdot b_k$$

$$= \lim_{n \longrightarrow \infty} \left\{ \sum_{j=1}^{n} a_j \right\} \cdot \lim_{m \longrightarrow \infty} \left\{ \sum_{k=1}^{m} b_k \right\}$$

$$= \sum_{n=1}^{\infty} a_n \cdot \sum_{m=1}^{\infty} b_m.$$

This result can also be derived using product measures (see Proposition 5.16 and Section 7.7).

By Exercise 3.31, $\sum_{n=0}^{\infty} x^n/n!$ is absolutely convergent for all $x \in \mathbf{R}$ and hence, by Proposition 7.1, it always converges. If $x, y \in \mathbf{R}$, then

$$
\begin{aligned}
\exp x \cdot \exp y &= \Big(\sum_{n=0}^{\infty} \frac{x^n}{n!}\Big) \cdot \Big(\sum_{m=0}^{\infty} \frac{y^m}{m!}\Big) \\
&= \sum_{n=0}^{\infty} \Big\{\sum_{j=0}^{n} \frac{x^j}{j!} \cdot \frac{y^{n-j}}{(n-j)!}\Big\} \\
&= \sum_{n=0}^{\infty} \frac{1}{n!}\Big\{\sum_{j=0}^{n} \frac{n!}{j!(n-j)!} x^j y^{n-j}\Big\} \\
&= \sum_{n=0}^{\infty} \frac{(x+y)^n}{n!} \\
&= \exp(x+y).
\end{aligned}
$$

Example 7.2. The above results easily extend to *almost surely countably valued* random variables, that is random variables X on $(\Omega, \mathcal{F}, P)$ for which there exists a countable set $A \subset \mathbf{R}$ such that $P(\{\omega \in \Omega : X(\omega) \in A\}) = P_X(A) = 1$. If $A = \{c_n\}_{n=1}^{\infty}$, $X = \sum_{n=1}^{\infty} c_n \mathbf{1}_{X^{-1}(\{c_n\})}$ almost surely. By the Monotone Convergence Theorem X is integrable if and only if $\sum_{n=1}^{\infty} |c_n| P(X^{-1}(\{c_n\})) = \sum_{n=1}^{\infty} |c_n| P_X(\{c_n\}) < \infty$ and

$$
\mathbb{E}[X] = \sum_{n=1}^{\infty} c_n P(X^{-1}(\{c_n\})) = \sum_{n=1}^{\infty} c_n P_X(\{c_n\}).
$$

This extends Example 6.4 from random variables with finite range to random variables which are almost surely countably valued and, in particular, to random variables with countable range.

If the random variable X is Poisson with parameter $\alpha > 0$, then $P[X = n] = e^{-\alpha}\alpha^n/n!$ for $n \in \mathbf{N}^*$. By Example 5.4, $\sum_{n=0}^{\infty} e^{-\alpha}\alpha^n/n! = 1$ and X is almost surely countably generated. Since $X \geq 0$, and

$$
\sum_{n=0}^{\infty} \frac{n e^{-\alpha}\alpha^n}{n!} = \alpha e^{-\alpha} \sum_{n=1}^{\infty} \frac{\alpha^{n-1}}{(n-1)!} = \alpha e^{-\alpha} e^{\alpha} = \alpha,
$$

X is integrable and $\mathbb{E}[X] = \alpha$.

7.2. Continuous Functions on Closed Bounded Intervals

In Proposition 6.29(b) we proved one of the most fundamental facts about sequences of real numbers: *every bounded sequence of real numbers contains a convergent subsequence.* We use this result to prove some basic properties of continuous real-valued functions.

Proposition 7.3. (*Intermediate Value Theorem*) *If* $f : [a, b] \longrightarrow \mathbf{R}$ *is continuous and* $f(a)f(b) < 0$, *then there exists* $c \in (a, b)$ *such that* $f(c) = 0$.

Proof. Since $a < b$ there exists a positive integer n_0 such that $a + \frac{1}{n} < b$ for all $n \geq n_0$. Suppose $f(a) > 0$. Let

$$A = \{x \in [a, b] : f(y) \geq 0 \text{ all } y \in [a, x]\}.$$

Since $A \subset [a, b]$ the set A is bounded above and the least upper bound of A, c, belongs to $[a, b]$. We first claim that $c > a$. Otherwise, we could find for every $n > n_0, x_n \in [a, a + \frac{1}{n}]$ such that $f(x_n) < 0$. Since $a \leq x_n \leq a + \frac{1}{n}, \lim_{n \to \infty} x_n = a$ and, by continuity, $f(a) = \lim_{n \to \infty} f(x_n) \leq 0$. This contradiction shows that $c > a$. A similar argument shows that $c < b$.

For all n sufficiently large we have $a \leq c - \frac{1}{n} < c$. Since $f(c - \frac{1}{n}) \geq 0$ continuity implies $f(c) \geq 0$. If $\delta > 0$, $c < \delta < b$ and $f(x) \geq 0$ for all $x \in [c, \delta]$, then $f(x) \geq 0$ in $[a, \delta]$, and this contradicts the definition of c. Thus, for all n sufficiently large we can find $y_n, c \leq y_n \leq c + \frac{1}{n}$ such that $f(y_n) < 0$. Hence $f(c) = f(\lim_{n \to \infty} y_n) = \lim_{n \to \infty} f(y_n) \leq 0$. This implies $f(c) = 0$ and completes the proof. □

The hypothesis on f in the Intermediate Value Theorem says that f takes *positive* and *negative* values at the endpoints of the interval $[a, b]$.

Corollary 7.4. *If* I *is an interval in* $\mathbf{R}$ *and* $f : I \mapsto \mathbf{R}$ *is continuous, then* $f(I) := \{f(x) : x \in I\}$ *is an interval.*

Proof. Let $a, b \in I$ and $a < b$. Suppose $f(a) < f(b)$. Let $f(a) < \alpha < f(b)$. The function $g := f - \alpha$, restricted to $[a, b]$, is continuous and

$$g(a)g(b) = (f(a) - \alpha) \cdot (f(b) - \alpha) < 0.$$

By the Intermediate Value Theorem there exists $c, a < c < b$, such that $g(c) = 0$. Hence $f(c) = \alpha$ and $[f(a), f(b)] \subset f(I)$. A similar proof works when $f(a) > f(b)$. Let $m := glb\{f(x) : x \in I\}$ if this set is bounded below; otherwise let $m = -\infty$. Let $M := lub\{f(x) : x \in I\}$ if this set is bounded above; otherwise let $M = +\infty$. If $m < y_1 < y_2 < M$, then there exist x_1 and x_2 in I such that $f(x_1) \leq y_1 < y_2 \leq f(x_2)$. The above argument applied to f on $[x_1, x_2]$ shows[2] that $[y_1, y_2] \subset f(I)$, and on taking a union of such sets, we obtain $(m, M) \subset f(I)$. Hence $f(I)$ is either (m, M) or this interval with one or both of the end-points included. In either case $f(I)$ is an interval. This completes the proof. □

---

[2]Assuming $x_1 < x_2$. Otherwise we consider f on $[x_2, x_1]$.

Proposition 7.5. (*Fundamental Existence Theorem for Maxima and Minima*)
*If $f : [a, b] \mapsto \mathbf{R}$ is continuous, then $\{f(x) : x \in [a, b]\}$ is the closed bounded
interval $[m, M]$, where*

$$m = \min\{f(x) : x \in [a, b]\}$$

and

$$M = \max\{f(x) : x \in [a, b]\}.$$

*Moreover, if f is also one-to-one or injective, then f is either strictly increasing
or strictly decreasing.*

Proof. Suppose the set $\{f(x) : x \in [a, b]\}$ is not bounded above. Then for each
integer n there exists $x_n \in [a, b]$ such that $f(x_n) > n$. By Proposition 6.29(b)
the sequence $(x_n)_{n=1}^\infty$ contains a subsequence $(x_{n_j})_{j=1}^\infty$ which converges to $x \in
[a, b]$. By continuity $\lim_{j \to \infty} f(x_{n_j}) = f(x)$ and this contradicts the fact that
$f(x_{n_j}) > n_j$ for all j. Hence $\{f(x) : x \in [a, b]\}$ is bounded above. Let $M =
lub\{f(x) : x \in [a, b]\}$. For each positive integer n there exists $y_n \in [a, b]$
such that $f(y_n) > M - \frac{1}{n}$. Again, by Proposition 6.29(b) we can choose a
subsequence of $(y_n)_{n=1}^\infty$ which converges to $y \in [a, b]$. By continuity $f(y) = M$.
Similarly we can show that $\{f(x) : x \in [a, b]\}$ is bounded below and there
exists $z \in [a, b]$ such that $f(z) = m := glb\{f(x) : x \in [a, b]\}$. By Corollary 7.4,
$\{f(x) : x \in [a, b]\} = [m, M]$.

Now suppose f is injective. Let $f(c) = M$. If $a < c < b$, then $f([a, c]) =
[m_1, M]$ and $f([c, b]) = [m_2, M]$, where $m_i \le M$ for $i = 1, 2$. If either $m_1 = M$ or
$m_2 = M$, f is constant on an interval of positive length, and this contradicts our
hypothesis that f is injective. Otherwise, there exists $m_3 \in [m_1, M) \cap [m_2, M)$,
$x \in [a, c)$ and $y \in (c, b]$ such that $f(x) = f(y)$. This again contradicts injectivity.
Hence f achieves its maximum, and similarly its minimum, over $[a, b]$ at end-
points of the interval. If $f(a) < f(b)$, then $f(a) < f(x) < f(b)$ for all $x \in (a, b)$,
and if $a < x < y < b$, then, since f is also injective on $[a, y]$, we have $f(a) <
f(x) < f(y)$ and f is strictly increasing. If $f(a) > f(b)$, a similar argument
shows that f is strictly decreasing. This completes the proof. $\square$

The predecessor of the Lebesgue Integral, the Riemann Integral (see Section 7.4), used extensively the following strengthened form of continuity.

Definition 7.6. *A function $f : A \subset \mathbf{R} \mapsto \mathbf{R}$ is uniformly continuous if for
every $\epsilon > 0$ there exists $\delta > 0$ such that for any $x, y \in A$ we have*

$$(7.1) \qquad\qquad |f(x) - f(y)| < \epsilon \qquad whenever \ |x - y| < \delta.$$

Proposition 7.7. *A function $f : [a, b] \mapsto \mathbf{R}$ is continuous if and only if it is
uniformly continuous.*

Proof. Clearly every uniformly continuous function is continuous and it suffices to prove the converse. Suppose $f : [a,b] \mapsto \mathbf{R}$ is continuous. If f is not uniformly continuous, then for some $\epsilon > 0$ we can find for every positive integer n, x_n and y_n in $[a,b]$, such that $|x_n - y_n| < 1/n$ and $|f(x_n) - f(y_n)| \geq \epsilon$. By Proposition 6.29(b) the sequence $(x_n)_{n=1}^{\infty}$ has a subsequence, $(x_{n_j})_{j=1}^{\infty}$, which converges to some point $x \in [a,b]$. This implies

$$\lim_{j \to \infty} y_{n_j} = \lim_{j \to \infty} x_{n_j} + \lim_{j \to \infty} (y_{n_j} - x_{n_j}) = x.$$

By continuity $\lim_{j \to \infty} f(x_{n_j}) = \lim_{j \to \infty} f(y_{n_j}) = f(x)$. This contradicts the fact that $|f(x_{n_j}) - f(y_{n_j})| > \epsilon$ for all j and completes the proof. $\square$

7.3. Independent Random Variables

We begin this section by extending Proposition 6.6(b) to arbitrary integrable random variables. Afterwards we characterize independent integrable random variables using expected values.

Proposition 7.8. *If X and Y are independent integrable random variables on the probability space $(\Omega, \mathcal{F}, P)$, then $X \cdot Y$ is integrable[3] and*

$$\mathbb{E}[X \cdot Y] = \mathbb{E}[X] \cdot \mathbb{E}[Y].$$

Proof. First suppose X and Y are positive integrable random variables. By Proposition 6.24, X and Y are the pointwise limit of increasing sequences of simple positive $\mathcal{F}_X$ and $\mathcal{F}_Y$ measurable random variables $(X_n)_{n=1}^{\infty}$ and $(Y_n)_{n=1}^{\infty}$, respectively. By Proposition 5.19 and Lemma 6.6(b), X_n and Y_n are simple independent random variable and $\mathbb{E}[X_n \cdot Y_n] = \mathbb{E}[X_n] \cdot \mathbb{E}[Y_n]$ for all n. Hence $\lim_{n \to \infty} \mathbb{E}[X_n \cdot Y_n] = \lim_{n \to \infty} \mathbb{E}[X_n] \cdot \lim_{n \to \infty} \mathbb{E}[Y_n] < \infty$. Since $X_n \cdot Y_n \leq X_{n+1} \cdot Y_n \leq X_{n+1} \cdot Y_{n+1}$ for all n, $(X_n \cdot Y_n)_{n=1}^{\infty}$ is an increasing sequence of positive simple random variables which converges pointwise to $X \cdot Y$. By Proposition 6.23, $X \cdot Y$ is integrable and $\mathbb{E}[X \cdot Y] = \lim_{n \to \infty} \mathbb{E}[X_n \cdot Y_n] = \lim_{n \to \infty} \mathbb{E}[X_n] \cdot \lim_{n \to \infty} \mathbb{E}[Y_n] = \mathbb{E}[X] \cdot \mathbb{E}[Y]$. This completes the proof when X and Y are positive.

Suppose X and Y are arbitrary. By Example 4.13, $X^{\pm}$ and $Y^{\pm}$ are, respectively, $\mathcal{F}_X$ and $\mathcal{F}_Y$ measurable. Since $\mathcal{F}_X$ and $\mathcal{F}_Y$ are independent σ-fields, $X^{\pm}$ and $Y^{\pm}$ are independent positive random variables. The result for positive

---

[3]The converse is almost true. If X and Y are independent random variables neither of which vanishes almost surely, $X \cdot Y$ is integrable if and only if X and Y are both integrable.

random variables implies

$$\begin{aligned}
\mathbb{E}[X \cdot Y] &= \mathbb{E}[X^+ \cdot Y^+] - \mathbb{E}[X^+ \cdot Y^-] - \mathbb{E}[X^- \cdot Y^+] + \mathbb{E}[X^- \cdot Y^-] \\
&= \mathbb{E}[X^+] \cdot \mathbb{E}[Y^+] - \mathbb{E}[X^+] \cdot \mathbb{E}[Y^-] - \mathbb{E}[X^-] \cdot \mathbb{E}[Y^+] + \mathbb{E}[X^-] \cdot \mathbb{E}[Y^-] \\
&= (\mathbb{E}[X^+] - \mathbb{E}[X^-]) \cdot (\mathbb{E}[Y^+] - \mathbb{E}[Y^-]) \\
&= \mathbb{E}[X] \cdot \mathbb{E}[Y].
\end{aligned}$$

This completes the proof. $\qquad\qquad\qquad\qquad\qquad\qquad\qquad\qquad\qquad\quad$ □

Proposition 7.9. *If X and Y are random variables on $(\Omega, \mathcal{F}, P)$, the following conditions are equivalent:*

(a) *X and Y are independent random variables;*

(b) *for any pair of Borel measurable functions f and g such that $f(X)$ and $g(Y)$ are integrable,*

$$\mathbb{E}[f(X)g(Y)] = \mathbb{E}[f(X)] \cdot \mathbb{E}[g(Y)];$$

(c) *for any bounded Borel measurable functions f and g,*

$$\mathbb{E}[f(X)g(Y)] = \mathbb{E}[f(X)] \cdot \mathbb{E}[g(Y)].$$

Proof. If (a) holds, Proposition 5.19 implies $f(X)$ and $g(Y)$ are independent for any pair of Borel measurable functions and, by Proposition 7.8, (b) holds. Since bounded random variables are integrable (b) implies (c). Suppose (c) holds. If $A \in \mathcal{F}_X$ and $B \in \mathcal{F}_Y$, we can find by the proof of Proposition 5.19, f and g, Borel measurable functions, such that $\mathbf{1}_A = f(X)$ and $\mathbf{1}_B = g(Y)$. By (c)

$$\begin{aligned}
P(A \cap B) = \mathbb{E}[\mathbf{1}_{A \cap B}] &= \mathbb{E}[\mathbf{1}_A \cdot \mathbf{1}_B] = \mathbb{E}[f(X) \cdot g(Y)] \\
= \mathbb{E}[f(X)] \cdot \mathbb{E}[g(Y)] &= \mathbb{E}[\mathbf{1}_A] \cdot \mathbb{E}[\mathbf{1}_B] = P(A) \cdot P(B)
\end{aligned}$$

and the random variables X and Y are independent. Hence (c) implies (a), and this completes the proof. $\qquad\qquad\qquad\qquad\qquad\qquad\qquad\qquad\qquad\qquad$ □

Our next proposition is useful for calculating expected values.

Proposition 7.10. *If X is a random variable on the probability space $(\Omega, \mathcal{F}, P)$, $g : \mathbf{R} \longrightarrow \mathbf{R}$ is Borel measurable and $g(X)$ is integrable, then*

$$(7.2) \qquad\qquad\qquad \mathbb{E}[g(X)] = \int_{\mathbf{R}} g \, dP_X.$$

Proof. If g is a simple Borel measurable function with canonical representation $\sum_{i=1}^n g(x_i)\mathbf{1}_{A_i}$, where $x_i \in A_i$ and A_i is a Borel subset of $\mathbf{R}$ for all[4] i,

$$g(X) = \sum_{i=1}^n g(x_i)\mathbf{1}_{X^{-1}(A_i)}$$

is a simple random variable and $(X^{-1}(A_i))_{i=1}^n$ partitions Ω into $\mathcal{F}$ measurable sets. By Lemma 6.3,

$$\mathbb{E}[g(X)] = \sum_{i=1}^n g(x_i)P(X^{-1}(A_i)) = \sum_{i=1}^n g(x_i)P_X(A_i) = \int_{\mathbf{R}} g\, dP_X.$$

This proves the result when g is a simple function. If g is arbitrary it suffices, since $g(X)^+ = g^+(X)$ and $g(X)^- = g^-(X)$, to prove the result for $g \geq 0$. By Proposition 6.24 there exists an increasing sequence of positive simple random variables, $(g_n)_{n=1}^\infty$, on the probability space $(\mathbf{R}, \mathcal{B}(\mathbf{R}), P_X)$ which converges pointwise to g. This implies the sequence $(g_n(X))_{n=1}^\infty$ is increasing, simple, positive and converges pointwise to $g(X)$ in $(\Omega, \mathcal{F}, P)$. *Two* applications of the Monotone Convergence Theorem show $\int_\Omega g_n(X)dP \longrightarrow \int_\Omega g(X)dP$ and $\int_{\mathbf{R}} g_n dP_X \longrightarrow \int_{\mathbf{R}} g\, dP_X$ as $n \longrightarrow \infty$. By the result for simple Borel measurable functions, we have

$$\mathbb{E}[g(X)] = \lim_{n\to\infty} \mathbb{E}[g_n(X)] = \lim_{n\to\infty} \int_{\mathbf{R}} g_n dP_X = \int_{\mathbf{R}} g\, dP_X.$$

This completes the proof. $\qquad\qquad\qquad\qquad\qquad\qquad\qquad\qquad\qquad\square$

The expected value is usually the most important real number that we can associate with a random variable, as it gives the average value of the function with the expected frequencies factored into the calculation. Following traditional practice, and at times for convenience, we call $\mathbb{E}[X]$ the *mean* of the random variable X and write μ or μ_X in place of $\mathbb{E}[X]$. Real numbers of this type are called *parameters* [5] and act as a summary of important information. The *Central Limit Theorem* studies the limiting behavior of sums of identically distributed independent random variables. This requires random variables which are not too widely dispersed. To quantify this notion we introduce the second most important parameter associated with a random variable, the *variance*.

Suppose X is a random variable on the probability space $(\Omega, \mathcal{F}, P)$ and X^2 is integrable. If $A := \{\omega \in \Omega : |X(\omega)| \leq 1\} = X^{-1}([-1, +1])$, then $A \in \mathcal{F}$ and $Y := \mathbf{1}_A + X^2 \cdot \mathbf{1}_{A^c}$ is an integrable random variable on $(\Omega, \mathcal{F}, P)$. If $\omega \in A$, $|X(\omega)| \leq 1 \leq \mathbf{1}_A(\omega) \leq Y(\omega)$; while if $\omega \in A^c$, $|X(\omega)| > 1$ and $|X(\omega)| < X^2(\omega) = Y(\omega)$. This accounts for all $\omega \in \Omega$ and implies $|X| \leq Y$. By

---

[4]See the proof of Proposition 5.18.

[5]From the Greek *para* beside and *meteon* to measure.

Proposition 6.28(d), X is integrable.[6] Since $(X - \mu_X)^2 = X^2 - 2\mu_X X + \mu_X^2$, $(X - \mu_X)^2$ is also integrable.

Definition 7.11. *If X is a random variable on the probability space $(\Omega, \mathcal{F}, P)$ and X^2 is integrable, let*

$$Var(X) = \sigma_X^2 = \mathbb{E}[(X - \mu_X)^2].$$

We call $Var(X)$ the variance[7] of X and let $\mathbf{L}^2(\Omega, \mathcal{F}, P)$ denote the set of all random variables X on $(\Omega, \mathcal{F}, P)$ with $\mathbb{E}[X^2] < \infty$.

Our next proposition shows how variance measures spread.

Proposition 7.12. (*Chebyshev's Inequality*)[8] *Let $X \in \mathbf{L}^2(\Omega, \mathcal{F}, P)$ and let $t > 0$. If $\mu = \mathbb{E}[X]$ and $\sigma^2 = Var(X) > 0$, then*

$$(7.3) \qquad P\Big[\omega \in \Omega : \Big|\frac{X(\omega) - \mu}{\sigma}\Big| \geq t\Big] \leq \frac{1}{t^2}.$$

Proof. If $A = \{\omega \in \Omega : |X(\omega) - \mu| \geq \sigma t\}$, then

$$\begin{aligned}
\sigma^2 &= \int_\Omega (X - \mu)^2 dP \geq \int_A (X - \mu)^2 dP \\
&\geq \int_A (\sigma t)^2 dP = \sigma^2 t^2 \int_A dP \\
&= \sigma^2 t^2 P(A) = \sigma^2 t^2 P[\{\omega \in \Omega : |X(\omega) - \mu| \geq t\sigma\}].
\end{aligned}$$

Hence

$$P\big[\{\omega \in \Omega : \big|\frac{X(\omega) - \mu}{\sigma}\big| \geq t\}\big] = P[\{\omega \in \Omega : |X(\omega) - \mu| \geq t\sigma\}] \leq \frac{\sigma^2}{\sigma^2 t^2} = \frac{1}{t^2}.$$

This completes the proof. $\qquad\qquad\qquad\qquad\qquad\qquad\qquad\qquad\qquad\qquad\qquad$ $\square$

For example, if $t = 10$ in Chebyshev's Inequality, then with probability greater than .99, an element chosen at random from a population distributed like X will lie in the interval $[\mu - 10\sigma, \mu + 10\sigma]$. Equivalently we can be 99% confident that an element chosen at random from the population will fall within this interval. The variance is also used as a measure of *risk*. The following example contains a key ingredient in the construction of *portfolios* to minimise risk (see Exercises 7.18 and 7.19).

---

[6]Other proofs follow from *Jensen's Inequality* and the *Cauchy-Schwarz inequality*. See Propositions 7.29 and 11.4.

[7]σ_X or σ is called, in statistics, the *standard deviation* of X.

[8]Pafnuty Chebyshev (1821-1894) was a major figure in Russian mathematics during the 19th century. He came from an upper-class family and remained rich all his life, helped no doubt by his interest in buying property. He had a wide range of mathematical interests: number theory, approximation theory, probability theory, mechanics and computational mathematics. Kolmogorov said that Chebyshev was the first to use precisely and clearly the notions of *random variable* and *expected value*. He invented mechanical objects, seven of which, including a special bicycle for women, were exhibited at the World's Exhibition in Chicago in 1893.

Example 7.13. Let $X_1, \ldots, X_n$ denote random variables in $\mathbf{L}^2(\Omega, \mathcal{F}, P)$. If $\mu_i = \mathbb{E}[X_i]$, then $\mathbb{E}[\sum_{i=1}^n X_i] = \sum_{i=1}^n \mathbb{E}[X_i] = \sum_{i=1}^n \mu_i$ and

$$
\begin{aligned}
\mathrm{Var}\Big(\sum_{i=1}^n X_i\Big) &= \mathbb{E}\Big[\Big(\sum_{i=1}^n X_i - \sum_{i=1}^n \mu_i\Big)^2\Big] = \mathbb{E}\Big[\Big(\sum_{i=1}^n (X_i - \mu_i)\Big)^2\Big] \\
&= \mathbb{E}\Big[\sum_{i,j=1}^n (X_i - \mu_i)(X_j - \mu_j)\Big] \\
&= \sum_{i=1}^n \mathbb{E}[(X_i - \mu_i)^2] + \sum_{i,j=1, i \neq j}^n \mathbb{E}[(X_i - \mu_i)(X_j - \mu_j)].
\end{aligned}
$$

If the random variables are independent and $\sigma_i^2 = \mathrm{Var}(X_i)$ for all i, then, by Proposition 7.8,

$$
\begin{aligned}
\mathrm{Var}\Big(\sum_{i=1}^n X_i\Big) &= \sum_{i=1}^n \sigma_i^2 + \sum_{i,j=1, i \neq j}^n \mathbb{E}[X_i - \mu_i]\mathbb{E}[X_j - \mu_j] \\
&= \sum_{i=1}^n \sigma_i^2.
\end{aligned}
$$

If $\mu_i = \mu$, $\sigma_i = \sigma$ for all i and $\bar{X} = \frac{1}{n}\sum_{i=1}^n X_i$, then $\mathbb{E}[\bar{X}] = \mu$ and $\mathrm{Var}(\bar{X}) = n\sigma^2/n^2 = \sigma^2/n.$[9]

7.4. The Riemann Integral

Many of the most important random variables, for example normal and exponential random variables, were defined and extensively studied, and important results, such as the Central Limit Theorem and the Law of Large Numbers, were established using the *Riemann Integral* prior to the development of the Lebesgue integral. To employ this integral we need to show that the Riemann and Lebesgue integrals give the same value when applied to the standard functions. Connecting the two confers benefits on both and leads to a method of computing specific Lebesgue integrals.

We could run through the details rapidly but feel a historical diversion may help restore the reader's sense of perspective and act as an antidote to the technicalities in Chapter 6.

Integration theory has a long history and our attention has focused on a relatively modern period. The Greeks used an exhaustion method and approximations over two thousand years ago. The discovery of the differential calculus

---

[9]Such sequences arise when an *unbiased* sample of size n is drawn from a population with finite variance. The result in this example can be used to determine the sample size necessary to find a confidence interval of prescribed length and preassigned probability which contains the mean of the population.

in the seventeenth century led to new ways of evaluating integrals, and by the end of the eighteenth century integrals of many particular functions had been calculated but no general definition had been introduced. It was generally accepted that either geometric arguments or physical realities were sufficient to prove existence: *circles exist and therefore the area of a circle exists.* This led to problems when the mathematical analysis of vibrating strings and heat conduction led to the generation of functions, using infinite series, which did not conform to the widely held belief at that time that all authentic mathematical functions could be described by algebraic or analytic expressions. Functions which were not continuous[10] or which were described by different formulae on different parts of their domain were regarded as suspect.[11] This problem was not resolved overnight and exercised the minds of some very talented mathematicians. The modern student, presented with the final definition or concept, may struggle, consciously or unconsciously, with the same difficulties that surrounded their introduction. Thus asking and attempting to answer questions such as : *what is the difference between a function and a formula?* are not only relevant and an essential part of the learning process but follow a good tradition. The history of mathematics can put in perspective some of the difficulties encountered by students.

Around 1820, when controversy still surrounded the concept of function, A. L. Cauchy was developing his ideas on analysis and the differential calculus[12] and was concerned that his work might be drawn into the controversy. To pre-empt his critics he laid out clearly the mathematical environment in which he worked. His point of departure was the abstract definition of function, which had been around for almost a century but which was only then becoming widely accepted. He defined *limits, continuous functions, convergent series*, and gave the *first formal definition of the integral* of a bounded function, continuous except perhaps at a finite set of points. We still follow his approach today. Forty years later Riemann showed that Cauchy's approach could be extended

---

[10]Continuity was a rather informal notion at that time.

[11]Standard mathematical notation gives some idea of the controversy and resistance that often accompanied new developments. It suffices to mention the adjectives used to name different kinds of numbers: *negative, imaginary* and *complex.* Negative numbers caused the most difficulties and were called *absurd* and *fictitious* by some. Many could not accept that the product of two negative numbers was positive; it looked like two wrongs making a right. As late as the second half of the eighteenth century some mathematics books did not allow the use of negative numbers.

[12]A. L. Cauchy, Résumé des leçons données a l'École Royal Polytechnique, Paris. Augustin Louis Cauchy (1789-1857) from Paris was an extremely prolific mathematician who took great pride in his ability to produce *new* mathematical results *each week* for presentation to his colleagues at the academy in Paris. Cauchy was a strong supporter of the Bourbons and on refusing to take an oath of loyalty to Louis Philippe, was excluded from public employment during the eighteen years of the July monarchy. He experienced prejudice and discrimination because of his strongly held political and religious beliefs, but he himself also behaved in a rather bigoted fashion.

to considerably enlarge the collection of integrable functions. Afterwards the integral became known as *the Riemann integral*.[13]

The Riemann integral of the function f over the closed interval $[a, b]$ is usually written $\int_a^b f(x)dx$. Instead of constructing this integral we deconstruct it, guided by our informal remarks in Chapter 6. The x refers to the horizontal or x-axis. Informally we expect the integral to be limits of sums $\sum_{i=1}^n f(\bar{x}_i)\Delta x_i$ where $(\Delta x_i)_{i=1}^n$ is derived from a partition of $[a, b]$. In the case of the Riemann[14] integral the domain $[a, b]$ is partitioned into a finite number of *adjacent* intervals. The partition is specified by an ordered finite set of points $\{a = x_1 < x_2 < \ldots < x_{n+1} = b\}$ and Δx_i is defined to be the *length* of the interval $[x_i, x_{i+1}]$, that is $\Delta x_i = x_{i+1} - x_i$. The point $\bar{x}_i$ is chosen arbitrarily in $[x_i, x_{i+1}]$. This gives us the *Riemann Sum*

$$(7.4) \qquad \sum_{i=1}^n f(\bar{x}_i)\Delta x_i \;=\; \sum_{i=1}^n f(\bar{x}_i)(x_{i+1} - x_i).$$

A Riemann sum for $f \geq 0$ is shown in Figure 7.1. The *mesh* of the partition is

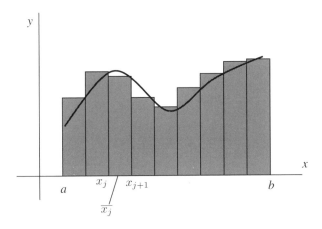

Figure 7.1

defined to be $\max_{1 \leq i \leq n} |x_{i+1} - x_i|$. If, as we let the mesh tend to zero and take *all possible choices* of $(\bar{x}_i)_{i=1}^n$, the Riemann sums in (7.4) converge, then we say that f is *Riemann integrable* and denote the limit, the Riemann integral of f over $[a, b]$, by $\int_a^b f(x)dx$. The Riemann integral of a positive function f can be

---

[13]The *Cauchy-Riemann integral* would be more appropriate. Cauchy developed, after gradually overcoming his own prejudices against "imaginaries", much of the theory of *Functions of One Complex Variable* and in doing so developed another integral which still bears his name.

[14]Bernard Riemann (1826-1866) was an extremely intuitive German mathematician who introduced the key initial ideas for what are today whole areas within mathematics. The most famous unsolved problem within mathematics today is due to Riemann, *The Riemann Hypothesis*.

interpreted as the area under the graph of f bounded below by the x-axis, on the left by the line $x = a$, and on the right by the line $x = b$.

Consider a *bounded* function on the closed interval $[a, b]$ and denote by $\mathcal{P}$ the partition given above. For each $i, 1 \leq i \leq n$, let $M_i = \sup\{f(x) : x \in [x_i, x_{i+1}]$ and $m_i = \inf\{f(x) : x \in [x_i, x_{i+1}]\}$. The difference $M_i - m_i$ is the *variation* of f over the ith interval. In contrast to the situation for the Lebesgue integral this may not tend to zero as we take finer and finer partitions. It is fairly easy to see that f is Riemann integrable if and only if

$$\lim_{\text{mesh}(\mathcal{P}) \longrightarrow 0} \sum_{i=1}^{n} (M_i - m_i) \Delta x_i = 0.$$

By Proposition 7.7 every continuous real-valued function f on a closed bounded interval is uniformly continuous. This implies that for every $\epsilon > 0$ there exists $\delta > 0$ such that $|\sum_{\mathcal{P}} (M_i - m_i) \Delta x_i| \leq \epsilon(b - a)$ whenever $\text{mesh}(\mathcal{P}) \leq \delta$ and f is Riemann integrable.

To establish a link between the Riemann and Lebesgue integrals we introduce measures which generalize probability measures.

Definition 7.14. *A mapping $\mu : \mathcal{F} \longrightarrow [0, +\infty)$, where $(\Omega, \mathcal{F})$ is a measurable space, is a measure if $\mu(\emptyset) = 0$ and for any pairwise disjoint sequence of sets in $\mathcal{F}$, $(A_n)_{n=1}^{\infty}$,*

$$(7.5) \qquad\qquad \mu\left(\bigcup_{n=1}^{\infty} A_n \right) = \sum_{n=1}^{\infty} \mu(A_n).$$

The triple $(\Omega, \mathcal{F}, \mu)$ is called a measure space.

The second axiom for a probability space (5.4) is just (7.5). All the results, including the Monotone Convergence Theorem and the Dominated Convergence Theorem, already established for probability measures, extend to arbitrary measures and with practically the same proofs if Ω admits a countable partition into sets of finite measure.[15] These results cannot, however, be interpreted as expected values. To make our presentation[16] complete we reduce proofs to probability measures by using the observation that a measure μ on $(\Omega, \mathcal{F})$ is a probability measure if and only if $\mu(\Omega) = 1$. Our next result, stated without proof[17], is the fundamental result of Henri Lebesgue. It shows that our geometric concept of length extends to define a measure in the sense of Definition 7.14.

---

[15]These are called σ-finite measures. If $\mu(\Omega) < \infty$, we call μ a finite measure.

[16]This approach may appear clumsy to the reader familiar with abstract measure theory. However, since we are not going to develop the theory for arbitrary measures, this allows us to extend results, such as the Dominated Convergence Theorem, that we have already proved for probability measures.

[17]See Example 9.6.

Proposition 7.15. *There exists a unique measure* $\mathbf{m}$ *on* $(\mathbf{R}, \mathcal{B}(\mathbf{R}))$ *such that* $\mathbf{m}([a,b]) = b-a$ *for all closed intervals* $[a,b] \subset \mathbf{R}$. *We call* $\mathbf{m}$ *Lebesgue measure on* $\mathbf{R}$.

If $[a,b] \subset \mathbf{R}$ and $l_{[a,b]}(B) = \mathbf{m}(B)/(b-a)$ for any Borel set[18] B in $[a,b]$, then $([a,b], \mathcal{B}([a,b]), l_{[a,b]})$ is a probability space.

We now define the Lebesgue integral of a function over a closed finite interval $I \subset \mathbf{R}$ with respect to Lebesgue measure. If $f : I \longrightarrow \mathbf{R}$ we extend f to $\mathbf{R}$ by letting $\tilde{f}(x) = f(x)$ if $x \in I$ and $\tilde{f}(x) = 0$ if $x \notin I$. It is easily verified that

$$(b-a) \int_{[a,b]} \tilde{f} dl_{[a,b]} = (d-c) \int_{[c,d]} \tilde{f} dl_{[c,d]}$$

whenever $[a,b]$ and $[c,d]$ are intervals containing I. This shows that the following definition of the Lebesgue integral of a Borel measurable function on $[a,b]$ is unambiguous. If $f : [a,b] \longrightarrow \mathbf{R}$ and $\tilde{f}$ is $l_{[a,b]}$ integrable, we let

$$\int_{[a,b]} f d\mathbf{m} = (b-a) \int_{[a,b]} \tilde{f} dl_{[a,b]}.$$

If $f : \mathbf{R} \longrightarrow \mathbf{R}$ is Borel measurable and the restriction of f to each interval $[-n,n]$ is Lebesgue integrable, we let $\int_{\mathbf{R}} f d\mathbf{m} = \lim_{n \to \infty} \int_{[-n,n]} f d\mathbf{m}$ whenever this limit is finite. Clearly, $\int_{[a,b]} f d\mathbf{m} = \int_{\mathbf{R}} f \cdot \mathbf{1}_{[a,b]} d\mathbf{m}$.

Proposition 7.16. *If* f *is a continuous function on* $[a,b]$, *then*

$$\int_a^b f(x) dx = \int_{[a,b]} f d\mathbf{m}.$$

Proof. If $\{x_1, x_1, \ldots, x_{n+1}\}$ partitions $[a,b]$ into n adjacent intervals, each of length $(b-a)/n$, and $f_n = \sum_{i=1}^n f(x_i) \mathbf{1}_{[x_i, x_{i+1})}$, then

$$(7.6) \qquad \sum_{i=1}^n f(x_i)(x_{i+1} - x_i) = \int_{[a,b]} f_n d\mathbf{m}.$$

Since f is Riemann integrable over $[a,b]$ the left-hand side of (7.6) tends to $\int_a^b f(x) dx$ as $n \longrightarrow \infty$. On the other hand, the sequence $(f_n)_{n=1}^{\infty}$ is a bounded sequence which converges pointwise to f as $n \longrightarrow \infty$. An application of the Dominated Convergence Theorem to the sequence $(f_n)_{n=1}^{\infty}$ on the probability space $([a,b], \mathcal{B}([a,b]), l_{[a,b]})$ shows that the right-hand side of (7.6) tends to $\int_{[a,b]} f d\mathbf{m}$. This completes the proof. $\qquad \square$

---

[18]A set $B \subset [a,b]$ is Borel if $B = [a,b] \cap \tilde{B}$ for some Borel set $\tilde{B} \subset \mathbf{R}$.

One can easily show, and we require this result later, that $\sum_{i=1}^{n} c_i \mathbf{1}_{[a_i,b_i]}$ is Riemann integrable and, if $[a_i, b_i] \subset [a, b]$ for all i, then

$$\int_a^b \Big(\sum_{i=1}^{n} c_i \mathbf{1}_{[a_i,b_i]} \Big) dx \;=\; \sum_{i=1}^{n} c_i (b_i - a_i).$$

Not all functions are Riemann integrable. If $f = \mathbf{1}_{\mathbf{Q} \cap [0,1]}$, then on every interval we have points where $f = 0$ and points where $f = 1$. Hence for any partition $\mathcal{P}$ of $[0,1]$, $M_i - m_i = 1$ for all i and f is not Riemann integrable.[19]

The essential difference between the Riemann and Lebesgue integrals lies in the method in which we partitioned the domain and hence calculated the finite sums. Lebesgue used a grouping so that the function varied very little when restricted to any set in the partition (compare (6.10) and (7.6)). It is only in the limit that differences appear. Lebesgue[20] himself gave an interesting lecture on the development of the integral. In it he explained the difference by analogy, and it is worth repeating his example. He used counting in his example, but measuring is just counting in which we use fractions and real numbers.

In Riemann's approach one operated as did a merchant who counted coins and bills randomly in the order in which they fell into his hands, while we (Lebesgue) operate like the methodical merchant who separated the coins and bills into groups of the same denomination. The two procedures will certainly lead the merchant to the same answer because, as rich as he might be, he has only a finite amount to count. But for Riemann and us the sum is infinite because it is being divided up into smaller and smaller parts, and it is only in the limit that any difference shows up.

Clearly Lebesgue's method is more efficient. When both give answers we expect them to coincide, and we have seen this to be the case. This suggests that we should be able to handle more functions using Lebesgue's theory and again this is true. The real power of Lebesgue's integral, however, lies in the robustness with which it allows limits to be taken under very weak assumptions and to give meaning to the limits.

A positive-valued Borel measurable function f with domain $\mathbf{R}$ is called a *density function* if $\int_{\mathbf{R}} f d\mathbf{m} = 1$. Proposition 6.26 shows how density functions can be used to define Borel probability measures on $\mathbf{R}$. A random variable X defined on the probability space $(\Omega, \mathcal{F}, P)$ has a density if there exists a density

---

[19]The following is an elegant characterization of bounded Riemann integrable functions using Lebesgue measure: a bounded function $f : [a, b] \longrightarrow \mathbf{R}$ is Riemann integrable *if and only if* the set of points where f is not continuous has Lebesgue measure 0.

[20]*The development of the notion of integral*, Lecture given in Copenhagen, 1926. This appeared in translation as an appendix in *Lebesgue Integration* by S. B. Chae, Marcel Dekker, 1980. A comprehensive historical study of the development of the Riemann and Lebesgue integrals, and of many other intermediate integrals, can be found in I. N. Pesin, *Classical and Modern Integration Theories*, Academic Press, New York and London, 1970.

function f such that for all closed intervals $[a, b]$

(7.7) $$P[\omega \in \Omega : a \le X(\omega) \le b] = P_X([a, b]) = \int_{[a,b]} f \, d\mathbf{m}.$$

With respect to Lebesgue measure, any two density functions for X are almost surely equal and, for all practical purposes, the density function associated with a random variable is unique. With this qualification we denote the density of X by f_X. When f_X is Riemann integrable, (7.7) implies

$$P_X([a, b]) = \int_a^b f_X(x) dx.$$

If f_X is continuous, except perhaps at a finite set of points, $\alpha, \beta \in \mathbf{R}$ and $\alpha > 0$, then, using the change of variable $y = (x - \beta)/\alpha$, we obtain

$$
\begin{aligned}
P_{\alpha X + \beta}([a, b]) &= P(\{\omega \in \Omega : a \le \alpha X(\omega) + \beta \le b\}) \\
&= P_X\left(\left[\frac{a - \beta}{\alpha}, \frac{b - \beta}{\alpha}\right]\right) = \int_{\frac{a-\beta}{\alpha}}^{\frac{b-\beta}{\alpha}} f_X(x) dx \\
&= \int_a^b \frac{1}{\alpha} f_X\left(\frac{y - \beta}{\alpha}\right) dy
\end{aligned}
$$

and

(7.8) $$f_{\alpha X + \beta}(x) = \frac{1}{\alpha} f_X\left(\frac{x - \beta}{\alpha}\right).$$

Example 7.17. For any $\alpha > 0$ the function

$$f(x) = \begin{cases} \alpha \exp(-x/\alpha) & , \ x \ge 0 \\ 0 & , \ x < 0 \end{cases}$$

is a density function. A random variable X with this density is called an *exponential random variable* with parameter α.

Density functions are particularly useful in calculating expected values, and the following result is a straightforward consequence of Proposition 7.10.

Proposition 7.18. *If the random variable X on $(\Omega, \mathcal{F}, P)$ has density function f_X and g is a Borel measurable function such that $g(X) f_X$ is Riemann integrable, then $g(X)$ is an integrable random variable and*

(7.9) $$\mathbb{E}[g(X)] = \int_{-\infty}^{+\infty} g(x) f_X(x) dx.$$

We complete this section by considering the most important density function in probability theory, the function $(2\pi)^{-1/2} e^{-x^2/2}$. Since it is used so frequently we feel every student should have, at some stage, the opportunity to see at least the sketch of a proof. It is an unexpected[21] proof, and having seen it, one can only say, how did anyone ever think of it? The reader may not feel the same way, but some day you will be struck by something other than the difficulty of a proof: by its beauty, by its ingenuity, by its obviousness, by its necessity, by the fact that it makes other things fall into place, by the urge to improve it or to generalize it, and at that stage you will have reached a higher level and you will know it because afterwards things will not be the same. Any student who studies any subject to any real depth will have these moments of truth.

We return now to the function. By the symmetry $e^{-x^2/2} = e^{-(-x)^2/2}$ we have

$$\int_{\mathbf{R}} e^{-x^2/2} dx = 2 \int_0^\infty e^{-x^2/2} dx = 2 \lim_{n \to \infty} \int_0^n e^{-x^2/2} dx.$$

Although our problem involves a single variable, it is by going to two variables that we obtain a solution. We have

$$\left(\int_0^n e^{-x^2/2} dx \right)^2 = \left(\int_0^n e^{-x^2/2} dx \right) \cdot \left(\int_0^n e^{-y^2/2} dy \right) = \int \int_{I_n} e^{-(x^2+y^2)/2} dx dy$$

where I_n denotes the square with vertices $(0,0), (0,n), (n,0)$ and (n,n). Both the Lebesgue and Riemann integrals extend to $\mathbf{R}^2$ and coincide for continuous functions on bounded rectangular regions. Let J_n denote the first quadrant of the circle centered at the origin with radius n and let $f(x,y) = e^{-(x^2+y^2)/2}$. Since $f \geq 0$ and $J_n \subset I_n \subset J_{n\sqrt{2}}$ we have $\int \int_{J_n} f \leq \int \int_{I_n} f \leq \int \int_{J_{n\sqrt{2}}} f$. These inequalities and the upper bound principle imply that $\lim_{n \to \infty} \int \int_{J_n} f < \infty$ if and only if $\lim_{n \to \infty} \int \int_{I_n} f < \infty$ and if the limits exist they are equal. To evaluate $\int \int_{J_n} f$ we look at a typical Riemann, sum but instead of using the usual vertical and horizontal lines to partition J_n, we use curves that take advantage of the geometry of J_n (see Figure 7.2).

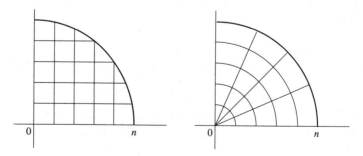

Figure 7.2

---

[21]The original proof was based on approximating the probability that the number of successes in n independent trials lies in $[a, b]$, given that the probability of success in any one trial is p. It involved complicated estimates of sums of terms from binomial expansions. The proof given here is due to K. F. Gauss.

We partition $[0, n]$ using $\{0 = r_1, \ldots, r_i, \ldots, r_l = n\}$ and let $\Delta r_i = r_{i+1} - r_i$, and partition $[0, \pi]$ using $\{0 = \theta_1, \ldots, \theta_j, \ldots, \theta_m = \pi/2\}$ and let $\Delta\theta_j = \theta_{j+1} - \theta_j$. If A is the sector of the circle of radius r supported by an angle θ at the center (see Figure 7.3), then $Area(A)/\pi r^2 = \theta/2\pi$. Hence $Area(A) = \theta r^2/2$ and the

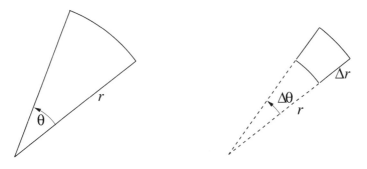

Figure 7.3

area of a typical set in our partition is

$$\left(\Delta\theta_j(r_i + \Delta_i)^2 - \Delta\theta_j r_i^2\right)/2 = r_i \Delta r_i \Delta\theta_j + (\Delta r_i)^2 \Delta\theta_j/2.$$

The second term on the right-hand side can be discarded, as it is much smaller than the first term when Δr_i is small. By Pythagoras' Theorem $r^2 = x^2 + y^2$ and thus $f(x, y)$ is close to $e^{-r^2/2}$ on a typical set in the partition. Our Riemann sum now has the appearance

$$\sum_{i,j=0}^{l-1,m-1} r_i e^{-r_i^2/2} \Delta r_i \Delta\theta_j,$$

and this sum can be rewritten as

$$\left(\sum_{i=0}^{l-1} r_i e^{-r_i^2/2} \Delta r_i\right) \cdot \left(\sum_{j=0}^{m-1} \Delta\theta_j\right).$$

This is now recognizable as the product of Riemann sums of two one-variable functions, and, on using finer and finer partitions, we obtain in the limit

$$\int\int_{J_n} e^{-(x^2+y^2)/2} dx dy = \int_0^n r e^{-r^2/2} dr \cdot \int_0^{\pi/2} d\theta.$$

On making the substitution $u = -r^2/2, du = -r dr$ we obtain

$$\int_0^n r e^{-r^2/2} dr = \int -e^u du = -e^u = -e^{-r^2/2}\Big]_0^n = 1 - e^{-n^2/2}.$$

By Exercise 1.2

$$\int\int_{J_n} e^{-(x^2+y^2)} dx dy = (1 - e^{-n^2/2}) \cdot \pi/2 \longrightarrow \pi/2$$

as $n \longrightarrow \infty$. This implies $\frac{1}{\sqrt{2\pi}} \int_{\mathbf{R}} e^{-x^2/2} dx = \frac{1}{\sqrt{2\pi}} \cdot 2 \cdot \left(\frac{\pi}{2}\right)^{1/2} = 1$. By (7.8), $(2\pi\sigma^2)^{-1/2} \exp\left\{-(x - \mu)^2/2\sigma^2\right\}$ is a density function. A *normal*,[22] or $N(\mu, \sigma^2)$ distributed, random variable is a random variable X with density $f_X(x) = (2\pi\sigma^2)^{-1/2} \exp\left\{-(x - \mu)^2/2\sigma^2\right\}, x \in \mathbf{R}$. An $N(\mu, \sigma^2)$ distributed random variable has mean μ and variance σ^2 (see Lemma 9.14). A random variable X has a *lognormal distribution* if $\log X$ has a normal distribution. It is generally accepted that most share prices at any fixed future time are lognormally distributed and hence fully determined by just two parameters, the mean and the variance (see Chapter 10).

7.5. The Central Limit Theorem

In this section we present without proof [23] one of the main results in probability theory, the Central Limit Theorem.[24]

Proposition 7.19. (*The Central Limit Theorem*) *Let* $(X_n)_{n=1}^{\infty}$ *be a sequence of independent* [25] *identically distributed random variables in* $\mathbf{L}^2(\Omega, \mathcal{F}, P)$ *and, for all* n, *let* $Y_n = \frac{1}{n} \sum_{i=1}^{n} X_i$. *If* $\mathbb{E}[X_i] = \mu$ *and* $Var(X_i) = \sigma^2$ *for all* i, *then*

$$\lim_{n \longrightarrow \infty} P\left[\frac{Y_n - \mu}{\sigma/\sqrt{n}} \leq x\right] = \lim_{n \longrightarrow \infty} P\left[\frac{\sum_{i=1}^{n} X_i - n\mu}{\sqrt{n}\sigma} \leq x\right] = \frac{1}{\sqrt{2\pi}} \int_{-\infty}^{x} e^{-y^2/2} dy$$

for all $x \in \mathbf{R}$.

---

[22]It is also said to have a Gaussian distribution after Karl Friedrich Gauss (1777-1855), although it was used in probability theory before Gauss by both de Moivre and Laplace. Gauss made fundamental contributions to number theory, algebra, differential geometry, celestial mechanics, electricity and magnetism and geodesy. His interest in astronomy led him to investigate the distribution of errors, a topic also considered by Laplace. When n observations are drawn at random from a population, one has a set of n independent random variables and the average, as both Gauss and Laplace proved, tends to be approximately normally distributed when n is large. This is essentially the *Central Limit Theorem*.

[23]The usual modern proof of the Central Limit Theorem uses *characteristic functions*. A direct proof, using the *Banach Contraction Principle* (see Exercise 7.7), is given in H. F. Trotter, *An Elementary Proof of the Central Limit Theorem*, Arch. Math., 10, 1959, pp. 226-234. Trotter's proof uses only the fact that normally distributed random variables have finite variance and that the sum of independent normal random variables is again normal (see Example 7.34.).

[24]The Central Limit Theorem was first *stated* by Abraham de Moivre (1667-1754) in 1732 for a sequence $(X_n)_{n=1}^{\infty}$ where $P(\{X_n = 0\}) = P(\{X_n = 1\}) = 1/2$, but this result was *proved*, and generalized to $P(\{X_n = 0\}) = p, P(\{X_n = 1\}) = 1 - p$, only in 1801 by Pierre Simon Laplace (1749-1827). de Moivre, a Huguenot, fled France as a teenager to escape religious persecution after the revocation of the edict of Nantes and settled in London for the remainder of his life. He supported himself by private tutoring in mathematics and acting as a consultant on games of chance and annuities. Laplace made important contributions to mathematics, astronomy, probability theory and applied mathematics. A number of particular cases of the Central Limit Theorem were proved after Laplace, but it was only in the first quarter of the twentieth century that the Russian mathematicians A. Liapounov and J.W. Lindeberg obtained a general form of the result which included Proposition 7.19.

[25]It is not sufficient that the sequence be pairwise independent. We require that for all n and any sequence of Borel sets, $(B_i)_{i=1}^{n}$, that $P\{\omega \in \Omega : X_i(\omega) \in B_i \text{ for all } i\} = \prod_{i=1}^{n} P\{\omega \in \Omega : X_i \in B_i\}$.

We restate this result by introducing a new type of convergence. The *distribution* function F_X of a random variable X on $(\Omega, \mathcal{F}, P)$ is defined as $F_X(x) := P(\{\omega \in \Omega : X(\omega) \leq x\})$ for all $x \in \mathbf{R}$. If F_X is continuously differentiable, then X has a density and $F'_X = f_X$. Since $P(\{\omega \in \Omega : x - h < X(\omega) \leq x + h\}) = F_X(x + h) - F_X(x - h)$ for all $h > 0$, $P(\{\omega \in \Omega : X(\omega) = x\}) = 0$ at all points x where F_X is continuous.

Definition 7.20. *A sequence of random variables* $(X_n)_{n=1}^{\infty}$ *on* $(\Omega, \mathcal{F}, P)$ *converges in distribution to the random variable* X *if*

$$\lim_{n \longrightarrow \infty} P\big[\{\omega \in \Omega : X_n(\omega) \leq x\}\big] \quad = \quad P\big[\{\omega \in \Omega : X(\omega) \leq x\}\big]$$

at all points x *where* F_X *is continuous. We write* $X_n \xrightarrow{D} X$ *when* X_n *tends to* X *in distribution.*[26]

The Central Limit Theorem states that the normalized[27] average of n independent identically distributed random variables with finite variance tends in distribution to an $N(0, 1)$ distributed random variable.

Proposition 7.21. *If* $(X_n)_{n=1}^{\infty}$ *is a sequence of random variables on the probability space* $(\Omega, \mathcal{F}, P)$ *which converges almost surely to the random variable* X, *then* $X_n \xrightarrow{D} X$ *as* $n \longrightarrow \infty$.

Proof. Let x denote a point of continuity of F_X, and let $A = \{\omega \in \Omega : X(\omega) \neq x\}$. By hypothesis there exists an $\mathcal{F}$ measurable set B such that $P(B) = 1$ and $X_n \longrightarrow X$ pointwise on B. Since[28] $P(A) = 1$ and

$$1 \geq P(A \cap B) = P(A) + P(B) - P(A \cup B) = 2 - P(A \cup B) \geq 1$$

we have $P(A \cap B) = 1$.

Let $f = \mathbf{1}_{(-\infty, x]}$. By the proof of Proposition 5.17

$$\mathbb{E}[f(Y)] = \mathbb{E}[\mathbf{1}_{Y^{-1}((-\infty, x])}] = P[Y^{-1}((-\infty, x])] = P[\{\omega \in \Omega : Y \leq x\}]$$

for any random variable Y, and it suffices to show $\mathbb{E}[f(X_n)] \longrightarrow \mathbb{E}[f(X)]$ as $n \longrightarrow \infty$. If $\omega \in A \cap B$ and $X(\omega) < x$, then $X_n(\omega) < x$ for all n sufficiently large, and $f(X_n)(\omega) = f(X)(\omega) = 1$ for n large. Similarly, if $\omega \in A \cap B$ and $X(\omega) > x$, then $f(X_n)(\omega) = f(X)(\omega) = 0$ for all n large. Hence $f(X_n) \longrightarrow f(X)$ almost surely as $n \longrightarrow \infty$. Since $|f(X_n)(\omega)| \leq 1$ for all n and ω the Dominated Convergence Theorem implies $\mathbb{E}[f(X_n)] \longrightarrow \mathbb{E}[f(X)]$ as $n \longrightarrow \infty$ as required. This completes the proof. $\qquad \square$

---

[26]The term *weakly convergent* is also used since $X_n \xrightarrow{D} X$ if and only if $\mathbb{E}[f(X_n)] \longrightarrow \mathbb{E}[f(X)]$ for all continuous bounded functions $f : \mathbf{R} \mapsto \mathbf{R}$.

[27]The normalized version of X is the random variable $Y := (X - \mu)/\sigma$ where $\mu = \mathbb{E}[X]$ and $\sigma^2 = \mathrm{Var}(X)$. The random variable Y had mean 0 and variance 1.

[28]See Exercise 5.27.

Example 7.22. Let P denote a probability measure on $(\mathbf{R}, \mathcal{B}(\mathbf{R}))$ such that $P[\{0\}] = P[\{1\}] = 1/2$. For each positive integer n let $X_n(x) = |x| + \frac{1}{n}$ for all $x \in \mathbf{R}$. Let $X(x) = |x|$ for $x \in \mathbf{R}$. Then $X_n \longrightarrow X$ pointwise, and hence almost surely, as $n \longrightarrow \infty$. Since $X_n(x) > 0$ for all $x \in \mathbf{R}$ we have $P[X_n \leq 0] = 0$. On the other hand, $X(x) \leq 0$ if and only if $x = 0$. Hence $P[X \leq 0] = P[X = 0] = P[\{0\}] = 1/2$ and $\lim_{n\to\infty} P[X_n \leq 0] \neq P[X \leq 0]$. This shows that points of continuity in Definition 7.20 do make a difference.

7.6. Convex Functions

The main result in this section, *Jensen's Inequality*, involves the introduction and analysis of a class of functions which occupy a special place in mathematical economics, convex functions. Our methods show how analysis and geometry combine to make concrete a class of functions originally defined in a rather abstract way.

Definition 7.23. *A function* $\phi : (a, b) \subset \mathbf{R} \longrightarrow \mathbf{R}$ *is convex if for all* $x, y, a < x < y < b$ *and all* $t, 0 < t < 1$,

$$(7.10) \qquad \phi(tx + (1 - t)y) \leq t\phi(x) + (1 - t)\phi(y).$$

The defining inequality (7.10) admits immediate geometric, analytic and probabilistic interpretations. Geometrically ϕ is convex if and only if the straight line joining any two points on the graph of ϕ lies above the graph; see Figure 7.4.

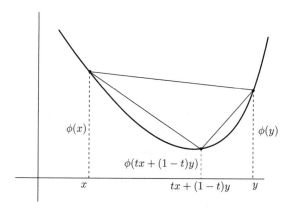

Figure 7.4

This suggests some useful examples, and $\phi(x) = |x|, \phi(x) = x^2$ and $\phi(x) = e^{\alpha x}, \alpha \in \mathbf{R}$, are all easily seen to be convex. Analytically we see that a non-constant convex function restricted to any closed interval $[x, y] \subset (a, b)$ cannot have a maximum over $[x, y]$ at any interior point $z \in (x, y)$. As regards probability theory we note that both sides of (7.10) are averages and this may be expressed transparently using expected values. If $a < x < y < b$, $0 < t < 1$, $\Omega = \{x, y\}$, $\mathcal{F} = 2^{\Omega}$, $P(\{x\}) = t$, $P(\{y\}) = 1 - t$, then $(\Omega, \mathcal{F}, P)$ is a probability space and (7.10) can be rewritten as

$$(7.11) \qquad \phi(\mathbb{E}[X]) \leq \mathbb{E}[\phi(X)]$$

where X is the identity function on $\mathbf{R}$; that is $X(x) = x$ for all $x \in \mathbf{R}$. The main result in this section, *Jensen's Inequality*, extends this inequality to arbitrary random variables. The following are immediate from the definition: if ϕ and ψ are defined and convex functions on (a, b) and α and β are *positive* real numbers, then $\alpha\phi + \beta\psi$ is convex, and ζ, defined by $\zeta(x) = \phi(-x)$ for all $x \in (-b, -a)$, is convex. Moreover, the restriction of a convex function to any *interval* in its domain of definition is convex.

Proposition 7.24. *If $\phi : (a, b) \subset \mathbf{R} \longrightarrow \mathbf{R}$, then the following conditions are equivalent:*

(a) *ϕ is convex;*

(b) *if $a < x_1 < x_2 < \ldots < x_n < b$, $0 < t_i < 1$ and $\sum_{i=1}^{n} t_i = 1$, then*

$$(7.12) \qquad \phi\left(\sum_{i=1}^{n} t_i x_i\right) \leq \sum_{i=1}^{n} t_i \phi(x_i);$$

(c) *if $a < x < y < z < b$, then*

$$(7.13) \qquad \frac{\phi(x) - \phi(y)}{x - y} \leq \frac{\phi(y) - \phi(z)}{y - z}.$$

Proof. If we let $n = 2$ in (b), we obtain (a) and hence (b) implies (a). We show (a) $\Longrightarrow$ (b) by induction on n, $n \geq 2$. With the above notation we have

$$\phi\left(\sum_{i=1}^{n+1} t_i x_i\right) = \phi\left((1 - t_{n+1})\left(\sum_{i=1}^{n} \frac{t_i}{1 - t_{n+1}} x_i\right) + t_{n+1} x_{n+1}\right)$$

$$\leq (1 - t_{n+1})\phi\left(\sum_{i=1}^{n} \frac{t_i}{1 - t_{n+1}} x_i\right) + t_{n+1}\phi(x_{n+1})$$

$$\leq (1 - t_{n+1})\left(\sum_{i=1}^{n} \frac{t_i}{1 - t_{n+1}} \phi(x_i)\right) + t_{n+1}\phi(x_{n+1})$$

$$\leq \sum_{i=1}^{n} t_i \phi(x_i) + t_{n+1}\phi(x_{n+1})$$

$$= \sum_{i=1}^{n+1} t_i \phi(x_i).$$

This shows that (a) and (b) are equivalent.

If $a < x < y < z < b$, then $y = tx + (1-t)z$ for some $t, 0 < t < 1$, and hence (7.13) can be rewritten as

$$\frac{\phi(x) - \phi(tx + (1-t)z)}{x - (tx + (1-t)z)} \leq \frac{\phi(tx + (1-t)z) - \phi(z)}{(tx + (1-t)z) - z} \quad ;$$

that is

$$\frac{\phi(x) - \phi(tx + (1-t)z)}{(1-t)(x-z)} \leq \frac{\phi(tx + (1-t)z) - \phi(z)}{t(x-z)}.$$

Since $0 < t < 1$ and $x < z$ this is equivalent to

$$t(\phi(x) - \phi(tx + (1-t)z)) \geq (1-t)(\phi(tx + (1-t)z) - \phi(z)) \quad ;$$

that is

$$t\phi(x) + (1-t)\phi(z) \geq ((1-t) + t)(\phi(tx + (1-t)z))$$
$$= \phi(tx + (1-t)z).$$

Hence (a) and (c) are equivalent, and this completes the proof. $\qquad\square$

Proposition 7.24(c) says that the lines joining three consecutive points on the graph of a convex function form a **V**; see Figure 7.4.

Corollary 7.25. *If ϕ is a twice continuously differentiable function defined on (a, b), then ϕ is convex if and only if $\phi'' \geq 0$.*

Proof. If $\phi'' \geq 0$, then ϕ' is an increasing function. Suppose $x < y < z$. By the *Mean Value Theorem* there exist x^* and y^*, $x < x^* < y < y^* < z$ such that

$$\frac{\phi(x) - \phi(y)}{x - y} = \phi'(x^*) \leq \phi'(y^*) = \frac{\phi(y) - \phi(z)}{y - z}.$$

By Proposition 7.24, ϕ is convex.

Conversely suppose ϕ is convex. Let x and $v, x < v$, lie in the domain of ϕ. Two applications of (7.13) show that

$$\frac{\phi(x) - \phi(y)}{x - y} \leq \frac{\phi(u) - \phi(v)}{u - v}$$

whenever $a < x < y < u < v < b$. Hence

$$\phi'(x) = \lim_{y \to x} \frac{\phi(x) - \phi(y)}{x - y} \leq \lim_{u \to v} \frac{\phi(u) - \phi(v)}{u - v} = \phi'(v)$$

and ϕ' is increasing. This implies $\phi'' \geq 0$ and completes the proof. $\qquad\square$

Corollary 7.26. *Convex functions are continuous.*

Proof. If $\phi : (a, b) \longrightarrow \mathbf{R}$ is convex and $x \in (a, b)$, then, applying (7.13) a few times, we obtain

$$\frac{\phi(u) - \phi(v)}{u - v} \leq \frac{\phi(x) - \phi(y)}{x - y} \leq \frac{\phi(z) - \phi(w)}{z - w}$$

for $a < u < v < z < w < b$ and $\{x, y\} \subset (v, z), y \neq x$. On fixing v and z this implies $(\phi(x) - \phi(y))/(x - y), x \neq y$, is bounded above and below on $[v, z]$. If $y \longrightarrow x$, then $x - y \longrightarrow 0$ and hence $\phi(x) - \phi(y) \longrightarrow 0$. This shows that ϕ is continuous at x, and as x was arbitrary this completes the proof. $\qquad\square$

Proposition 7.27. *If ϕ is a convex function with domain (a, b), then[29] either ϕ is always increasing or always decreasing on (a, b) or there exists $c \in (a, b)$ such that ϕ is decreasing on (a, c), increasing on (c, b), and ϕ has an absolute minimum over (a, b) at c.*

Proof. First suppose that ϕ achieves its minimum m over (a, b) at c. If $a < x < y < c$, then, by (7.13) and as $\phi(y) - \phi(c) \geq 0$ and $y - c < 0$, we have

$$\frac{\phi(x) - \phi(y)}{x - y} \leq \frac{\phi(y) - \phi(c)}{y - c} \leq 0.$$

Since $x - y < 0$ this implies $\phi(x) - \phi(y) \geq 0$ and ϕ is decreasing on (a, c). A similar argument shows that ϕ is increasing on (c, b). Hence ϕ has an absolute minimum over (a, b) at c.

We now suppose that ϕ does not have a minimum over (a, b). If $x < y$ and $\phi(x) = \phi(y)$, then, for $a < x_1 < x < y < y_1 < b$, we have

$$\frac{\phi(x_1) - \phi(x)}{x_1 - x} \leq \frac{\phi(x) - \phi(y)}{x - y} = 0 \leq \frac{\phi(y) - \phi(y_1)}{y - y_1}$$

and hence $\phi(x_1) \geq \phi(x)$ and $\phi(y) \leq \phi(y_1)$. This implies that ϕ achieves its minimum over (a, b) at some point in $[x, y]$ and contradicts our hypothesis. Hence ϕ is one-to-one or injective, and by Proposition 7.5 it is either strictly increasing or strictly decreasing on every closed subinterval in $[a, b]$.

If $x, y \in (a, b)$ and $x \neq y$, then $\phi(x) \neq \phi(y)$. Suppose $\phi(x) < \phi(y)$. Choose n_0, a positive integer, such that $a + \frac{1}{n} < x$ and $y < b - \frac{1}{n}$ for all $n > n_0$. Then ϕ is strictly increasing on $[a + \frac{1}{n}, b - \frac{1}{n}]$ for all $n > n_0$ and hence on $(a, b) = \bigcup_{n > n_0} [a + \frac{1}{n}, b - \frac{1}{n}]$. Similarly, if $\phi(x) > \phi(y)$, then ϕ is strictly decreasing on (a, b). This completes the proof. $\qquad\square$

The functions x^2, e^x and e^{-x} show that all possibilities occur.

Corollary 7.28. *If $\phi : (a, b) \longrightarrow \mathbf{R}$ is convex, then $\phi = \phi_1 + \phi_2$ where ϕ_1 is convex and increasing and ϕ_2 is convex and decreasing.*

---

[29]These different possibilities are not *mutually exclusive*, for example constant functions satisfy all of them. What the proposition says is that every convex function satisfies *at least* one of them.

Proof. We consider the three possible cases given in the previous proposition. If ϕ is increasing, let $\phi_1 = \phi$ and $\phi_2 = 0$. If ϕ is decreasing, let $\phi_1 = 0$ and $\phi_2 = \phi$. If ϕ is convex and not covered by the above cases, then there exists $c \in (a, b)$ such that ϕ is decreasing on $(a, c]$ and increasing on $[c, b)$. Let $\phi_1 = \phi \mathbf{1}_{[c,b)} - m\mathbf{1}_{[c,b)}$ and $\phi_2 = \phi \cdot \mathbf{1}_{(a,c)} + m\mathbf{1}_{[c,b)}$ where $m = \phi(c)$. Equation (7.10) is easily seen to hold for ϕ_1 and ϕ_2 (see Figure 7.4), and this completes the proof. $\qquad\square$

In our next proposition we suppose that ϕ is defined on $\mathbf{R}$, although it is easily seen that we need suppose only that $X(\Omega) \subset \mathrm{domain}(\phi)$.

Proposition 7.29. (*Jensen's Inequality*)[30] *If X is an integrable random variable on $(\Omega, \mathcal{F}, P)$, $\phi : \mathbf{R} \longrightarrow \mathbf{R}$ is convex and $\phi(X)$ is integrable then*

$$(7.14) \qquad \phi(\mathbb{E}[X]) \ \leq \ \mathbb{E}[\phi(X)].$$

Proof. By Proposition 6.28(a), X is the pointwise limit of a sequence of simple random variables $(X_n)_{n=1}^\infty$ satisfying $|X_n| \leq |X|$ for all n. By the Dominated Convergence Theorem, $\mathbb{E}[X_n] \longrightarrow \mathbb{E}[X]$ as $n \longrightarrow \infty$. Since ϕ is continuous, $\phi(\mathbb{E}[X_n]) \longrightarrow \phi(\mathbb{E}[X])$ as $n \longrightarrow \infty$. If $X_n = \sum_{i=1}^k a_i \mathbf{1}_{A_i}$ is a canonical representation, then $\mathbb{E}[X_n] = \sum_{i=1}^k a_i P(A_i)$ and $\sum_{i=1}^k P(A_i) = 1$. Since ϕ is convex, (7.10) implies

$$(7.15) \qquad \phi(\mathbb{E}[X_n]) \leq \sum_{i=1}^k P(A_i)\phi(a_i) = \mathbb{E}[\phi(X_n)].$$

By continuity $\phi(X_n)$ converges pointwise to $\phi(X)$ as $n \longrightarrow \infty$. If ϕ is increasing, then

$$|\phi(X_n)(\omega)| = |\phi(X_n(\omega))| \leq |\phi(X(\omega))|.$$

By the Dominated Convergence Theorem, $\mathbb{E}[\phi(X_n)] \longrightarrow \mathbb{E}[\phi(X)]$ as $n \longrightarrow \infty$ and, by (7.15), $\phi(\mathbb{E}[X]) \leq \mathbb{E}[\phi(X)]$. If ϕ is decreasing, let $\theta(x) = \phi(-x)$. Then θ is convex and increasing and $\phi(X_n(\omega)) = \theta(-X_n(\omega))$ for all n and ω. By the above $\phi(\mathbb{E}[X]) = \theta(\mathbb{E}[-X]) \leq \mathbb{E}[\theta(-X)] = \mathbb{E}[\phi(X)]$. This proves Jensen's inequality when ϕ is either increasing or decreasing and, by Corollary 7.28, we complete the proof by combining these two cases. $\qquad\square$

---

[30]Johan Jensen (1859-1925) from Nakskov (Denmark) studied a range of sciences, including mathematics, at university but was essentially self taught as a research mathematician and never held an academic position. He had a successful professional career as a technical engineer with the Bell Telephone Company in Copenhagen from 1881 until 1924 and devoted his spare time to mathematics. He published high-quality research in complex and real analysis. Jensen's Inequality, first published in 1906, is regarded, along with the Cauchy-Schwarz inequality, as one of the fundamental inequalities in analysis.

7.7. Product Measures

We make extensive use of products of probability measures in this book. In Proposition 5.16 we constructed the product of two probability measures when both underlying σ-fields were countably generated. The main result on product measures proved in this section, Proposition 7.33, is considerably more involved but still only a special case of a result we use later but do not prove. The Monotone Convergence Theorem (Propositions 6.23 and 6.25) is the crucial ingredient in the proof, and to use it efficiently we introduce a new approach to generating σ-fields, based on increasing and decreasing sequences of sets (see Proposition 5.3). The reader may wish to skip this technical section on a first reading.

Definition 7.30. *A collection $\mathcal{M}$ of subsets of a set Ω is called a monotone class if the union of every increasing sequence and the intersection of every decreasing sequence of sets in $\mathcal{M}$ belong to $\mathcal{M}$.*

If $\mathcal{A}$ is a non-empty collection of subsets of Ω, then the intersection in 2^{Ω} of all monotone classes containing $\mathcal{A}$ is easily seen to be the smallest monotone class containing $\mathcal{A}$ (see the proof of Proposition 3.7). It is called the monotone class generated by $\mathcal{A}$ and is denoted by $\mathcal{M}(\mathcal{A})$. By the proof of Proposition 5.3 every σ-field is a monotone class and hence $\mathcal{M}(\mathcal{A}) \subset \mathcal{F}(\mathcal{A})$. In the following lemma we give conditions under which $\mathcal{M}(\mathcal{A}) = \mathcal{F}(\mathcal{A})$.

Lemma 7.31. *If $\mathcal{A}$ is a non-empty collection of subsets of Ω such that the finite union and complement of sets from $\mathcal{A}$ belong to $\mathcal{A}$, then $\mathcal{M}(\mathcal{A}) = \mathcal{F}(\mathcal{A})$.*

Proof. It suffices to show that $\mathcal{M}(\mathcal{A})$ is a σ-field. If $A \in \mathcal{A}$ then $A^c \in \mathcal{A}$ and hence $\Omega = A \cup A^c \in \mathcal{A}$.

If $A \in \mathcal{A}$, let

$$\mathcal{M}_{\mathbf{A}} = \{B \in \mathcal{M}(\mathcal{A}) : A \cup B \in \mathcal{M}(\mathcal{A})\}.$$

Since finite unions in $\mathcal{A}$ belong to $\mathcal{A}$, $\mathcal{A} \subset \mathcal{M}_{\mathbf{A}}$. If $(B_n)_{n=1}^{\infty}$ is an increasing sequence in $\mathcal{M}_{\mathbf{A}}$, then $(A \cup B_n)_{n=1}^{\infty}$ is an increasing sequence in $\mathcal{M}(\mathcal{A})$. Hence $\bigcup_{n=1}^{\infty}(A \cup B_n) = A \cup \left(\bigcup_{n=1}^{\infty} B_n\right) \in \mathcal{M}(\mathcal{A})$ and $\bigcup_{n=1}^{\infty} B_n \in \mathcal{M}_{\mathbf{A}}$. Similarly, if $(B_n)_{n=1}^{\infty}$ is an decreasing sequence in $\mathcal{M}_{\mathbf{A}}$, then the intersection $\bigcap_{n=1}^{\infty} B_n \in \mathcal{M}_{\mathbf{A}}$. Hence $\mathcal{M}_{\mathbf{A}}$ is a monotone class containing $\mathcal{A}$ and contained in $\mathcal{M}(\mathcal{A})$. Since $\mathcal{M}(\mathcal{A})$ is the smallest monotone class containing $\mathcal{A}$, this means $\mathcal{M}_{\mathbf{A}} = \mathcal{M}(\mathcal{A})$, and as A was arbitrary this shows that $A \cup B \in \mathcal{M}(\mathcal{A})$ whenever $A \in \mathcal{A}$ and $B \in \mathcal{M}(\mathcal{A})$.

Now let

$$\mathcal{M}_{\mathcal{A}} = \{B \in \mathcal{M}(\mathcal{A}) : A \cup B \in \mathcal{M}(\mathcal{A}) \text{ for all } A \in \mathcal{M}(\mathcal{A})\}.$$

The above argument shows that $\mathcal{M}_A$ is a monotone class, and as we already know that $\mathcal{A} \subset \mathcal{M}_A$, this implies that $\mathcal{M}_A = \mathcal{M}(\mathcal{A})$. Hence the union of any two sets in $\mathcal{M}(\mathcal{A})$ lies in $\mathcal{M}(\mathcal{A})$. By induction finite unions of sets in $\mathcal{M}(\mathcal{A})$ also lie in $\mathcal{M}(\mathcal{A})$ and, as $\mathcal{M}(\mathcal{A})$ is a monotone class, any countable union of sets in $\mathcal{M}(\mathcal{A})$ also belongs to $\mathcal{M}(\mathcal{A})$.

Let $\mathcal{M}_A^c = \{B \in \mathcal{M}(\mathcal{A}) : B^c \in \mathcal{M}(\mathcal{A})\}$. Since the complement of any set in $\mathcal{A}$ also lies in $\mathcal{A}$, we have $\mathcal{A} \subset \mathcal{M}_A^c$. If $(B_n)_{n=1}^\infty$ is an increasing sequence in $\mathcal{M}_A^c$, then $B_n^c \in \mathcal{M}(\mathcal{A})$ for all n and, as $\mathcal{M}(\mathcal{A})$ is a monotone class and $(B_n^c)_{n=1}^\infty$ is a decreasing sequence in $\mathcal{M}(\mathcal{A})$, $\bigcap_{n=1}^\infty B_n^c = \left(\bigcup_{n=1}^\infty B_n\right)^c \in \mathcal{M}(\mathcal{A})$ and $\bigcup_{n=1}^\infty B_n \in \mathcal{M}_A^c$. Similarly any decreasing sequence of sets in $\mathcal{M}_A^c$ also lies in $\mathcal{M}_A^c$ and $\mathcal{M}_A^c$ is a monotone class containing $\mathcal{A}$. Hence $\mathcal{M}_A^c = \mathcal{M}(\mathcal{A})$ and the complement of any set in $\mathcal{M}(\mathcal{A})$ also belongs to $\mathcal{M}(\mathcal{A})$. This shows that $\mathcal{M}(\mathcal{A})$ is a σ-field and completes the proof. $\square$

We fix, once and for all, the notation that we use throughout the remainder of this section. Let $(\Omega_1, \mathcal{F}_1, P_1)$ and $(\Omega_2, \mathcal{F}_2, P_2)$ denote probability spaces and let $\Omega := \Omega_1 \times \Omega_2$ denote the product of the sample spaces. Let $\mathcal{F} := \mathcal{F}_1 \times \mathcal{F}_2$ denote the σ-field on Ω generated by $A \times B$ where $A \in \mathcal{F}_1$ and $B \in \mathcal{F}_2$. Sets of the form $A \times B, A \in \mathcal{F}_1, B \in \mathcal{F}_2$ are called *measurable rectangles*. Let

$$\mathcal{G} := \Big\{ \bigcup_{i=1}^n A_i \times B_i : A_i \in \mathcal{F}_1, B_i \in \mathcal{F}_2, (A_i \times B_i) \cap (A_j \times B_j) = \emptyset \text{ for } i \neq j \Big\}$$

denote the set of all finite unions of *pairwise disjoint* measurable rectangles. If

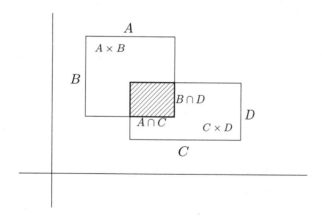

Figure 7.5

$(A_i \times B_i)_{i=1}^n$ and $(C_j \times D_j)_{j=1}^m$ belong to $\mathcal{G}$, then (see Figure 7.5)

$$\Big(\bigcup_{i=1}^n A_i \times B_i\Big) \cap \Big(\bigcup_{j=1}^m C_j \times D_j\Big) = \bigcup_{i=1,j=1}^{n,m} (A_i \cap C_j) \times (B_i \cap D_j);$$

and if $i \neq k$ or $j \neq l$,

$$
\begin{aligned}
&\left[(A_i \cap C_j) \times (B_i \cap D_j)\right] \cap \left[(A_k \cap C_l) \times (B_k \cap D_l)\right] \\
&= (A_i \cap A_k \cap C_j \cap C_l) \times (B_i \cap B_k \cap D_j \cap D_l) \\
&= (A_i \times B_i) \cap (A_k \times B_k) \cap (C_j \times D_j) \cap (C_l \times D_l) \\
&= \emptyset.
\end{aligned}
$$

Hence the intersection of two sets in $\mathcal{G}$ lies in $\mathcal{G}$, and by induction the intersection of any finite number of sets in $\mathcal{G}$ also lies in $\mathcal{G}$. Since $\left[\bigcup_{i=1}^{n}(A_i \times B_i)\right]^c = \bigcap_{i=1}^{n}(A_i \times B_i)^c$ and $(A_i \times B_i)^c = (A_i^c \times B_i) \cup (A_i \times B_i^c) \cup (A_i^c \times B_i^c)$ and as these sets are pairwise disjoint, the complement of any set in $\mathcal{G}$ is also in $\mathcal{G}$. If G_1 and G_2 belong to $\mathcal{G}$, then $G_1 \cup G_2 = (G_1 \cup G_2)^{cc} = (G_1^c \cap G_2^c)^c \in \mathcal{G}$, and by induction any finite union of sets in $\mathcal{G}$ also lies in $\mathcal{G}$. By Lemma 7.31, $\mathcal{M}(\mathcal{G}) = \mathcal{F}(\mathcal{G}) = \mathcal{F}$.

If $X : \Omega_1 \times \Omega_2 \longrightarrow \mathbf{R}$, then X defines the following two new functions:

$$
[X(\cdot, \omega_2)](\omega_1) := [X(\omega_1, \cdot)](\omega_2) := X(\omega_1, \omega_2).
$$

Since $(\mathbf{1}_{A \times B}(\omega_1, \cdot))(\omega_2) = \mathbf{1}_{A \times B}(\omega_1, \omega_2) = \mathbf{1}_A(\omega_1) \cdot \mathbf{1}_B(\omega_2) = (\mathbf{1}_A(\omega_1) \cdot \mathbf{1}_B)(\omega_2) = (\mathbf{1}_{A \times B}(\cdot, \omega_2))(\omega_1)$, we have

$$
(7.16) \quad \mathbf{1}_{A \times B}(\omega_1, \cdot) = \mathbf{1}_A(\omega_1) \cdot \mathbf{1}_B \quad \text{and} \quad \mathbf{1}_{A \times B}(\cdot, \omega_2) = \mathbf{1}_B(\omega_2) \cdot \mathbf{1}_A.
$$

Let

$$
\mathcal{G}_1 = \{G \in \mathcal{F} : \mathbf{1}_G(\omega_1, \cdot) \text{ is } \mathcal{F}_2 \text{ measurable for all } \omega_1 \in \Omega_1\}.
$$

By (7.16), $\mathcal{G}_1$ contains all measurable rectangles. If $A, B \subset \Omega$, then

$$
(7.17) \quad \mathbf{1}_{A \cup B}(\omega_1, \cdot) = \mathbf{1}_A(\omega_1, \cdot) + \mathbf{1}_B(\omega_1, \cdot) - \mathbf{1}_A(\omega_1, \cdot) \cdot \mathbf{1}_B(\omega_1, \cdot).
$$

By (7.17), Proposition 4.9 and induction finite unions of sets in $\mathcal{G}_1$ also belong to $\mathcal{G}_1$. Since $\mathbf{1}_{\bigcup_{n=1}^{\infty} A_n}(\omega_1, \cdot) = \lim_{n \to \infty} \mathbf{1}_{A_n}(\omega_1, \cdot)$, pointwise on Ω_2, for any increasing sequence of sets $(A_n)_{n=1}^{\infty}$, Proposition 4.22 shows that countable unions of sets in $\mathcal{G}_1$ also lie in $\mathcal{G}_1$. By (7.17), $\mathbf{1}_\Omega = \mathbf{1}_G + \mathbf{1}_{G^c}$. Hence $G^c \in \mathcal{G}_1$ whenever $G \in \mathcal{G}_1$ and $\mathcal{G}_1$ is a σ-field containing all measurable rectangles. This implies $\mathcal{G}_1 = \mathcal{F}$ and proves (a) of the following proposition. By symmetry we obtain (b).

Proposition 7.32. *Let $(\Omega_1, \mathcal{F}_1, P_1)$ and $(\Omega_2, \mathcal{F}_2, P_2)$ denote two probability spaces. Let $\mathcal{F} := \mathcal{F}_1 \times \mathcal{F}_2$ denote the σ-field on $\Omega := \Omega_1 \times \Omega_2$ generated by all measurable rectangles. The following hold for all $G \in \mathcal{F}$:*

    (a) *$\mathbf{1}_G(\omega_1, \cdot)$ is $\mathcal{F}_2$ measurable for all $\omega_1 \in \Omega_1$;*

    (b) *$\mathbf{1}_G(\cdot, \omega_2)$ is $\mathcal{F}_1$ measurable for all $\omega_2 \in \Omega_2$;*

    (c) *$\omega_1 \mapsto \mathbb{E}[\mathbf{1}_G(\omega_1, \cdot)] = \int_{\Omega_2} \mathbf{1}_G(\omega_1, \cdot) dP_2$ is $\mathcal{F}_1$ measurable;*

    (d) *$\omega_2 \mapsto \mathbb{E}[\mathbf{1}_G(\cdot, \omega_2)] = \int_{\Omega_1} \mathbf{1}_G(\cdot, \omega_2) dP_1$ is $\mathcal{F}_2$ measurable;*

(e) *if $G \in \mathcal{F}$, then*

$$P_1 \times P_2(G) \quad := \quad \int_{\Omega_2} \Big\{ \int_{\Omega_1} \mathbf{1}_G(\cdot, \omega_2) dP_1 \Big\} dP_2 = \int_{\Omega_1} \Big\{ \int_{\Omega_2} \mathbf{1}_G(\omega_1, \cdot) dP_2 \Big\} dP_1$$

defines a probability measure on $(\Omega, \mathcal{F})$ satisfying $P_1 \times P_2(A \times B) = P_1(A) \cdot P_2(B)$ for all measurable rectangles $A \times B$.

Proof. By (a) and (b) the formulae in (c) and (d) are well defined. We prove (c); (d) follows by symmetry. Let

$$\mathcal{G}_2 = \{G \in \mathcal{F} : \omega_1 \mapsto \mathbb{E}[\mathbf{1}_G(\omega_1, \cdot)] \text{ is } \mathcal{F}_1 \text{ measurable}\}.$$

Since $\mathbb{E}[\mathbf{1}_{A \times B}(\omega_1, \cdot)] = \mathbb{E}[\mathbf{1}_A(\omega_1)\mathbf{1}_B] = P_2(B)\mathbf{1}_A(\omega_1)$ for all $A \in \mathcal{F}_1$ and all $B \in \mathcal{F}_2$, all measurable rectangles belong to $\mathcal{G}_2$. If $(A_i \times B_i)_{i=1}^n$ are pairwise disjoint, then

$$(7.18) \qquad \mathbb{E}[\mathbf{1}_{\bigcup_{i=1}^n A_i \times B_i}(\omega_1, \cdot)] = \Big(\sum_{i=1}^n P_2(B_i)\mathbf{1}_{A_i} \Big)(\omega_1)$$

and $\bigcup_{i=1}^n A_i \times B_i \in \mathcal{G}_2$; hence $\mathcal{G} \subset \mathcal{G}_2$.

If $(G_n)_{n=1}^\infty$ is an increasing or decreasing sequence of sets in $\mathcal{G}_2$, then, for all $\omega_1 \in \Omega_1$, $(\mathbf{1}_{G_n}(\omega_1, \cdot))_{n=1}^\infty$ converges pointwise to $\mathbf{1}_G(\omega_1, \cdot)$ in Ω_2 where $G = \bigcup_{n=1}^\infty G_n$ if $(G_n)_{n=1}^\infty$ is increasing and $G = \bigcap_{n=1}^\infty G_n$ if $(G_n)_{n=1}^\infty$ is decreasing. Since indicator functions are bounded, the Monotone Convergence Theorem implies $\mathbb{E}[\mathbf{1}_{G_n}(\omega_1, \cdot)] \longrightarrow \mathbb{E}[\mathbf{1}_G(\omega_1, \cdot)]$ as $n \longrightarrow \infty$ for all $\omega_1 \in \Omega_1$. By Proposition 4.22 the pointwise limit of a sequence of measurable functions is measurable. Hence $G \in \mathcal{G}_2$, $\mathcal{G}_2$ is a monotone class and $\mathcal{F} = \mathcal{M}(\mathcal{G}) \subset \mathcal{M}(\mathcal{G}_2) = \mathcal{G}_2 \subset \mathcal{F}$. This completes the proof of (c).

By (c) and (d) the formulae in (e) are well defined. It remains to show that they are equal and define a measure on $(\Omega_1 \times \Omega_2, \mathcal{F}_1 \times \mathcal{F}_2) = (\Omega, \mathcal{F})$. Let

$$\mathcal{K} = \{K \in \mathcal{F} : \text{ for which (e) holds}\}.$$

If $A \times B$ is a measurable rectangle, then

$$\int_{\Omega_2} \Big\{ \int_{\Omega_1} \mathbf{1}_{A \times B}(\cdot, \omega_2) dP_1 \Big\} dP_2 = \int_{\Omega_2} P_1(A)\mathbf{1}_B dP_2 = P_1(A) \cdot P_2(B).$$

Similarly $\int_{\Omega_1} \{ \int_{\Omega_2} \mathbf{1}_{A \times B}(\omega_1, \cdot) dP_2 \} dP_1 = P_1(A) \cdot P_2(B)$. Hence all measurable rectangles belong to $\mathcal{K}$ and $P_1 \times P_2(A \times B) = P_1(A) \cdot P_2(B)$. By (7.16), $\mathcal{G} \subset \mathcal{K}$. If $(K_n)_{n=1}^\infty$ is an increasing sequence of sets in $\mathcal{K}$ and $K = \bigcup_{n=1}^\infty K_n$, then, by the Monotone Convergence Theorem,

$$\int_{\Omega_1} \mathbf{1}_{K_n}(\cdot, \omega_2) dP_1 \longrightarrow \int_{\Omega_1} \mathbf{1}_K(\cdot, \omega_2) dP_1 \quad \text{as } n \longrightarrow \infty$$

for all $\omega_2 \in \Omega_2$, and a further application of the Monotone Convergence Theorem implies

$$\lim_{n \longrightarrow \infty} \int_{\Omega_2} \left\{ \int_{\Omega_1} \mathbf{1}_{K_n}(\cdot, \omega_2) dP_1 \right\} dP_2 = \int_{\Omega_2} \left\{ \int_{\Omega_1} \mathbf{1}_K(\cdot, \omega_2) dP_1 \right\} dP_2.$$

Since $K_n \in \mathcal{K}$ this implies $K \in \mathcal{K}$, and as a similar result holds for decreasing sequences in $\mathcal{K}$, $\mathcal{K}$ is a monotone class. Since $\mathcal{G} \subset \mathcal{K}$ this implies $\mathcal{F} = \mathcal{M}(\mathcal{G}) \subset \mathcal{M}(\mathcal{K}) = \mathcal{K} \subset \mathcal{F}$ and $\mathcal{K} = \mathcal{F}$.

If $(G_n)_{n=1}^\infty$ is a pairwise disjoint sequence in $\mathcal{F}$ and $G = \bigcup_{n=1}^\infty G_n$, then $\mathbf{1}_G = \sum_{n=1}^\infty \mathbf{1}_{G_n}$. By the Monotone Convergence Theorem

$$\begin{aligned}
P_1 \times P_2(G) &= \int_{\Omega_2} \left\{ \int_{\Omega_1} \mathbf{1}_G(\cdot, \omega_2) dP_1 \right\} dP_2 \\
&= \int_{\Omega_2} \left\{ \lim_{n \longrightarrow \infty} \int_{\Omega_1} \sum_{i=1}^n \mathbf{1}_{G_i}(\cdot, \omega_2) dP_1 \right\} dP_2 \\
&= \lim_{n \longrightarrow \infty} \int_{\Omega_2} \left\{ \int_{\Omega_1} \sum_{i=1}^n \mathbf{1}_{G_i}(\cdot, \omega_2) dP_1 \right\} dP_2 \\
&= \lim_{n \longrightarrow \infty} \sum_{i=1}^n P_1 \times P_2(G_i) \\
&= \sum_{n=1}^\infty P_1 \times P_2(G_i).
\end{aligned}$$

Since $(P_1 \times P_2)(\Omega_1 \times \Omega_2) = P_1(\Omega_1) \cdot P_2(\Omega_2) = 1$, this shows that $P_1 \times P_2$ is a probability measure on (Ω, P). This completes the proof. □

Our final result in this section is a criterion for integrability on a product space which shows also that such integrals can be evaluated by iteration.

Proposition 7.33. (*Fubini's Theorem*)[31] *Let X denote a random variable on the probability space* $(\Omega, \mathcal{F}, P) := (\Omega_1 \times \Omega_2, \mathcal{F}_1 \times \mathcal{F}_2, P_1 \times P_2)$. *Then*

(a) *$X(\omega_1, \cdot)$ is measurable for all $\omega_1 \in \Omega_1$ and $X(\cdot, \omega_2)$ is measurable for all $\omega_2 \in \Omega_2$;*

(b) *X is integrable if and only if*

$$P_1\{\omega_1 : X(\omega_1, \cdot) \text{ is integrable}\} = P_2\{\omega_2 : X(\cdot, \omega_2) \text{ is integrable}\} = 1$$

---

[31]Guido Fubini (1859-1943) was born in Venice and educated at Scuola Normale Superiore di Pisa. He had wide-ranging interests in pure and applied mathematics: differential and projective geometry, harmonic functions, calculus of variations, several complex variables, Lebesgue integration, continuous groups, acoustics, electricity and the application of mathematics to engineering. He was a professor of mathematics at Turin from 1908 to 1938, but, as a Jew, he was forced to resign in 1938. For his own and his family's safety he emigrated to the USA in 1939.

and one, and hence all, of the following are finite:

$$\int_{\Omega_1}\Big\{\int_{\Omega_2}|X(\omega_1,\cdot)|dP_2\Big\}dP_1 \;=\; \int_{\Omega_2}\Big\{\int_{\Omega_1}|X(\cdot,\omega_2)|dP_1\Big\}dP_2$$

$$=\; \int\int_{\Omega_1\times\Omega_2}|X|d(P_1\times P_2);$$

(c) *if X is integrable, then*

$$\int_{\Omega_1}\Big\{\int_{\Omega_2}X(\omega_1,\cdot)dP_2\Big\}dP_1 \;=\; \int_{\Omega_2}\Big\{\int_{\Omega_1}X(\cdot,\omega_2)dP_1\Big\}dP_2$$

$$=\; \int\int_{\Omega_1\times\Omega_2}Xd(P_1\times P_2).$$

Proof. By Proposition 7.32(e) and linearity the proposition holds for simple integrable random variables. Since every random variable is the pointwise limit of a sequence of simple random variables, (a) follows from Proposition 7.32(a). To prove (b) we first suppose X is positive. Then X is the pointwise limit of an increasing sequence of simple positive random variables, $(X_n)_{n=1}^{\infty}$, and, by Propositions 6.23 and 7.23(e), X is integrable if and only if

$$(7.19) \qquad\qquad \lim_{n\to\infty}\int_{\Omega_1}\Big\{\int_{\Omega_2}X_n(\omega_1,\cdot)dP_2\Big\}dP_1 < \infty.$$

Since $(X_n)_{n=1}^{\infty}$ is increasing Proposition 6.23 implies

$$\lim_{n\to\infty}\int_{\Omega_1}\Big\{\int_{\Omega_2}X_n(\omega_1,\cdot)dP_2\Big\}dP_1 \;=\; \int_{\Omega_1}\Big\{\lim_{n\to\infty}\int_{\Omega_2}X_n(\omega_1,\cdot)dP_2\Big\}dP_1,$$

and a further application of Proposition 6.23 implies that (7.19) holds if and only if

$$P\Big[\omega_1\in\Omega_1 : \lim_{n\to\infty}\int_{\Omega_2}X_n(\omega_1,\cdot)dP_2 < \infty\Big] = 1$$

and

$$\int_{\Omega_1}\Big\{\int_{\Omega_2}\lim_{n\to\infty}X_n(\omega_1,\cdot)dP_2\Big\}dP_1 = \int\int_{\Omega}Xd(P_1\times P_2) < \infty.$$

By the Monotone Convergence Theorem

$$\int_{\Omega}Xd(P_1\times P_2) \;=\; \lim_{n\to\infty}\Big(\int_{\Omega_1}\Big\{\int_{\Omega_2}X_n(\omega_1,\cdot)dP_2\Big\}dP_1\Big)$$

$$=\; \int_{\Omega_1}\lim_{n\to\infty}\Big\{\int_{\Omega_2}X_n(\omega_1,\cdot)dP_2\Big\}dP_1$$

$$=\; \int_{\Omega_1}\Big\{\int_{\Omega_2}X(\omega_1,\cdot)dP_2\Big\}dP_1.$$

On interchanging $(\Omega_1, \mathcal{F}_1, P_1)$ and $(\Omega_2, \mathcal{F}_2, P_2)$ we obtain (b) and (c) for X positive and integrable. The remaining parts of (b) and (c) are obtained by using the decomposition $X = X^+ - X^-$ and Proposition 6.28. This[32] completes the proof.   □

Example 7.34. If X and Y are independent random variables on $(\Omega, \mathcal{F}, P)$ with densities f_X and f_Y, respectively, and $(x, y) \in \mathbf{R}^2$, then

$$
\begin{aligned}
P[\omega \in \Omega : X(\omega) \le x, Y(\omega) \le y] &= P[\omega \in \Omega : X(\omega) \le x] P[\omega \in \Omega : Y(\omega) \le y] \\
&= \left(\int_{-\infty}^x f_X(u) du \right) \cdot \left(\int_{-\infty}^y f_Y(v) dv \right) \\
&= \int_{-\infty}^x \int_{-\infty}^y f_X(u) f_Y(v) du dv.
\end{aligned}
$$

Hence, if A is any Borel[33] subset of $\mathbf{R}^2$, then

$$
P\{\omega \in \Omega : (X(\omega), Y(\omega)) \in A\} = \int \int_A f_X(x) f_Y(y) dx dy.
$$

If $Z = X + Y$, then, by the change of variable $x = w - y$ and Fubini's Theorem,

$$
\begin{aligned}
P[\omega \in \Omega : (X + Y)(\omega) \le z] &= \int \int_{\{(x,y):x+y\le z\}} f_X(x) f_Y(y) dx dy \\
&= \int_{-\infty}^{+\infty} \left\{ \int_{-\infty}^{z-y} f_X(x) f_Y(y) dx \right\} dy \\
&= \int_{-\infty}^{+\infty} \left\{ \int_{-\infty}^z f_X(w - y) f_Y(y) dw \right\} dy \\
&= \int_{-\infty}^z \left\{ \int_{-\infty}^\infty f_X(w - y) f_Y(y) dy \right\} dw
\end{aligned}
$$

and[34]

$$
(7.20) \qquad f_X * f_Y(z) := f_{X+Y}(z) = \int_{-\infty}^{+\infty} f_X(z - y) f_Y(y) dy
$$

---

[32]It is possible that the *iterated* integrals in Proposition 7.33(c) are both finite and do not coincide.

[33]The Borel subsets of $\mathbf{R}^2$, $\mathcal{B}(\mathbf{R}^2)$, are generated by the classical rectangles (products of intervals) and $\mathcal{B}(\mathbf{R}^2) = \mathcal{B}(\mathbf{R}) \times \mathcal{B}(\mathbf{R})$.

[34]The function $f_X * f_Y$ is called the *convolution* of f_X and f_Y.

is a density for $X + Y$. If X and Y are independent $N(0,1)$ distributed random variables, we obtain, on completing squares,

$$
\begin{aligned}
f_{X+Y}(z) &= \frac{1}{2\pi} \int_{-\infty}^{\infty} \exp\{-\frac{1}{2}(z-y)^2 - \frac{1}{2}y^2\} dy \\
&= \frac{e^{-z^2/4}}{2\pi} \int_{-\infty}^{+\infty} \exp\{-(y - (z/2))^2\} dy \\
&= \frac{1}{2\sqrt{\pi}} \exp\{-z^2/4\}
\end{aligned}
$$

since $y \mapsto \frac{1}{\sqrt{\pi}} \exp\{-(y - (z/2))^2\}$ is the density of an $N(z/2, 1/2)$ distributed random variable. This shows that $X + Y$ is $N(0,2)$. A useful semi-converse to the above result characterizes normal random variables:

If X and Y are independent random variables and there exist non-zero real numbers a and b such that $aX + bY$ and $bX - aY$ are independent, then X and Y are normally distributed random variables with the same variance and $aX + bY$ and $bX - aY$ are independent for all $(a, b) \in \mathbf{R}^2$.

7.8. Exercises

(7.1) Use the Cauchy criterion to show that the series of real numbers $\sum_{n=1}^{\infty} a_n$ converges if $\sum_{n=1}^{\infty} |a_n| < \infty$.

(7.2) Let k denote a fixed positive number and let $f : (a, b) \mapsto \mathbf{R}$. Show that f is continuous at $x \in (a, b)$ if and only if for every $\epsilon > 0$ there exists $\delta > 0$ such that $|f(x) - f(y)| < k\epsilon$ whenever $|x - y| < \delta$.

(7.3) Show that $f : (0,1) \mapsto \mathbf{R}, f(x) = 1/x$ and $g : \mathbf{R} \mapsto \mathbf{R}, g(x) = x^2$ are not uniformly continuous.

(7.4) Show that $f : (a, b) \mapsto \mathbf{R}$ is uniformly continuous if and only if f is the restriction to (a, b) of a continuous function on $[a, b]$.

(7.5) If $f : \mathbf{R} \longrightarrow \mathbf{R}$ and $x \in \mathbf{R}$, let $f^-(x) = \lim_{y \to x, y < x} f(y)$ and $f^+(x) = \lim_{y \to x, y > x} f(y)$ whenever these limits exist. If f is increasing, show that both limits exist and that $f(b) - f(a) \geq \sum_{a < x < b} (f^+(x) - f^-(x))$ for any pair of real numbers $a, b, a < b$. Using this result and Exercise 3.3 show that the set of points where an increasing function is not continuous is countable.

(7.6) Let $\mathcal{B}([a, b]) := \{f : [a, b] \mapsto \mathbf{R}, f \text{ bounded}\}$ and $\|f\| := lub\{|f(x)| : a \leq x \leq b\}$. Let $\mathcal{C}([a, b]) := \{f : [a, b] \mapsto \mathbf{R}, f \text{ continuous}\}$. If $(f_n)_{n=1}^{\infty} \subset \mathcal{B}([a, b])$ and $f \in \mathcal{B}([a, b])$, we say $(f_n)_{n=1}^{\infty}$ converges *uniformly* to f if $\lim_{n \to \infty} \|f_n - f\| = 0$ and write $\lim_{n \to \infty} f_n = f$. If $(f_n)_{n=1}^{\infty} \subset \mathcal{C}([a, b])$ and $\lim_{n \to \infty} f_n = f$, show that $f \in \mathcal{C}([a, b])$. If $(g_n)_{n=1}^{\infty} \subset \mathcal{C}([a, b])$ and $\lim_{n,m \to \infty} \|g_n - g_m\| = 0$, show there exists $g \in \mathcal{C}([a, b])$ such that $\lim_{n \to \infty} \|g_n - g\| = 0$.

(7.7) Let $T : \mathcal{C}([a,b]) \mapsto \mathcal{C}([a,b])$ and suppose there exists $k, 0 < k < 1$ such that $\|T(f) - T(g)\| \le k\|f - g\|$ for all $f, g \in \mathcal{C}([a,b])$. Let $h \in \mathcal{C}([a,b])$ be arbitrary and let $h_n := T \circ T \circ \cdots \circ T(h)$ for every positive integer n. If $m \ge n$, show that

$$\|h_m - h_n\| \le k^n \|h_{m-n} - h\| \le k^n (1-k)^{-1} \|T(h) - h\|.$$

Hence show that there exists a unique $f \in \mathcal{C}([a,b])$ such that $T(f) = f$.

(7.8) Let $f(x) = x^2$ for $x \in [0,1]$. Find the Riemann sum for f when $[0,1]$ is partitioned into n adjacent subintervals each of length $1/n$. By taking a limit, find $\int_0^1 x^2 dx$.

(7.9) If X is an $N(0,1)$ distributed random variable, find $\mathbb{E}[e^X]$, $\mathbb{E}[Xe^X]$ and $\mathbb{E}[(X-2)^+]$.

(7.10) If $X \in \mathbf{L}^2(\Omega, \mathcal{F}, P)$, show that $\mathrm{Var}(X) = \mathbb{E}[X^2] - \mathbb{E}[X]^2$. If a and b are real numbers, show that $\mathrm{Var}(aX + b) = a^2 \mathrm{Var}(X)$. Show that $\mathrm{Var}(X) = 0$ if and only if there exists a real number c such that $X = c$ almost surely.

(7.11) Show that the random variables X and Y on $(\Omega, \mathcal{F}, P)$ are independent if and only if $F_{X,Y}(x,y) := P(\{\omega : X(\omega) \le x, Y(\omega) \le y\}) = P(\{\omega : X(\omega) \le x\}) \cdot P(\{\omega : Y(\omega) \le y\}) = F_X(x) \cdot F_Y(y)$ for all $(x,y) \in \mathbf{R}^2$.

(7.12) Write ϕ, where $\phi(x) = x^2$, as a sum of an increasing convex function and a decreasing convex function.

(7.13) Use Jensen's inequality to prove the *arithmetic-geometric mean inequality*: if $(x_i)_{i=1}^n$ is a finite set of positive real numbers, then

$$(x_1 \cdots x_n)^{1/n} \le \frac{x_1 + \cdots + x_n}{n}.$$

(7.14) If $X(\omega_1, \omega_2) = X_1(\omega_1) \cdot X_2(\omega_2)$ where X_i is an integrable random variable on $(\Omega_i, \mathcal{F}_i, P_i)$ and $A_i \in \mathcal{F}$ for $i = 1, 2$, show that

$$\int_{A_1 \times A_2} X dP = \left(\int_{A_1} X_1 dP_1 \right) \cdot \left(\int_{A_2} X_2 dP_2 \right).$$

(7.15) If X is $N(\mu_1, \sigma_1^2)$ and Y is $N(\mu_2, \sigma_2^2)$ and X and Y are independent, show that $X + Y$ is $N(\mu_1 + \mu_2, \sigma_1^2 + \sigma_2^2)$.

(7.16) If X and Y are independent Poisson random variables on the same probability space with parameters α and β, show that $X + Y$ is Poisson with parameter $\alpha + \beta$.

(7.17) A random variable X is called Bernoulli with parameter p if $P_X(\{1\}) = p$ and $P_X(\{0\}) = 1 - p$, and a random variable Y is called binomial with parameters (n,p) if $P_Y(\{r\}) = \binom{n}{r} p^r (1-p)^{n-r}$ for all integers $r, 0 \le r \le n$. If $(X_i)_{i=1}^n$ are n independent Bernoulli random variables with parameter p defined on the same space, show that $\sum_{i=1}^n X_i$ is a binomial random variable with parameters (n,p). Use this result to show that the sum of independent binomial random variables on the same probability space with parameters (n, p) and (m, p), respectively, is binomial with parameters $(n + m, p)$.

(7.18) Suppose the profit on a certain project is a random variable X with mean 1000 and standard deviation 200 and X is symmetrically distributed about its mean; that is $P(|X - 1000| > c) = 2P(X - 1000 > c)$ for all $c \geq 0$. Find, using Chebyshev's Inequality, an upper bound on the probability that the project will lose money.

(7.19) Consider stocks A and B with share prices \$20 an \$15 today. Assuming that the share prices in one year's time, X_A and X_B, are random variables with expected values 22 and 19 and variances 1 and 16, respectively, and that $\mathbb{E}[(X_A - 22)(X_B - 19)] = -3$, find the proportion of A and B shares in a portfolio that minimizes risk.

(7.20) If $f : (a, b) \mapsto \mathbf{R}$ is continuous and has no local maxima and no local minima, show that f is injective and either strictly increasing or strictly decreasing.

(7.21) If ϕ_1 and ϕ_2 are convex functions on $(a, b) \subset \mathbf{R}$, show that $\phi_1 + \phi_2$ and $\max\{\phi_1, \phi_2\}$ are convex.

(7.22) If $\phi : (a, b) \mapsto \mathbf{R}$ is convex and constant on an interval $[c, d] \subset (a, b)$, show that $\phi(x) \geq \phi(c)$ for all $x \in (a, b)$.

(7.23) Give a short proof of Proposition 7.27 for convex functions which are twice continuously differentiable.

Chapter 8

Conditional Expectation

Information and probability are the two main tools in a rational decision procedure. Information increases in time and can sometimes make the probabilistic point of view ultimately obsolete.

Paul Malliavin, *Stochastic Analysis*, 1997

Summary

Using a binomial model we price a call option with information available and trading allowed at one intermediate time. Conditional expectations are introduced to express this mathematically. A balanced portfolio to hedge any claim on the option is constructed.

8.1. Call Options 2

In Example 5.5 we set up our first model for pricing a call option. While the hypotheses were somewhat unrealistic our analysis did unearth fundamental principles that will be retained in any refined model. Central to our approach was the method by which the buyer determined a fair price. The risk neutral probabilities were found by assuming that the expected return on investing directly in shares would, when discounted back to the present, equal the initial investment. We call this the *fair game principle*. The risk neutral probabilities were then used to price the call option. We now apply the same principle to a slightly more complex model.

Example 8.1. Consider the following call option: strike price \$22, maturity date six months, interest rate[1] 12%, share price today \$20, in three months' time either \$24 or \$19, and in six months it will either go from \$24 to \$21 or \$26 or from \$19 to \$21 or \$17. The new feature in this example is the introduction of supplementary information at an intermediate time. We make two assumptions:

(a) *the future depends only on the present and is independent of the past,*[2]

(b) *the option can be bought or sold at $t = .25$.*

We display the information provided in a *binomial tree diagram* (Figure 8.1).

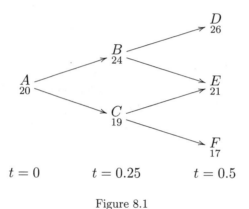

$$t = 0 \qquad\qquad t = 0.25 \qquad\qquad t = 0.5$$

Figure 8.1

We analyze this information using the methods developed in Example 5.5 and at each stage reorganize the material in the language of probability theory. This clarifies the situation and suggests how to proceed.

The points labeled $A, B, \ldots$ are called *nodes*. Information is received at nodes and shares, and options can be bought and sold at nodes A, B and C. The total set of possible outcomes consists of the paths that may be followed from $t = 0$ to $t = .50$: $\{ABD\}, \{ABE\}, \{ACE\}$ and $\{ACF\}$. Each *path* is an example of what *may* happen to the share price over the duration of the option. Let Ω denote the set of all paths and let $\mathcal{F} = 2^{\Omega}$. Each pair $(t, \omega), \omega \in \Omega$, determines a *unique* node and hence any function on the nodes can be pulled back to define a function of (t, ω). Let X denote the share price and let $X_t, t = 0, .25, .5$ be the share price at time t. Decomposing Figure 8.1 we obtain Figure 8.2.

---

[1]Interest rates are always given per annum and are continuously compounded.

[2]That is whether or not the share price goes up or down after $t = .25$ *does not depend* on whether it went up or down prior to $t = .25$.

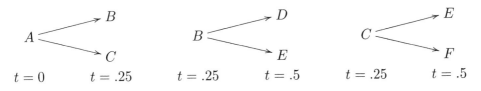

Figure 8.2

By Proposition 5.6

$$p = \frac{\text{initial price } e^{.25 \times .12} - \text{lower price}}{\text{higher price } - \text{lower price}}$$

is the risk neutral probability that the share price will rise in each of the three diagrams in Figure 8.2.

Hence $p_A = \frac{20e^{.03} - 19}{24 - 19} = .32$, $p_B = \frac{24e^{.03} - 21}{26 - 21} = .75$, $p_C = \frac{19e^{.03} - 17}{19 - 17} = .64$ where the initial node is used as a subscript for identification. Combining these we obtain Figure 8.3. Using the independence assumption (a) we assign probabilities to all paths in Ω and obtain

$$
\begin{aligned}
P[ABD \text{ occurs }] &= P[AB \text{ occurs and } BD \text{ occurs }] \\
&= P[AB \text{ occurs }] \cdot P[BD \text{ occurs }] \\
&= (.32) \times (.75) = .24,
\end{aligned}
$$

$P[ABE] = .08, P[ACE] = .44$ and $P[ACF] = .24$. With these probabilities in place we have constructed the *risk neutral probability space* $(\Omega, \mathcal{F}, P)$.

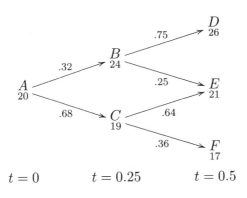

Figure 8.3

Our next step is to interpret $X_t, t = 0, .25, .50$ as random variables on $(\Omega, \mathcal{F}, P)$. On each path the share price achieves a *unique* price at time t and defines X_t as a function on Ω. We have $X_0(\omega) = 20$ for all $\omega \in \Omega$, $X_{.25}(ABD) = X_{.25}(ABE) = 24$, $X_{.25}(ACE) = X_{.25}(ACF) = 19$, $X_{.5}(ABD) = 26$, $X_{.5}(ABE) = X_{.5}(ACE) = 21$ and $X_{.5}(ACF) = 17$. Since $\mathcal{F} = 2^\Omega$ each X_t

is a random variable on $(\Omega, \mathcal{F}, P)$. Let $\mathcal{F}_t$, $t = 0, .25, .5$, denote the σ-field of events involving the share price that are known or have been decided by time t. At $t = 0$, $X_0 = 20$, and as this is the only information that we will ever have about X_0, $\mathcal{F}_0$ is the σ-field generated by X_0. Hence $X_0(\omega) = 20$ for all $\omega \in \Omega$ and $\mathcal{F}_0 = \mathcal{F}_\emptyset = \{\emptyset, \Omega\}$. At $t = .25$ we have precise information about X_0 and $X_{.25}$ and nothing more. Hence $\mathcal{F}_{.25}$ is the smallest σ-field for which X_0 and $X_{.25}$ are measurable. Since $X_{.25}^{-1}(24) = \{ABD, ABE\}$ and $X_{.25}^{-1}(19) = \{ACE, ACF\}$, $\mathcal{F}_{.25}$ is generated by the partition $\{ABD, ABE\}, \{ACE, ACF\}$ of Ω (see Figure 8.4). At $t = .5$ all events are known and this implies $\mathcal{F}_{.5} = 2^\Omega = \mathcal{F}$. On the other hand the σ-field generated by $\{X_0, X_{.25}$ and $X_{.5}\}$ contains the sets $\{ABD, ABE\}, \{ACE, ACF\}$ and $X_{.5}^{-1}(21) = \{ABE, ACE\}$ and hence contains all subsets of Ω. This shows that $\mathcal{F}_{.5}$ is generated by $X_0, X_{.25}$ and $X_{.5}$ and thus $\mathcal{F}_t$ is the σ-field generated by $(X_s)_{s \le t}$ for $t = 0, .25, .5$. The three σ-fields[3] are given in Figure 8.4.

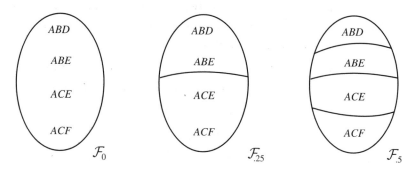

Figure 8.4

Since $\mathcal{F}_0 \subset \mathcal{F}_{.25} \subset \mathcal{F}_{.5} = \mathcal{F}$, $(\mathcal{F}_t)_{t=0,.25,.5}$ is a *discrete filtration* of $(\Omega, \mathcal{F})$ and, by Definitions 5.20 and 5.21, $(X_t)_{t=0,.25,.5}$, is a *stochastic process* on $(\Omega, \mathcal{F}, P)$ adapted to the *filtration* $(\mathcal{F}_t)_{t=0,.25,.5}$. We interpret $\mathcal{F}_t$ as the history of the process up to (and including) time t.

We now rephrase the applications of the fair game principle used to find the risk neutral probabilities in terms of the above random variables. From Figure 8.3 we see that our first calculation was

(8.1) $$X_0 = e^{-.25 \times .12} \mathbb{E}[X_{.25}].$$

The other two calculations were *conditional* on what happened at $t = .25$. The first says that the *expectation* of $X_{.5}$ *is* 24 *if* the share price increased in the first period, that is *given* that either path ABD or ABE is followed. We introduce temporary notation to highlight what is happening and afterwards rewrite it

---

[3]This is very similar to the situation discussed in Section 3.5.

using permanent notation. The calculations are

(8.2) $$e^{-.25\times.12}\mathbb{E}[X_{.5}|\{ABD, ABE\}] = 24$$

and

(8.3) $$e^{-.25\times.12}\mathbb{E}[X_{.5}|\{ACE, ACF\}] = 19.$$

The expected values in (8.2) and (8.3), unlike the expected value in (8.1), are not constant but a function of the path being followed. Since the events on which it is conditional, $\{ABD, ABE\}, \{ACE, ACF\}$, generate $\mathcal{F}_{.25}$, we rewrite (8.2) and (8.3) as

$$e^{-.25\times.12}\mathbb{E}[X_{.5}|\mathcal{F}_{.25}](\omega) = 24 = X_{.25}(\omega) \text{ if } \omega = ABD \text{ or } ABE,$$

$$e^{-.25\times.12}\mathbb{E}[X_{.5}|\mathcal{F}_{.25}](\omega) = 19 = X_{.25}(\omega) \text{ if } \omega = ACE \text{ or } ACF.$$

We call $\mathbb{E}[X_{.5}|\mathcal{F}_{.25}]$ the *conditional expectation* of $X_{.5}$ given $\mathcal{F}_{.25}$. By definition it is a *random variable* on $(\Omega, \mathcal{F}, P)$. We can now rewrite (8.2) and (8.3) as a single equation involving *two random variables*,

(8.4) $$e^{-.25\times.12}\mathbb{E}[X_{.5}|\mathcal{F}_{.25}] = X_{.25},$$

and note that the risk neutral probabilities are derived from (8.1) and (8.4).

Let V denote the buyer's price for the option and let V_t denote the price at time t. We are interested in calculating V_0. Since V_0 will not change with time, we identify V_0 with the constant random variable defined by $V_0(\omega) = V_0$ for all $\omega \in \Omega$. This means that V_0 is an $\mathcal{F}_0$ measurable random variable on $(\Omega, \mathcal{F}, P)$.

Since the strike price is \$22, the option will be exercised only if the share price follows path ABD, that is if it moves up twice. Hence at $t = .5$ we have $V_{.5} = 4$ if the share price is \$26, and otherwise it is worthless. Thus, for each path ω, we can assign a unique value to $V_{.5}$, and let $V_{.5}(ABD) = 4, V_{.5}(ABE) = V_{.5}(ACE) = V_{.5}(ACF) = 0$. Hence $V_{.5}$ is an $\mathcal{F}_{.5}$ measurable random variable on $(\Omega, \mathcal{F}, P)$. The relationship between the random variables X and V becomes visible at $t = .5$ and

(8.5) $$V_{.5} = (X_{.5} - 22)^+.$$

The fair game principle applied to the option price says that V_0 is the expected value of $V_{.5}$ discounted back to $t = 0$. This observation and (8.5) imply

(8.6) $$V_0 = e^{-.5\times.12}\mathbb{E}[V_{.5}] = e^{-.5\times.12}\mathbb{E}[(X_{.5} - 22)^+].$$

Since the expected return is $4 \times .24$, we obtain, on discounting back to the present,

$$V_0 = 4 \times .24 \times e^{-.12\times.5} = .90.$$

We now consider the impact of changing the information provided at the intermediate stage while keeping the same initial and final data. For example, the price of the option with the data given in Figure 8.5, in which the risk

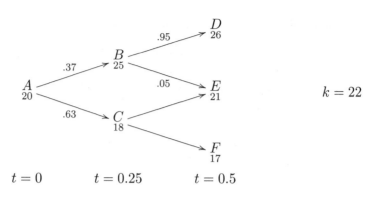

$$t = 0 \qquad\qquad t = 0.25 \qquad\qquad t = 0.5$$

Figure 8.5

neutral probabilities have been calculated and included, is $1.34. This price is higher than the price of the original option and shows that the intermediate information, over which the buyer has no control, may affect the price. This should, assuming that the price is *arbitrage free*, be balanced by something over which the buyer has control.

This appears as the buyer's right to sell the option at $t = .25$. We now wish to find this price for the original data, and, naturally, denote it by $V_{.25}$. At $t = 0$ we cannot make any *definite* statements about the situation at $t = .25$, but we can make a number of "if...then" statements. *If* the share price is $24 at $t = .25$, *then* the expected discounted return on buying the option at $t = .25$ is

$$.75 \times 4 \times e^{-.25 \times .12} + .25 \times 0 \times e^{.25 \times .12} = 2.90.$$

If the share price is $19 at $t = .25$, then the option is worthless. We can now associate with each path a unique value for $V_{.25}$ and consider $V_{.25}$ as a random variable on $(\Omega, \mathcal{F}, P)$. We have $V_{.25}(ABD) = V_{.25}(ABE) = 2.90$ and $V_{.25}(ACE) = V_{.25}(ACF) = 0$. Clearly $V_{.25}$ is $\mathcal{F}_{.25}$ measurable. Moreover, as with the share price, $(V_t)_{t=0,.25,.5}$ is a finite discrete stochastic process adapted to the filtration $(\mathcal{F}_t)_{t=0,.25,.5}$. Rephrasing some of the above (see (8.2), (8.3) and (8.4)) we obtain

(8.7) $$\qquad\qquad e^{-.25 \times .12}\mathbb{E}[V_{.5}|\{ABD, ABE\}] = 2.90,$$
(8.8) $$\qquad\qquad e^{-.25 \times .12}\mathbb{E}[V_{.5}|\{ACE, ACF\}] = 0.$$

Rewriting (8.7) and (8.8), using the σ-field $\mathcal{F}_{.25}$, we obtain:

$$e^{-.25 \times .12}\mathbb{E}[V_{.5}|\mathcal{F}_{.25}](\omega) = 2.90 = V_{.25}(\omega) \text{ if } \omega = ABD \text{ or } ABE,$$
$$e^{-.25 \times .12}\mathbb{E}[V_{.5}|\mathcal{F}_{.25}](\omega) = 0 = V_{.25}(\omega) \text{ if } \omega = ACE \text{ or } ACF.$$

We call $\mathbb{E}[V_{.5}|\mathcal{F}_{.25}]$ the *conditional expectation* of $V_{.5}$ given $\mathcal{F}_{.25}$. By definition it is a *random variable* on $(\Omega, \mathcal{F}, P)$. Equations (8.7) and (8.8) may be combined into a single equation involving *two random variables*:

$$e^{-.25 \times .12} \mathbb{E}[V_{.5}|\mathcal{F}_{.25}] = V_{.25}. \tag{8.9}$$

Equations (8.6) and (8.9) summarize all the relevant information regarding the option price. In Example 8.11 we show that the seller can hedge any claim on the option.

Example 8.2. This example is an abstract version of the previous example. Since the analysis is precisely the same, it suffices to clarify the notation and record the conclusions. Suppose we have a call option with maturity date T, strike price k, intermediate information provided at time $t, 0 < t < T$, and interest rate r. By (8.1) and (8.4) and some simple cross multiplication we see that the risk neutral probabilities are calculated from the following two equations:

$$\mathbb{E}[e^{-rt} X_t] = X_0, \tag{8.10}$$

$$\mathbb{E}[e^{-rT} X_T|\mathcal{F}_t] = e^{-rt} X_t. \tag{8.11}$$

By (8.6) and (8.9) the prices of the call option at times 0 and t are calculated from the following equations:

$$\mathbb{E}[e^{-rT} V_T] = V_0, \tag{8.12}$$

$$\mathbb{E}[e^{-rT} V_T|\mathcal{F}_t] = e^{-rt} V_t, \tag{8.13}$$

and from $V_T = (X_T - k)^+$ and (8.6) we obtain

$$V_0 = \mathbb{E}[e^{-rT} (X_T - k)^+]. \tag{8.14}$$

The similarity between the two pairs of equations is not mere coincidence and in Chapter 9 we will see, using *martingales*, that they form part of a larger picture.

In our analysis we introduced special cases of a new concept: *conditional expectation*. This allows us to express in a concise fashion all relevant information connected with pricing a call option. Conditional expectations are a modified version of expected values and may be analyzed using the integration theory from Chapter 6. *The crucial difference is that conditional expectations are random variables.*

8.2. Conditional Expectation

If X denotes the number of heads that appear when a fair coin is tossed three times in succession, then $\mathbb{E}[X] = 1.5$. If, however, it is *known* that the first toss resulted in a head, then $\mathbb{E}[X|$ First toss is a head $] = 2$ and similarly

$\mathbb{E}[X|$ First toss is a tail $] = 1$. Our *expectation* changes as new *information* becomes available. More generally, if X is a random variable on $(\Omega, \mathcal{F}, P)$, where Ω is finite, $\mathcal{F} = 2^{\Omega}, P(\{\omega\}) > 0$ for all $\omega \in \Omega$ and $A \in \mathcal{F}, 0 < P(A) < 1$, we let

$$\mathbb{E}[X|A] = \sum_{\omega \in \Omega} X(\omega) P(\{\omega\}|A).$$

By Proposition 5.10,

$$P(\{\omega\}|A) = \frac{P(\{\omega\} \cap A)}{P(A)} \quad = \quad \begin{cases} P(\{\omega\})/P(A) & \text{if } \omega \in A, \\ 0 & \text{if } \omega \notin A. \end{cases}$$

Hence

$$\mathbb{E}[X|A] = \sum_{\omega \in A} X(\omega) \frac{P(\{\omega\})}{P(A)} = \frac{1}{P(A)} \int_A X dP$$

and similarly

$$\mathbb{E}[X|A^c] = \frac{1}{P(A^c)} \int_{A^c} X dP.$$

The σ-field generated by A, $\mathcal{A}$, consists of the sets $\{\emptyset, A, A^c, \Omega\}$. Hence, if $B \in \mathcal{A}$ and $P(B) > 0$, then

$$\mathbb{E}[X|B] = \frac{1}{P(B)} \int_B X dP.$$

We rewrite this as a function on Ω. If $B \in \mathcal{A}, P(B) > 0$ and $\omega \in B$, let

$$\mathbb{E}[X|\mathcal{A}](\omega) = \frac{1}{P(B)} \int_B X dP.$$

This minor change of notation defines an $\mathcal{A}$ measurable *random variable* on $(\Omega, \mathcal{F}, P)$ and allows us to apply the theory already developed for random variables. Motivated by the above we define conditional expectations with respect to a σ-field generated by a countable partition. Afterwards we define the general concept and prove its main properties, but confine our proofs to the countably generated case.

Definition 8.3. *Let $(\Omega, \mathcal{F}, P)$ denote a probability space and let $\mathcal{G}$ denote a σ-field on Ω generated by a countable partition $(G_n)_{n=1}^{\infty}$ of Ω. Suppose $\mathcal{G} \subset \mathcal{F}$ and $P(G_n) > 0$ for all n. If X is an integrable[4] random variable on $(\Omega, \mathcal{F}, P)$, let*

(8.15) $$\mathbb{E}[X|\mathcal{G}](\omega) = \frac{1}{P(G_n)} \int_{G_n} X dP$$

---

[4]Since $|X \cdot \mathbf{1}_A| \leq |X|$ for any $A \in \mathcal{F}$, $X \cdot \mathbf{1}_A$ is integrable.

for all n and all $\omega \in G_n$. We call $\mathbb{E}[X|\mathcal{G}]$ the conditional expectation of X given $\mathcal{G}$. If $\mathcal{G}$ is generated by a random variable Y on $(\Omega, \mathcal{F}, P)$, we also write $\mathbb{E}[X|Y]$ in place of $\mathbb{E}[X|\mathcal{F}_Y]$.

Since $(G_n)_{n=1}^{\infty}$ partitions Ω each ω lies in *precisely one* G_n and (8.15) defines $\mathbb{E}[X|\mathcal{G}](\omega)$ for all $\omega \in \Omega$. The mapping

$$(8.16) \qquad \mathbb{E}[X|\mathcal{G}] : \Omega \longrightarrow \mathbf{R}$$

is constant on each G_n and hence $\mathcal{G}$ measurable, and, as $\mathcal{G} \subset \mathcal{F}$, it is also $\mathcal{F}$ measurable and $\mathbb{E}[X|\mathcal{G}]$ is a *random variable* on $(\Omega, \mathcal{F}, P)$. By (8.15), if $\omega_n \in G_n$, then $|\mathbb{E}[X|\mathcal{G}](\omega_n)| \leq \int_{G_n} |X| dP / P(G_n)$ and

$$\int_{\Omega} |\mathbb{E}[X|\mathcal{G}]| dP = \sum_{n=1}^{\infty} \int_{G_n} |\mathbb{E}[X|\mathcal{G}]| dP = \sum_{n=1}^{\infty} |\mathbb{E}[X|\mathcal{G}](\omega_n)| \cdot P(G_n)$$

$$\leq \sum_{n=1}^{\infty} \int_{G_n} |X| dP = \int_{\Omega} |X| dP = \mathbb{E}[|X|].$$

Hence $\mathbb{E}[X|\mathcal{G}]$ is integrable.

The trivial σ-field $\mathcal{F}_{\emptyset}$ is countably generated and, since $P(\Omega) = 1$, it follows $\mathbb{E}[X|\mathcal{F}_{\emptyset}](\omega) = \mathbb{E}[X]$ for all $\omega \in \Omega$. Hence we may *identify* $\mathbb{E}[X]$ and the constant random variable $\mathbb{E}[X|\mathcal{F}_{\emptyset}]$ and regard the expectation defined in the previous chapter as a special case of conditional expectation.

Our next result characterizes conditional expectations in the countably generated case and extends, although we do not prove it, with a slightly weaker form of uniqueness to arbitrary conditional expectations.

Proposition 8.4. *Let $(\Omega, \mathcal{F}, P)$ denote a probability space and let $\mathcal{G}$ denote a σ-field on Ω generated by a countable partition $(G_n)_{n=1}^{\infty}$ of Ω. We suppose $\mathcal{G} \subset \mathcal{F}$ and $P(G_n) > 0$ for all n. If X is an integrable random variable on $(\Omega, \mathcal{F}, P)$, then $\mathbb{E}[X|\mathcal{G}]$ is the unique $\mathcal{G}$ measurable integrable random variable on $(\Omega, \mathcal{F}, P)$ satisfying*

$$(8.17) \qquad \int_A \mathbb{E}[X|\mathcal{G}] dP = \int_A X dP$$

for all $A \in \mathcal{G}$.

Proof. Let n be arbitrary and let $\omega \in G_n$. Since $\mathbb{E}[X|\mathcal{G}]$ is constant on each G_n, it is $\mathcal{G}$ measurable and

$$\int_{G_n} \mathbb{E}[X|\mathcal{G}] dP = \mathbb{E}[X|\mathcal{G}](\omega) \cdot \int_{G_n} dP = \left(\frac{1}{P(G_n)} \int_{G_n} X dP \right) \cdot P(G_n)$$

$$= \int_{G_n} X dP.$$

If $A \in \mathcal{G}$, then $A = \bigcup_{n \in M} G_n$ for some $M \subset \mathbf{N}$. Hence

$$
\begin{aligned}
\int_A \mathbb{E}[X|\mathcal{G}]dP &= \int_{\bigcup_{n \in M} G_n} \mathbb{E}[X|\mathcal{G}]dP = \sum_{n \in M} \int_{G_n} \mathbb{E}[X|\mathcal{G}]dP \\
&= \sum_{n \in M} \int_{G_n} X dP = \int_{\bigcup_{n \in M} G_n} X dP \\
&= \int_A X dP.
\end{aligned}
$$

As uniqueness is easily established[5] this completes the proof. □

If $A = \Omega$ in (8.17), then

$$
(8.18) \qquad \mathbb{E}[\mathbb{E}[X|\mathcal{G}]] = \int_\Omega \mathbb{E}[X|\mathcal{G}]dP = \int_\Omega X dP = \mathbb{E}[X],
$$

which says that the average of the averages is the average.

Conditional expectation is a rather subtle concept and a much more powerful tool than its initial appearance suggests. We consider $\mathbb{E}[X|\mathcal{G}]$ as our expectation of X with all possible information about X, that can be derived from $\mathcal{G}$ events, incorporated. When $\mathcal{G}$ is countably generated, as in Proposition 8.4, we can interpret $\mathbb{E}[X|\mathcal{G}]$ *pointwise*. This is *not* possible in the general case. If $\mathcal{G}$ is generated by the countable partition $(G_n)_{n=1}^\infty$ with $P(G_n) > 0$ for all n and X is a random variable on $(\Omega, \mathcal{F}, P)$, then, for all n and all $\omega \in G_n$, we have

$$
\begin{aligned}
\mathbb{E}[X|\mathcal{G}](\omega) &= \text{Expected value of } X \text{ given that } G_n \text{ has occurred,} \\
&= \text{Expected value of } X \text{ with respect to the probability} \\
&\quad\ \text{measure } P(\cdot|G_n), \\
&= \text{Average of } X \text{ over } G_n, \\
&= \text{Average of } \mathbb{E}[X|\mathcal{G}] \text{ over } G_n.
\end{aligned}
$$

Our next example is simple but a useful first exercise in calculating conditional probabilities. Note the different roles played by the random variables X and Y.

Example 8.5. Let $\Omega = \{1, 2, 3, 4, 5, 6\}$, $\mathcal{F} = 2^\Omega$, $P(\{1\}) = P(\{2\}) = 1/16$, $P(\{3\}) = P(\{4\}) = 1/4$ and $P(\{5\}) = P(\{6\}) = 3/16$. Suppose $X(1) = X(2) = 2$, $X(3) = X(4) = X(5) = X(6) = 8$ and $Y = 41_{\{1,2,3\}} + 61_{\{4,5,6\}}$. We calculate $\mathbb{E}[X|Y]$. In Figure 8.6 we show the partitions which generate $\mathcal{F}_X$ and $\mathcal{F}_Y$. Since X lies between 2 and 8 on the set $\{1, 2, 3\}$ its average over the set should lie in the interval $[2, 8]$, but as the probability at 3 is much bigger than at the other two points we should expect the average to be closer to 8 than 2.

---

[5]See Exercise 8.8.

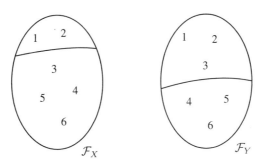

Figure 8.6

We have $P(\{1,2,3\}) = 3/8$ and

$$
\begin{aligned}
\mathbb{E}[X|Y](1) &= \mathbb{E}[X|Y](2) = \mathbb{E}[X|Y](3) \\
&= \frac{1}{P(\{1,2,3\})} \int_{\{1,2,3\}} X \, dP \\
&= \frac{1}{3/8} \big(X(1)P(\{1\}) + X(2)P(\{2\}) + X(3)P(\{3\}) \big) \\
&= \frac{8}{3} \big(2 \cdot \frac{1}{16} + 2 \cdot \frac{1}{16} + 8 \cdot \frac{1}{4} \big) = 6.
\end{aligned}
$$

Since $X(\omega) = 8$ for $\omega = 4, 5, 6$ the average over $\{4, 5, 6\}$ is 8 and $\mathbb{E}[X|Y](\omega) = 8$ when $\omega = 4, 5$ and 6. Combining these calculations we obtain

$$
\mathbb{E}[X|Y] = 6\mathbf{1}_{\{1,2,3\}} + 8\mathbf{1}_{\{4,5,6\}}.
$$

To prepare for the general definition of conditional expectation we return to the situation discussed in Proposition 6.26. Let X denote a positive integrable random variable on $(\Omega, \mathcal{F}, P)$. If $\mathcal{G}$ is a σ-field on Ω and $\mathcal{G} \subset \mathcal{F}$, let $Q(A) = \int_A X \, dP$ for all $A \in \mathcal{G}$. By modifying Proposition 6.26 one can show that Q is a finite measure on the measurable space $(\Omega, \mathcal{G})$ and $P(A) = 0$ implies $Q(A) = 0$. If $A \in \mathcal{G}, P(A) > 0$ and for every $\mathcal{G}$ measurable set B with $A \cap B \neq \emptyset$ we have $A \subset B$, then A cannot be partitioned into smaller $\mathcal{G}$ measurable sets, and it is natural to let $\mathbb{E}[X|\mathcal{G}](\omega) = \int_A X \, dP / P(A)$ for all $\omega \in A$. In particular, if $A = \{\omega\} \in \mathcal{G}$ and $P(\{\omega\}) > 0$, then $\int_{\{\omega\}} X \, dP = X(\omega) \cdot P(\{\omega\})$ and

$$
\mathbb{E}[X|\mathcal{G}](\omega) = \frac{X(\omega) \cdot P(\{\omega\})}{P(\{\omega\})} = X(\omega).
$$

However, this may not always be the case and we may have $\{\omega\} \in \mathcal{G}$ with $P(\{\omega\}) = 0$. If there exists a decreasing sequence of $\mathcal{G}$ measurable sets $(A_n)_{n=1}^{\infty}$, with $P(A_n) > 0$ for all n such that $\lim_{n \to \infty} A_n = \{\omega\}$, then $\lim_{n \to \infty} P(A_n) = \lim_{n \to \infty} Q(A_n) = 0$ by Proposition 5.3. In view of Definition 8.3 it is reasonable to attempt to define $\mathbb{E}[X|\mathcal{G}](\omega)$ by

$$\lim_{n \longrightarrow \infty} \left(\frac{1}{P(A_n)} \cdot \int_{A_n} X dP \right) = \lim_{n \longrightarrow \infty} \frac{Q(A_n)}{P(A_n)}.$$

This limit may not exist at *all points* but, by a deep converse to Proposition 6.26, the Radon-Nikodým Theorem, it can be shown to exist *almost surely* and to define a $\mathcal{G}$ measurable random variable on Ω. Writing $\Delta Q_n/\Delta P_n$ in place of $Q(A_n)/P(A_n)$ we can see why the almost sure limit is denoted by dQ/dP. We now present, without proof, the Radon-Nikodým Theorem.

Proposition 8.6. (*The Radon-Nikodým Theorem*)[6] *If P and Q are finite measures on the measurable space $(\Omega, \mathcal{F})$ and $Q(A) = 0$ whenever $A \in \mathcal{F}$ and $P(A) = 0$, then there exists a positive measurable function Y on Ω such that*

$$(8.19) \qquad\qquad Q(A) = \int_A Y dP$$

for all $A \in \mathcal{F}$. Moreover, any $\mathcal{F}$ measurable function Z on Ω satisfying (8.19) for all $A \in \mathcal{G}$ is equal to Y almost everywhere.

As a particular example suppose the random variable X on $(\Omega, \mathcal{F}, P)$ has a continuous density f_X. Since $\mathbf{m}\{[a, b]\} = b - a$, $P_X([a, b]) = \int_a^b f_X d\mathbf{m}$, and $\lim_{a \to b}(\int_a^b f_X(x)d\mathbf{m}/(b-a)) = f_X(b)$, we have $dP_X/d\mathbf{m} = f_X$ almost surely. If F_X is the distribution function of X, then $F_X' = f_X$ and (8.19), with $A = [a, b]$, reduces to the Fundamental Theorem of Calculus:

$$F_X(b) - F_X(a) = \int_a^b f_X(x)dx.$$

We now state, without proof, the main result on the existence of conditional expectations. This result is proved in Proposition 8.4 when $\mathcal{G}$ is generated by a countable partition $(G_n)_{n=1}^\infty$ with $P(G_n) > 0$ for all n.

---

[6]The Radon-Nikodým Theorem is the culmination of results extending the scope of the *Fundamental Theorem of Calculus* (Proposition 1.11). Key contributions were made by Lebesgue in 1904 and by Radon in 1913, both of whom worked with $\mathbf{R}^n$ as the domain, and the final step was taken by Nikodým in 1930. Johann Radon (1887-1956) from Bohemia, now part of the Czech Republic, worked in measure theory, analysis and differential geometry. He introduced the Radon transform, whose inverse is used to construct three-dimensional images from two-dimensional intensities. This forms the theoretical basis for *tomography*, a technique of X-ray photography now standard in medical CT-scans (*tomo* is the Greek word for "a part cut off". Otto Nikodým (1887-1974) was born in Galicia in what was then the Austro-Hungarian Empire but which is now part of Ukraine. Nikodým worked in various Polish universities but left Poland in 1946 and moved permanently to the USA in 1948. His mathematical contributions were mainly in measure theory, functional analysis, differential equations and the foundations of quantum mechanics. He had a strong commitment to mathematical education and wrote several books on the teaching of mathematics at second level and a number of undergraduate texts. He was an enthusiastic communicator of mathematics at all levels and presented a popular radio lecture series on pure mathematics, with titles such as *Logic and Intuition in Mathematics*, *On Infinity* and *On Paradoxes in Logic*.

Proposition 8.7. *If X is an integrable random variable on $(\Omega, \mathcal{F}, P)$ and $\mathcal{G}$ is a σ-field on Ω such that $\mathcal{G} \subset \mathcal{F}$, then there exists a $\mathcal{G}$ measurable integrable random variable on $(\Omega, \mathcal{F}, P)$, $\mathbb{E}[X|\mathcal{G}]$, such that*

$$(8.20) \qquad \int_A \mathbb{E}[X|\mathcal{G}]dP = \int_A X dP$$

for all $A \in \mathcal{G}$. Moreover, if Y is any $\mathcal{G}$ measurable integrable random variable satisfying

$$(8.21) \qquad \int_A Y dP = \int_A X dP$$

for all $A \in \mathcal{G}$, then $Y = \mathbb{E}[X|\mathcal{G}]$ almost surely in $(\Omega, \mathcal{G}, P)$. When Y is a random variable we let $\mathbb{E}[X|Y] = \mathbb{E}[X|\mathcal{F}_Y]$. We call $\mathbb{E}[X|\mathcal{G}]$ and $\mathbb{E}[X|Y]$ the conditional expectations of X given $\mathcal{G}$ and Y respectively.[7]

In view of (8.21) conditional expectations are not *unique*. However, any two conditional expectations of X with respect to $\mathcal{G}$ are *almost surely* equal as random variables on $(\Omega, \mathcal{G}, P)$, and, taking this into consideration, we may regard, for all practical purposes, conditional expectations as unique (see the remarks after Definition 6.20). This means that *all* general statements and results about conditional expectations are to be interpreted *almost surely*.[8] As a consequence of the lack of uniqueness we are not always able to interpret conditional expectations *pointwise*. However, by combining sufficiently many points to obtain a $\mathcal{G}$ measurable set with positive measure and averaging, we obtain a replacement and recover the final two equivalences that we had in the countably generated case. This is the content of (8.20). We continue regarding $\mathbb{E}[X|\mathcal{G}]$ as the expectation of X with all information about X that can be derived from $\mathcal{G}$ events incorporated. The role of Y in $\mathbb{E}[X|Y]$ consists solely in identifying those events. If $f : \mathbf{R} \mapsto \mathbf{R}$ is a bijective Borel measurable function, then $\mathcal{F}_Y = \mathcal{F}_{f(Y)}$ and $\mathbb{E}[X|Y] = \mathbb{E}[X|f(Y)]$.

Another interpretation looks at $\mathbb{E}[X|\mathcal{G}]$ as a *predictor* for X. If we consider $\mathrm{Var}(X - Y)$ as a measure of the difference between the random variables X and Y, then it can be shown, when X has finite variance, that $\mathbb{E}[X|\mathcal{G}]$ also has finite variance and $\mathrm{Var}(X - \mathbb{E}[X|\mathcal{G}]) \leq \mathrm{Var}(X - Y)$ for *any* $\mathcal{G}$ measurable random variable Y. This means that $\mathbb{E}[X|\mathcal{G}]$ is the best predictor of X within the collection of $\mathcal{G}$ measurable random variables with finite variance.[9]

---

[7]Conditional expectations were used prior to the introduction of a mathematically satisfactory definition by A. Kolmogorov in 1933. Later, J. L. Doob gave the above, equivalent but much more usable, definition.

[8]For example all three statements in Proposition 8.8 say that random variables are equal almost surely.

[9]This important property can also be used to define conditional expectations, without using the Radon-Nikodým Theorem, and is essential for more advanced studies.

Conditional expectations satisfy the usual laws such as $\mathbb{E}[X + Y|\mathcal{G}] = \mathbb{E}[X|\mathcal{G}] + \mathbb{E}[Y|\mathcal{G}]$, and these can easily be verified using (8.20) and the integration theory developed in Chapter 6. In addition, there are three important *named* laws that are essential in studying martingales.

Proposition 8.8. *Let X and Y denote integrable random variables on the probability space $(\Omega, \mathcal{F}, P)$ and let $\mathcal{G}$ and $\mathcal{H}$ denote σ-fields on Ω where $\mathcal{H} \subset \mathcal{G} \subset \mathcal{F}$.*

(a) **Taking out what is known.** *If $X \cdot Y$ is integrable and X is $\mathcal{G}$ measurable, then*

$$\mathbb{E}[X \cdot Y|\mathcal{G}] = X \cdot \mathbb{E}[Y|\mathcal{G}].$$

(b) **Independence drops out.** *If X and $\mathcal{G}$ are independent, that is if $\mathcal{F}_X \perp \mathcal{G}$, then*

$$\mathbb{E}[X|\mathcal{G}] = \mathbb{E}[X].$$

(c) **Tower Law.**

$$\mathbb{E}[\mathbb{E}[X|\mathcal{G}|\mathcal{H}]] = \mathbb{E}[X|\mathcal{H}].$$

Proof. We confine our proofs to the case where $\mathcal{G}$ is generated by a countable partition $(G_n)_{n=1}^{\infty}$ of Ω with $P(G_n) > 0$ for all n. This implies, since $\mathcal{H} \subset \mathcal{G}$, that $\mathcal{H}$ is also generated by a countable partition $(H_n)_{n=1}^{\infty}$ and each H_n is a finite or countable union of G_n's.

(a) If $\omega \in \Omega$, then there exists a unique n such that $\omega \in G_n$. Since the random variables $\mathbb{E}[X|\mathcal{G}]$ and X are constant on each G_n,

$$\begin{aligned}
\mathbb{E}[X \cdot Y|\mathcal{G}](\omega) &= \frac{1}{P(G_n)} \int_{G_n} X \cdot Y dP \\
&= \frac{1}{P(G_n)} \int_{G_n} X(\omega) \cdot Y dP \\
&= X(\omega) \cdot \frac{1}{P(G_n)} \int_{G_n} Y dP \\
&= X(\omega) \cdot \mathbb{E}[Y|\mathcal{G}](\omega).
\end{aligned}$$

Hence $\mathbb{E}[X \cdot Y|\mathcal{G}] = X \cdot \mathbb{E}[Y|\mathcal{G}]$.

(b) Since X and $\mathcal{G}$ are independent and $\mathbf{1}_{G_n}$ is $\mathcal{G}$ measurable, X and $\mathbf{1}_{G_n}$ are independent random variables. If $\omega \in G_n$, then

$$
\begin{aligned}
\mathbb{E}[X|\mathcal{G}](\omega) &= \frac{1}{P(G_n)} \int_{G_n} X dP = \frac{1}{P(G_n)} \int_\Omega X \cdot \mathbf{1}_{G_n} dP \\
&= \frac{1}{P(G_n)} \mathbb{E}[X \cdot \mathbf{1}_{G_n}] \\
&= \frac{1}{P(G_n)} \mathbb{E}[X] \cdot \mathbb{E}[\mathbf{1}_{G_n}], \text{ by Proposition 7.8,} \\
&= \frac{1}{P(G_n)} \mathbb{E}[X] \cdot P(G_n), \text{ by Definition 6.1,} \\
&= \mathbb{E}[X].
\end{aligned}
$$

Hence $\mathbb{E}[X|\mathcal{G}]$ is the constant random variable which is everywhere equal to $\mathbb{E}[X]$.

(c) Using Definition 8.7 twice and the fact that $\mathcal{H} \subset \mathcal{G}$ we obtain for $\omega \in H_n$

$$
\begin{aligned}
\mathbb{E}[\mathbb{E}[X|\mathcal{G}|\mathcal{H}]](\omega) &= \frac{1}{P(H_n)} \int_{H_n} \mathbb{E}[X|\mathcal{G}] dP \\
&= \frac{1}{P(H_n)} \int_{H_n} X dP \\
&= \mathbb{E}[X|\mathcal{H}](\omega).
\end{aligned}
$$

Since this holds for all $\omega \in \Omega$ we have $\mathbb{E}[\mathbb{E}[X|\mathcal{G}]|\mathcal{H}] = \mathbb{E}[X|\mathcal{H}]$. This completes the proof. $\qquad\square$

If X is $\mathcal{G}$ measurable, then $\mathcal{F}_X \subset \mathcal{G}$ and $\mathbb{E}[X|\mathcal{G}]$ contains complete information about all events involving X. Thus in (a) we are taking out what is known. A useful particular case arises when we replace X by $X \cdot \mathbf{1}_\Omega$ and suppose X is $\mathcal{G}$ measurable. We then have almost surely

$$
\mathbb{E}[X|\mathcal{G}] = \mathbb{E}[X \cdot \mathbf{1}_\Omega|\mathcal{G}] = X \cdot \mathbb{E}[\mathbf{1}_\Omega] = X.
$$

The opposite occurs when X, or equivalently $\mathcal{F}_X$, and $\mathcal{G}$ are independent. Then no $\mathcal{G}$ event contains information about X and, by (b), independence drops out. A useful special case, that we have previously considered from a different point of view, occurs when $\mathcal{F} = \mathcal{F}_\emptyset$. For any event A we have $P(A \cap \Omega) = P(A) = P(A) \cdot P(\Omega)$ and $P(A \cap \emptyset) = P(\emptyset) = 0 = P(A) \cdot P(\emptyset)$. Hence $\mathcal{F}_X$ and $\mathcal{F}_\emptyset$ are independent and (b) implies $\mathbb{E}[X|\mathcal{F}_\emptyset] = \mathbb{E}[X]$.

The tower law says, when $\mathcal{H} \subset \mathcal{G}$, that averaging first over $\mathcal{G}$ and then over $\mathcal{H}$ is the same as just averaging over $\mathcal{H}$. In particular, we recover (8.18), since

$$
\mathbb{E}[\mathbb{E}[X|\mathcal{G}]] = \mathbb{E}[\mathbb{E}[X|\mathcal{G}]|\mathcal{F}_\emptyset] = \mathbb{E}[X|\mathcal{F}_\emptyset] = \mathbb{E}[X].
$$

Example 8.9. Let $\Omega = \{1, 2, \ldots, 8\}, \mathcal{F} = 2^\Omega, P(\{i\}) = 1/10$ for $i \leq 4$ and $P(\{i\}) = 3/20$ for $i > 4$. Suppose $X = \mathbf{1}_{\{1,2,3,4\}} + 2\mathbf{1}_{\{5,6,7,8\}}$ and $Y = \mathbf{1}_{\{1,5\}} + 2\mathbf{1}_{\{2,3,4,6,7,8\}}$. Let $\mathcal{G}$ denote the σ-field generated by $(\{1,2\}, \{3,4\})$ and let $\mathcal{H}$ denote the σ-field generated by $\{1,2,3,4\}$. Our aim is to show

$$(8.22) \qquad\qquad \mathbb{E}[\mathbb{E}[X \cdot Y | \mathcal{G}] | \mathcal{H}] = X \cdot \mathbb{E}[Y].$$

We use two methods: direct calculation and applications of the three fundamental laws in Proposition 8.8. The following diagram (Figure 8.7) displays the σ-fields that arise in the example: $\mathcal{G}, \mathcal{H}, \mathcal{F}_X$ and $\mathcal{F}_Y$.

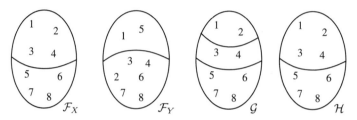

Figure 8.7

By inspection of Figure 8.7, $\mathcal{H} \subset \mathcal{G}$, $\mathcal{F}_X = \mathcal{H}$ and X is $\mathcal{H}$ measurable. We have

$$\mathbb{E}[Y] = \int_\Omega Y dP = \sum_{i=1}^8 Y(i) \cdot P(\{i\}),$$

$$= 1 \cdot \frac{1}{10} + 2 \cdot \frac{1}{10} + 2 \cdot \frac{1}{10} + 2 \cdot \frac{1}{10} + 1 \cdot \frac{3}{20} + 2 \cdot \frac{3}{20} + 2 \cdot \frac{3}{20} + 2 \cdot \frac{3}{20}$$

$$= \frac{7}{4}$$

and

$$(8.23) \qquad\qquad X \cdot \mathbb{E}[Y] = \frac{7}{4}\mathbf{1}_{\{1,2,3,4\}} + \frac{7}{2}\mathbf{1}_{\{5,6,7,8\}}.$$

Using $\mathbf{1}_A \cdot \mathbf{1}_B = \mathbf{1}_{A \cap B}$ we obtain

$$X \cdot Y = (\mathbf{1}_{\{1,2,3,4\}} + 2 \cdot \mathbf{1}_{\{5,6,7,8\}}) \cdot (\mathbf{1}_{\{1,5\}} + 2 \cdot \mathbf{1}_{\{2,3,4,6,7,8\}})$$

$$= \mathbf{1}_{\{1\}} + 2 \cdot \mathbf{1}_{\{5\}} + 2 \cdot \mathbf{1}_{\{2,3,4\}} + 4 \cdot \mathbf{1}_{\{6,7,8\}}$$

$$= \mathbf{1}_{\{1\}} + 2 \cdot \mathbf{1}_{\{2,3,4,5\}} + 4 \cdot \mathbf{1}_{\{6,7,8\}}.$$

Hence

$$\mathbb{E}[X \cdot Y | \mathcal{G}](\omega) = \frac{1}{1/5}(1 \cdot \frac{1}{10} + 2 \cdot \frac{1}{10}) = 3/2 \text{ when } \omega \in \{1,2\},$$

$$\mathbb{E}[X \cdot Y | \mathcal{G}](\omega) = 2, \omega = 3, 4 \text{ since } \{3,4\} \in \mathcal{G} \text{ and } X \cdot Y(3) = X \cdot Y(4) = 2,$$

$$\mathbb{E}[X \cdot Y | \mathcal{G}](\omega) = \frac{1}{3/5}(2 \cdot \frac{3}{20} + 4 \cdot \frac{3}{20} + 4 \cdot \frac{3}{20} + 4 \cdot \frac{3}{20}) = 7/2, \omega \in \{5,6,7,8\}.$$

Since $P(\{1,2,3,4\}) = 4/10$

$$\mathbb{E}[\mathbb{E}[X \cdot Y|\mathcal{G}]|\mathcal{H}](\omega) = \frac{1}{4/10}\left(\frac{1}{10} \cdot \frac{3}{2} + \frac{1}{10} \cdot \frac{3}{2} + \frac{1}{10} \cdot 2 + \frac{1}{10} \cdot 2\right) = \frac{7}{4}$$

when $\omega \in \{1,2,3,4\}$ and, as $\mathbb{E}[X \cdot Y|\mathcal{G}|\mathcal{H}]$ is constant on the $\mathcal{H}$ measurable set $\{5,6,7,8\}$, we have when $\omega \in \{5,6,7,8\}$

$$\mathbb{E}[\mathbb{E}[X \cdot Y|\mathcal{G}]|\mathcal{H}](\omega) = \frac{7}{2}.$$

Comparing this with (8.23) we obtain (8.22).

We now use Proposition 8.8 to establish the same result. We first show that $\mathcal{F}_Y \perp \mathcal{H}$. By Example 5.14 it suffices (see Figure 8.7) to show that $\{1,5\}$ and $\{1,2,3,4\}$ are independent events. We have $P(\{1,5\}) = 5/20$, $P(\{1,2,3,4\}) = 4/10$ and $P(\{1,5\} \cap \{1,2,3,4\}) = P(\{1\}) = 1/10$. Hence $P(\{1,5\}) \cdot P(\{1,2,3,4\}) = 1/10 = P(\{1,5\} \cap \{1,2,3,4\})$ and the σ-fields $\mathcal{F}_Y$ and $\mathcal{H}$ are independent. Hence

$$\mathbb{E}[\mathbb{E}[X \cdot Y|\mathcal{G}]|\mathcal{H}] = \mathbb{E}[X \cdot Y|\mathcal{H}] \text{ by the tower law since } \mathcal{H} \subset \mathcal{G}$$

$= X \cdot \mathbb{E}[Y|\mathcal{H}]$, taking out what is known since X is $\mathcal{H}$ measurable

$= X \cdot \mathbb{E}[Y]$, independence drops out as Y and $\mathcal{H}$ are independent.

Example 8.10. This example is a continuation of Example 8.2, and we use the same notation: X_t denotes the share price and V_t the call option price at time t. We call $Y_t := e^{-rt}X_t$ the *discounted share price* and $Z_t := e^{-rt}V_t$ the *discounted option price* at time t. Rewriting (8.10) and (8.11) with this notation, we obtain $\mathbb{E}[Y_t|\mathcal{F}_0] = Y_0$ and $\mathbb{E}[Y_T|\mathcal{F}_t] = Y_t$. Applying the Tower Law we obtain, since Y_0 is a constant random variable and $\mathcal{F}_0 = \mathcal{F}_\emptyset \subset \mathcal{F}_t$,

$$(8.24) \qquad \mathbb{E}[Y_T|\mathcal{F}_0] = \mathbb{E}[\mathbb{E}[Y_T|\mathcal{F}_t]|\mathcal{F}_0] = \mathbb{E}[Y_t|\mathcal{F}_0] = Y_0.$$

Similarly (8.12) and (8.13) can be rewritten as $\mathbb{E}[Z_T|\mathcal{F}_0] = Z_0$ and $\mathbb{E}[Z_T|\mathcal{F}_t] = Z_t$ and, using the Tower Law, we obtain

$$(8.25) \qquad \mathbb{E}[Z_t|\mathcal{F}_0] = \mathbb{E}[\mathbb{E}[Z_T|\mathcal{F}_t]|\mathcal{F}_0] = \mathbb{E}[Z_T|\mathcal{F}_0] = Z_0.$$

On taking out what is known, $\mathbb{E}[Y_u|\mathcal{F}_u] = Y_u$ and $\mathbb{E}[Z_u|\mathcal{F}_u] = Z_u$ for $u \in \{0,t,T\}$. We summarize both of these equations and (8.10), (8.11), (8,12), (8,13), (8.24) and (8.25) as follows:

$$(8.26) \qquad \mathbb{E}[Y_v|\mathcal{F}_u] = Y_u, \text{ when } u,v \in \{0,t,T\}, u \le v,$$

$$(8.27) \qquad \mathbb{E}[Z_v|\mathcal{F}_u] = Z_u, \text{ when } u,v \in \{0,t,T\}, u \le v.$$

Equation (8.26) is used to find the risk neutral probabilities while (8.27) implies

$$(8.28) \qquad Z_0 = e^{-rT}\mathbb{E}[(X_T - k)^+],$$

and this is the price of the call option. Our simple model now contains a probability space, a filtration, two finite stochastic processes, and two sets of equations using conditional expectation. In the next chapter, we will see that it also contains two martingales.

We have just seen a good example of how and why mathematics is both useful and difficult. Mathematics often summarizes large amounts of information in compact form. It does so by recognizing patterns and using efficient notation. The summary may take the form of a set of equations, as for example (8.26), (8.27) and (8.28), which together contain all we need to price a call option. On the other hand, since equations in mathematics often contain so much information, it is unreasonable to expect to understand them at a glance. Mathematics, in contrast to, say, economics, may summarize key information in one line instead of pages. To read and understand, even partially, almost any book on mathematics is a major task and should not be approached in the same way as a novel. One needs to go forward and backwards and to recognize that the difficulty encountered in coming to grips with a proposition or set of equations is usually proportional to the amount of information being conveyed and to the eventual progress that will follow. On the other hand, certain mathematical results and formulae can be used without understanding their significance. Then mathematics becomes a magic ritual which produces required results on reciting a meaningless formula. This may work for some time, but as we have seen, there are rules, hypotheses (or restrictions) and flexibilities surrounding any mathematical formulae; and without understanding the background, such a recipe-driven approach will either be very restrictive or lead to errors in application. The other interesting feature of the above set of equations is that, because of their compact form, they suggest how to go further and to obtain even deeper results. We will see the result in the next chapter.

8.3. Hedging

Example 8.11. In this example we show how the seller can set up a portfolio to cover or hedge any claim on the option in Example 8.1. We suppose, as previously, that the seller receives no commission and that the portfolio consists of shares and bonds. The portfolio will need to match the claim at *each* node. The option has value 4 at node D and value 0 at nodes C, E and F. This leaves only A and B. We denote by v_0 the seller's price for the option at $t = 0$ and by $v_{.25}$ the seller's price at $t = .25$. Our aim is to show that v_0 coincides with V_0, the buyer's price at $t = 0$, that $v_{.25}$ coincides with $V_{.25}$ the buyer's price at $t = .25$, and that these prices allow the seller to hedge any claim on the option. We consider the portfolio at each of the diagrams in Figure 8.2. If the share price goes to node C, the option will not be exercised no matter what happens at $t = .5$ and we need not consider the final diagram in Figure 8.2. Suppose the seller's portfolio contains Δ_0 shares at $t = 0$ and $\Delta_{.25}$ shares at $t = .25$.

At $t = 0$ the seller will receive v_0 and needs to borrow $20\Delta_0 - v_0$ to buy the shares. At $t = .25$ the portfolio will be worth $24\Delta_0 - e^{.25 \times .12}(20\Delta_0 - v_0)$ if the share price goes up and $19\Delta_0 - e^{.25 \times .12}(20\Delta_0 - v_0)$ if the share price goes down. Hence

$$(8.29) \qquad 24\Delta_0 - e^{.25 \times .12}(20\Delta_0 - v_0) = v_{.25},$$

$$(8.30) \qquad 19\Delta_0 - e^{.25 \times .12}(20\Delta_0 - v_0) = 0$$

and $\Delta_0 = v_{.25}/5$.

At node B the number of shares will change from Δ_0 to $\Delta_{.25}$ and require additional borrowings[10] of $24(\Delta_{.25} - \Delta_0)$. Hence, equating the portfolio with the claim at node D, we obtain

$$(8.31) \qquad 26\Delta_{.25} - 24(\Delta_{.25} - \Delta_0)e^{.25 \times .12} - (20\Delta_0 - v_0)e^{.5 \times .12} = 4$$

and at node E we have

$$(8.32) \qquad 21\Delta_{.25} - 24(\Delta_{.25} - \Delta_0)e^{.25 \times .12} - (20\Delta_0 - v_0)e^{.5 \times .12} = 0.$$

Subtracting (8.32) from (8.31) we obtain $\Delta_{.25} = .8$. By (8.30),

$$19\Delta_0 e^{.03} = e^{.06}(20\Delta_0 - v_0),$$

and on substituting this into (8.32) and using $\Delta_{.25} = .8$ we obtain

$$.8(21 - 24e^{.03}) = \Delta_0(19e^{.03} - 24e^{.03}) = -e^{.03}\Delta_0 5.$$

Hence $\Delta_0 = (24 - 21e^{-.03}) \cdot (.8)/5 = .58$ and

$$v_{.25} = 2.90 = V_{.25}.$$

By (8.30),

$$v_0 = (20 - 19e^{-.03})\Delta_0 = (20 - 19e^{-.03})(.58) = .90 = V_0.$$

The seller's hedging portfolio at $t = 0$ consists of .58 shares and borrowings of \$10.70 worth of bonds. If the share price increases at $t = .25$, the seller re-balances the portfolio by buying an extra .22 shares and increasing his borrowings to \$15.98; otherwise he sells his shares and repays his borrowings. This portfolio hedges any claim at any time on the option.

Two different approaches in Examples 8.1 and 8.11 led to the same agreed price. On the buyer's side the fair game principle was used to construct the risk neutral probability space, which was then used to price the option. The two steps were summarized by very similar formulae, (8.26) and (8.27). On the seller's side a hedging portfolio was constructed at each node and gave, at time 0, the seller's fair price for the option.

---

[10]If $\Delta_{.25} > \Delta_0$. It may happen that $\Delta_{.25} < \Delta_0$ in which case shares are sold.

The next step, in obtaining a more realistic *model* for pricing and hedging an option, is clear: partition $[0, T]$ into a large number of small intervals, provide information at the end points of every interval, and extend the method used in Examples 8.1, 8.2 and 8.11. By providing information at n different times, the share price can take any of $(i + 1)$ different values at the ith intermediate time and any of $(n + 1)$ values at the maturity date. This extension contains no surprises and is only complicated by the increased amount of data to be processed. Formulae (8.26) and (8.27) will be developed in Chapter 9 to overcome this problem. This involves the use of conditional expectations to define martingales. The martingales themselves will be seen as a mathematical formulation of a set of fair games. Afterwards, it is natural to take limits by letting the mesh of the partition tend to zero, and this leads to the *Black-Scholes formula* for pricing the option and covers the buyer's side of the story. We follow this approach, but, as we have already seen, taking limits is not always straightforward.

The sample space for the binomial model with information provided at times $\{0, \frac{T}{n}, \frac{2T}{n}, \ldots, T\}$ consists of paths similar to the one featured in Figure 8.8.

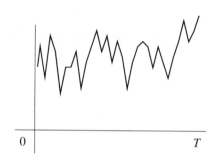

Figure 8.8

In the limit we obtain the sample space for a Wiener process. Each point in this space is a potential path for the share price over $[0, T]$ and defines a mapping from $[0, T]$ into $\mathbf{R}$. This gives us a *path*, but now new non-trivial questions emerge with mathematical implications. It is important to know how smooth the paths are in the sample space. It can be shown that almost surely all paths are *continuous*, but also almost surely all paths are *nowhere differentiable*. This means we can integrate but not differentiate along paths, and we briefly consider the implications for the *hedging strategy*.

Suppose information is given a finite number of times in $[0, T]$ and that $[t, t + \Delta t]$ is one such interval, where information is given at t and $t + \Delta t$ and nowhere in between. The portfolio that hedges the claim over the interval has to be in place at time t, using information available at time t, and must match the price of the call option at both ends of the interval. Suppose the portfolio consists of θ_t shares and β_t units of a *riskless bond* at time t. We let $B(t)$ denote the value of the bond at time t. In the usual case of a continuously compounded constant interest rate r with unit cost for the bond at $t = 0$, we have $B(t) = e^{rt}$. If the portfolio hedges the claim at all times, then

$$(8.33) \qquad V_t = \theta_t X_t + B(t)\beta_t$$

where V_t is the value of the claim at time t. Let $\omega \in \Omega$ be arbitrary and let $\widetilde{\omega}$ denote any path such that $X_t(\omega) = X_t(\widetilde{\omega})$ and $X_{t+\Delta t}(\omega) \neq X_{t+\Delta t}(\widetilde{\omega})$ (see Figure 8.9).

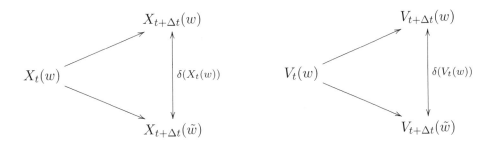

Figure 8.9

If the share price follows the path ω up to time t, then at time $t+\Delta t$ the share price will either be $X_{t+\Delta t}(\omega)$ with corresponding claim $V_{t+\Delta t}(\omega)$ or $X_{t+\Delta t}(\widetilde{\omega})$ with claim $V_{t+\Delta t}(\widetilde{\omega})$. Since the portfolio is unchanged over the interval $(t, t+\Delta t)$ and must match either of these possibilities at time $t + \Delta t$, we have, by (8.33),

$$(8.34) \qquad X_{t+\Delta t}(\omega)\theta_t(\omega) + B(t + \Delta t)\beta_t(\omega) = V_{t+\Delta t}(\omega)$$

and

$$(8.35) \qquad X_{t+\Delta t}(\widetilde{\omega})\theta_t(\omega) + B(t + \Delta t)\beta_t(\omega) = V_{t+\Delta t}(\widetilde{\omega}).$$

Let $\delta(X_t(\omega)) := X_{t+\Delta t}(\omega) - X_{t+\Delta t}(\widetilde{\omega})$ denote the gap between the two prices the stock may achieve at $t + \Delta t$ if it followed path ω up to time t, and let $\delta(V_t(\omega)) := V_{t+\Delta t}(\omega) - V_{t+\Delta t}(\widetilde{\omega})$ denote the corresponding gap in the value of the claim (see Figure 8.9). From (8.34) and (8.35) we obtain[11]

$$(8.36) \qquad \theta_t(\omega) = \theta_t(\widetilde{\omega}) = \frac{\delta(V_t(\omega))}{\delta(X_t(\omega))} = \frac{\delta(V_t(\widetilde{\omega}))}{\delta(X_t(\widetilde{\omega}))}$$

---

[11]Clearly $V_{t+\Delta t}(\omega) > V_{t+\Delta t}(\widetilde{\omega})$ if and only if $X_{t+\Delta t}(\omega) > X_{t+\Delta t}(\widetilde{\omega})$, and hence $\theta_t(\omega) > 0$. If $X_{t+\Delta t}(\omega) = X_{t+\Delta t}(\widetilde{\omega})$, then no hedging is necessary.

and hence

$$(8.37) \qquad \beta_t(\omega) \;=\; B(t+\Delta t)^{-1}\big(V_{t+\Delta t}(\omega) - X_{t+\Delta t}(\omega)\cdot\theta_t(\omega)\big)$$

$$(8.38) \qquad\qquad\;=\; B(t+\Delta t)^{-1}\big(V_{t+\Delta t}(\widetilde{\omega}) - X_{t+\Delta t}(\widetilde{\omega})\cdot\theta_t(\omega)\big).$$

As both θ_t and β_t are independent of what happens after time t, both are $\mathcal{F}_t$ measurable and we have an abstract version of the material in Example 8.11. Working backwards from time T, one can set up a portfolio which hedges the claim.

Let $\Delta X_t = X_{t+\Delta t} - X_t$, $\Delta B(t) = B(t+\Delta t) - B(t)$ and $\Delta V_t = V_{t+\Delta t} - V_t$. If $\mathcal{F}_t$ denotes the σ-field of events known by time t, then ΔX_t and ΔV_t are $\mathcal{F}_{t+\Delta t}$ measurable random variables. Subtracting

$$X_t(\omega)\theta_t(\omega) + B(t)\beta_t(\omega) = V_t(\omega)$$

from (8.34) we obtain the *basic* equation required to construct a hedging portfolio:

$$(8.39) \qquad\qquad \Delta X_t\cdot\theta_t + \Delta B(t)\cdot\beta_t = \Delta V_t.$$

It is tempting to divide (8.39) by Δt, to let $\Delta t \longrightarrow 0$ and write down the following *stochastic differential equation*:[12]

$$(8.40) \qquad\qquad X_t'\cdot\theta_t + B'(t)\cdot\beta_t = V_t',$$

hoping it will provide, in the limit, a continuous hedging strategy.

However, $\Delta X_t/\Delta t$ is not a real number but a random variable, and the limit should also be a random variable. In particular, we should be able to interpret $\lim_{\Delta t\to 0}\Delta X_t(\omega)/\Delta t$ for any path ω. Since, almost surely, paths are nowhere differentiable, this limit will very rarely exist and (8.40) has only a *symbolic meaning*. There is an alternative approach, as we saw in Chapter 1 while deriving (1.15). In place of taking limits in (8.39) take a similar term from each interval and add them together to form Riemann sums

$$(8.41) \qquad \sum_{i=1}^{n}\theta_{t_i}\Delta X_{t_i} + \sum_{i=1}^{n}\beta_{t_i}\Delta B_{t_i} = \sum_{i=1}^{n}\Delta V_{t_i}$$

and then take a limit to obtain, in place of (8.40), the *stochastic integral equation*

$$(8.42) \qquad \int_0^T \theta_t\,dX_t + \int_0^T \beta_t\,dB(t) = \int_0^T dV_t = V_T - V_0.$$

This involves two new kinds of integrals, the *Stochastic Riemann Integral* and the *Itô Integral*, that we rigorously define in Chapter 11. Although (8.40) does not have any rigorous mathematical meaning, it is useful as a shorthand for the mathematically meaningful stochastic integral equation (8.42). Equation (8.42) will be used later to construct a hedging portfolio.

---

[12]An equation involving the "derivative" of random variables.

8.4. Exercises

(8.1) Let $\Omega = \{1, 2, \dots, 10\}$, $\mathcal{F} = 2^{\Omega}$. If $P(\{i\}) = i^2/a$ for all i and $(\Omega, \mathcal{F}, P)$ is a probability space, find a. Let $X(i) = 1$ for $i \leq 5$ and $X(i) = i$ for $i \geq 6$. Express X as a simple random variable. Let $Y = 2 \cdot \mathbf{1}_{\{1,2,3\}} + 3 \cdot \mathbf{1}_{\{4,5,6\}}$. Find $\mathbb{E}[X|X], \mathbb{E}[X|Y], \mathbb{E}[Y|X], \mathbb{E}[X|Y^2], \mathbb{E}[X \cdot Y|\mathcal{F}_X]$ and $\mathbb{E}[\mathbb{E}[X|\mathcal{F}_Y]|\mathcal{F}_X]$.

(8.2) If $(\Omega, \mathcal{F}, P)$ is a probability space and $A, B \in \mathcal{F}$, find $\mathbb{E}[\mathbf{1}_A|\mathbf{1}_B]$.

(8.3) Let $(\Omega, \mathcal{F}, P)$ denote a probability space and suppose $\mathcal{F}$ is generated by a countable partition $(G_n)_{n=1}^{\infty}$ of Ω with $P(G_n) > 0$ for all n. Let $A \in \mathcal{F}$. Show that $\mathbb{E}[\mathbf{1}_A|\mathcal{F}](\omega) = P(G_n \cap A)/P(G_n)$ for all $\omega \in G_n$ and for all n.

(8.4) If X is an almost surely positive integrable random variable on $(\Omega, \mathcal{F}, P)$ and $\mathcal{G}$ is a σ-field on Ω with $\mathcal{G} \subset \mathcal{F}$, show that $\mathbb{E}[X|\mathcal{G}]$ is almost surely positive. Show that for any integrable random variable X, $|\mathbb{E}[X|\mathcal{G}]| \leq \mathbb{E}[|X||\mathcal{G}]$ almost surely, and that $\mathbb{E}[|\mathbb{E}[X|\mathcal{G}]|] \leq \mathbb{E}[|X|]$.

(8.5) Suppose the share price of a certain stock is \$8 today and that it will either be \$9 or \$7 in one month's time and will move, if at \$9, to either \$8 or \$12 and, if at \$7, to either \$8 or \$6. If the interest rate is 5%, describe portfolios consisting of shares and bonds which hedge the risk on (a) a call option on one share in two months' time, (b) a put option for one share in two months' time with strike price \$9 in both cases. Find the value of the options in one month in both cases.

(8.6) Suppose the average number of accidents per month at a given location is α and the average number injured per accident is β. If both the number of accidents and the number injured in each accident are random variables with a Poisson distribution, show that the average number injured per month is $\alpha\beta$.

(8.7) If $(\Omega, \mathcal{F}, P)$ is a probability space, $\mathcal{G}$ is a σ-field on Ω, $\mathcal{G} \subset \mathcal{F}$ and X is an integrable random variable, show that the following are equivalent: (a) X is $\mathcal{G}$ measurable, (b) $\mathbb{E}[X \cdot Y|\mathcal{G}] = X \cdot \mathbb{E}[Y|\mathcal{G}]$ for all integrable random variables Y such that $X \cdot Y$ is integrable, (c) $\mathbb{E}[X|\mathcal{G}] = X$.

(8.8) If X and Y are integrable random variables on $(\Omega, \mathcal{F}, P)$ and $\int_A X\,dP = \int_A Y\,dP$ for all $A \in \mathcal{F}$, show that $X = Y$ almost surely. Use this result to establish uniqueness in Propositions 8.4 and 8.7.

(8.9) Let $(\Omega, \mathcal{F}, P)$ be a probability space, $\mathcal{G}$ a σ-field on Ω, $\mathcal{G} \subset \mathcal{F}$ and suppose X is an integrable random variable on $(\Omega, \mathcal{F}, P)$. By considering $(X - \mathbb{E}[X|\mathcal{G}])^2$ show that $\mathbb{E}[X|\mathcal{G}]^2 \leq \mathbb{E}[X^2|\mathcal{G}]$.

(8.10) If $(\Omega, \mathcal{F}, P)$ is a probability space, $\mathcal{G}$ and $\mathcal{H}$ are σ-fields on Ω, $\mathcal{H} \subset \mathcal{G} \subset \mathcal{F}$, X and Y are integrable random variables on $(\Omega, \mathcal{F}, P)$, X is $\mathcal{G}$ measurable and $\mathcal{F}_Y$ and $\mathcal{G}$ are independent show that $\mathbb{E}[XY|\mathcal{H}] = \mathbb{E}[Y] \cdot \mathbb{E}[X|\mathcal{H}]$.

Chapter 9

Martingales

All things flow, and it is not possible to step into the same river twice for he who does will be washed by other waters.

Heraclitus, c. 540-480 BC

Summary

Discrete and continuous martingales are defined. Sequences of independent random variables, fair games and random walks are presented as examples. For martingales, $\mathbf{L}^1$ boundedness is shown to imply almost sure convergence and uniform integrability to imply $\mathbf{L}^1$ convergence.

9.1. Discrete Martingales

A martingale is a stochastic process satisfying a condition that removes bias. There are two basic types of martingales:[1] discrete and continuous. In this section we define and discuss discrete martingales. Equations (8.26) and (8.27)

---

[1]Martingales were defined in probability theory by Paul Pierre Lévy (1886-1971). Lévy was from Paris. His early research was in analysis, and his studies in probability theory began by accident. A promising young French mathematician, Rene Gateâux, began studying probability measures on infinite dimensional spaces, such as $\mathcal{C}([a,b])$, a couple of years prior to the start of World War I. He was killed early in the war and Lévy was asked to prepare his unfinished work for publication. While undertaking this task Lévy became interested in the subject and from then on devoted most of his time to probability theory. His substantial contributions include limit theorems, variations on the Central Limit Theorem, stable distributions, the introduction of many new stochastic processes, some of which are currently used in financial mathematics, and characterizations of Brownian motion/Weiner measure (see Chapter 10).

motivate the definition and provide simple examples. Four fundamental examples, all of which feature later in applications, are given.

Definition 9.1. *Let $(\mathcal{F}_n)_{n=1}^{\infty}$ be a filtration on the probability space $(\Omega, \mathcal{F}, P)$. A discrete martingale on $(\Omega, \mathcal{F}, P, (\mathcal{F}_n)_{n=1}^{\infty})$ is a sequence $(X_n)_{n=1}^{\infty}$ of integrable random variables on $(\Omega, \mathcal{F}, P)$, adapted to the filtration $(\mathcal{F}_n)_{n=1}^{\infty}$; that is X_n is $\mathcal{F}_n$ measurable for all n, such that*

$$(9.1) \qquad\qquad \mathbb{E}[X_{n+1}|\mathcal{F}_n] = X_n$$

for all $n \geq 1$.[2]

It is helpful to think of n as measuring time, for example days or weeks, with one experiment occurring in each time interval. The random variable X_n is associated with the nth experiment, and $\mathcal{F}_n$ is the history of the first n periods or the information available at the end of the nth time period.

Let $\mathcal{G}_n := \sigma(X_1, \ldots, X_n)$ denote the σ-field generated by $(X_i)_{i=1}^{n}$; that is $\mathcal{G}_n$ is the smallest σ-field on Ω for which $X_i, 1 \leq i \leq n$, are measurable. Since $\mathcal{F}_{X_n} \subset \mathcal{F}_n \subset \mathcal{F}$, $\mathcal{G}_n \subset \mathcal{F}_n$ and $(\mathcal{G}_n)_{n=1}^{\infty}$ is a filtration on $(\Omega, \mathcal{F}, P)$. Taking the conditional expectation in (9.1) with respect to $\mathcal{G}_n$ we obtain

$$(9.2) \qquad\qquad \mathbb{E}[\mathbb{E}[X_{n+1}|\mathcal{F}_n]|\mathcal{G}_n] = \mathbb{E}[X_n|\mathcal{G}_n].$$

On taking out what is known from the right-hand side of (9.2) and applying the Tower Law to the left-hand side, we obtain

$$\mathbb{E}[X_{n+1}|\mathcal{G}_n] = X_n.$$

This shows, since $(X_n)_{n=1}^{\infty}$ is adapted to the filtration $(\mathcal{G}_n)_{n=1}^{\infty}$, that $(X_n)_{n=1}^{\infty}$ is a martingale on $(\Omega, \mathcal{F}, P, (\mathcal{G}_n)_{n=1}^{\infty})$. In many examples we have $\mathcal{F}_n = \mathcal{G}_n$ for all n, and if we do not mention the filtration in defining or discussing martingales, we take it as understood that this is the case. In particular, we often write: let $(X_n)_{n=1}^{\infty}$ denote a martingale on $(\Omega, \mathcal{F}, P)$.

Example 9.2. This example shows that discrete martingales generalize the concept of a sequence of independent integrable random variables. Let $(X_n)_{n=1}^{\infty}$ denote a sequence of independent integrable random variables on the probability space $(\Omega, \mathcal{F}, P)$ and suppose $\mathbb{E}[X_n] = 0$ for all n. If $\mathcal{F}_n$ is the σ-field generated by $X_1, \ldots, X_n$, then $\mathcal{F}_n \subset \mathcal{F}$ for all n and $(\mathcal{F}_n)_{n=1}^{\infty}$ is a filtration on $(\Omega, \mathcal{F}, P)$. Let $Y_n = \sum_{i=1}^{n} X_i$ for all n. Since $|Y_n| \leq \sum_{i=1}^{n} |X_i|$ and each X_i is integrable, Proposition 6.28 implies that Y_n is integrable. The random variable Y_n, as a finite sum of $\mathcal{F}_n$ measurable functions, is $\mathcal{F}_n$ measurable. If $i \leq n$, the random variable X_{n+1} is independent of X_i, and hence also of $\mathcal{F}_n$. Since independence

---

[2]Equation (9.1), as well as the analogous formula for continuous martingales (see Definition 9.12), is called the *martingale property*.

drops out (Proposition 8.8(b)), $\mathbb{E}[X_{n+1}|\mathcal{F}_n] = \mathbb{E}[X_{n+1}] = 0$. On taking out what is known (Proposition 8.8(a)), we obtain

$$
\begin{aligned}
\mathbb{E}[Y_{n+1}|\mathcal{F}_n] &= \mathbb{E}[X_{n+1} + Y_n|\mathcal{F}_n] \\
&= \mathbb{E}[X_{n+1}|\mathcal{F}_n] + \mathbb{E}[Y_n|\mathcal{F}_n] \\
&= Y_n
\end{aligned}
$$

and $(Y_n)_{n=1}^\infty$ is a martingale adapted to the filtration $(\mathcal{F}_n)_{n=1}^\infty$.

Example 9.3. This example, although apparently rather special, will be shown, in Proposition 9.11, to occur quite frequently in disguise and is the key to presenting the price of a call option as a martingale. Let $(\mathcal{F}_n)_{n=1}^\infty$ denote a filtration on $(\Omega, \mathcal{F}, P)$ and let X denote an integrable random variable. For each n let $X_n = \mathbb{E}[X|\mathcal{F}_n]$. By Proposition 8.7, X_n is integrable and, by the definition of conditional expectation, $\mathcal{F}_n$ measurable. Hence $(X_n)_{n=1}^\infty$ is adapted to the filtration $(\mathcal{F}_n)_{n=1}^\infty$. Since $\mathcal{F}_n \subset \mathcal{F}_{n+1}$, the Tower Law, Proposition 8.8(c), implies

$$
\mathbb{E}[X_{n+1}|\mathcal{F}_n] = \mathbb{E}[\mathbb{E}[X|\mathcal{F}_{n+1}]|\mathcal{F}_n] = \mathbb{E}[X|\mathcal{F}_n] = X_n
$$

and $(X_n)_{n=1}^\infty$ is a martingale on $(\Omega, \mathcal{F}, P)$ adapted to the filtration $(\mathcal{F}_n)_{n=1}^\infty$.

The following proposition is the first test that should be applied when trying to decide if a given sequence of random variables is a martingale.

Proposition 9.4. *If $(X_n)_{n=1}^\infty$ is a martingale on $(\Omega, \mathcal{F}, P, (\mathcal{F}_n)_{n=1}^\infty)$, then*

$$
\mathbb{E}[X_n] = \mathbb{E}[X_m]
$$

for all n and m.

Proof. By Proposition 8.7,

$$
\mathbb{E}[X_n] = \int_\Omega X_n dP = \int_\Omega \mathbb{E}[X_{n+1}|\mathcal{F}_n] dP = \int_\Omega X_{n+1} dP = \mathbb{E}[X_{n+1}].
$$

Hence $\mathbb{E}[X_n] = \mathbb{E}[X_{n+1}] = \mathbb{E}[X_{n+2}] = \ldots = \mathbb{E}[X_m]$ for all n and m. This completes the proof.[3] $\qquad \square$

Example 9.5. Martingales[4] are the mathematical formulation of a sequence of *fair games*. Let X_n denote the winnings per unit stake on the nth game in a sequence of fair games. Then $\mathbb{E}[X_n] = 0$ and $Y_n := \sum_{i=1}^n X_n$ are the winnings accumulated by the end of the nth game. To place this in a mathematical

---

[3]One may also use the Tower Law to prove this result: since $\mathcal{F}_\emptyset$ is contained in any σ-field, we have $\mathbb{E}[X_n] = \mathbb{E}[X_n|\mathcal{F}_\emptyset] = \mathbb{E}[\mathbb{E}[X_{n+1}|\mathcal{F}_n]|\mathcal{F}_\emptyset] = \mathbb{E}[X_{n+1}|\mathcal{F}_\emptyset] = \mathbb{E}[X_{n+1}]$.

[4]*The martingale* was originally a betting system in which a player keeps doubling the bet on successive games so that the first win recoups all previous losses and leaves the player with an overall profit. It was popular in 19th century Parisian gambling circles but is today banned in most casinos. It looks as if playing the martingale will always be profitable, *but* the expected loss *prior* to winning is *infinite*. Note that we have two *precise*, but *different*, meanings to the word *martingale*, one in gambling and one in mathematics.

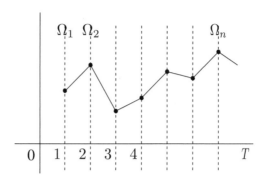

Figure 9.1

setting let Ω_n denote the set of outcomes of the nth game, and suppose there exists a σ-field $\mathcal{G}_n$ on Ω_n and a probability measure P_n on $(\Omega_n, \mathcal{G}_n)$ such that X_n is a random variable on $(\Omega_n, \mathcal{G}_n, P_n)$. If $\omega_n \in \Omega_n$, then $X_n(\omega_n)$ are the winnings per unit stake on the nth game when ω_n is the outcome. We cannot, however, immediately apply the result in Example 9.2 to conclude that the sequence $(Y_n)_{n=1}^{\infty}$ is a martingale because the random variables $(X_n)_{n=1}^{\infty}$ are *not* all defined on the *same* probability space. We met the same problem previously and resolved it in Example 5.15 and Propositions 5.16 and 7.32 by constructing a product probability space. Here we require a similar result for an infinite set of random variables, and this leads to an *infinite* product of probability measures on an infinite product of measurable spaces. We confine our discussion to an outline of the main highlights of one approach and omit the non-trivial technical details.

Since our sample space Ω must include all information about all *possible* games, we let $\Omega = \prod_{n=1}^{\infty} \Omega_n = \{(\omega_n)_{n=1}^{\infty} : \omega_n \in \Omega_n \text{ for all } n\}$. Thus Ω is the set of all sequences with the nth entry chosen from the space Ω_n. A typical point in Ω represents one possible set of results from a full set of games. In Figure 9.1 we sketch a *point* in Ω, assuming $\Omega_n \subset \mathbf{R}$ for all n.

In view of this representation each point in Ω is called a *path*. For each positive integer n we *identify* $X_n : \Omega_n \mapsto \mathbf{R}$ with $X_n : \Omega \mapsto \mathbf{R}$ where $X_n\big((\omega_m)_{m=1}^{\infty}\big) = X_n(\omega_n)$, and keep the same notation. Let $\mathcal{F}_n$ denote the σ-field on Ω generated by the random variables $(X_i)_{i=1}^{n}$. Clearly, $\mathcal{F}_n = \mathcal{G}_1 \times \cdots \times \mathcal{G}_n$ is generated by $A := A_1 \times A_2 \times \cdots \times A_n \times \Omega_{n+1} \times \Omega_{n+2} \times \cdots$ and A contains *all possible futures* of all points in $A_1 \times A_2 \times \cdots \times A_n$ (see Figure 9.2). Let $\mathcal{F}_{\infty} = \bigcup_{n=1}^{\infty} \mathcal{F}_n$ and let $\mathcal{F}$ denote the σ-field generated by $(X_i)_{i=1}^{\infty}$. For all n, $\mathcal{F}_n \subset \mathcal{F}_{\infty} \subset \mathcal{F}$. In general, $\mathcal{F}_{\infty}$ is not a σ-field, but it does have some useful properties: the *finite* union of sets in $\mathcal{F}_{\infty}$ still lies in $\mathcal{F}_{\infty}$; and if $A \in \mathcal{F}_{\infty}$, then $A^c \in \mathcal{F}_{\infty}$. Since $\mathcal{F}_1 \subset \mathcal{F}_2 \ldots \subset \mathcal{F}_n \ldots \subset \mathcal{F}$, $(\mathcal{F}_n)_{n=1}^{\infty}$ is a filtration on $(\Omega, \mathcal{F})$. As $\mathcal{F}_n$ contains all

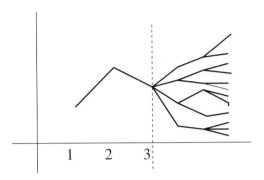

Figure 9.2

events from the first n games, it is the history of the process up to the end of the nth game. The σ-field $\mathcal{F}$ contains all events from all games.

Proposition 7.32 can be extended to show that there exists a measure Q_n on $(\Omega, \mathcal{F}_n)$ such that

$$Q_n(A_1 \times A_2 \times \cdots \times A_n \times \Omega_{n+1} \times \Omega_{n+2} \times \cdots) = P_1(A_1) \cdot P_2(A_2) \cdots P_n(A_n)$$

whenever $A_i \in \mathcal{G}_i$ for $i = 1, 2, \ldots, n$. Moreover, we have the following consistency relationship:

$$Q_{n+1}(A) = Q_n(A) \text{ for all } A \in \mathcal{F}_n.$$

This easily implies that there exists a mapping $P : \mathcal{F}_\infty \mapsto [0, 1]$ such that $P(\Omega) = 1$, $P(\bigcup_{i=1}^n A_i) = \sum_{i=1}^n P(A_i)$ for any *finite* sequence of pairwise disjoint sets in $\mathcal{F}_\infty$ and $P(A^c) = 1 - P(A)$ for all $A \in \mathcal{F}_\infty$. The two remaining problems are to show that P is countably additive, that is (5.4) holds, and to extend P to $\mathcal{F}$ and retain countable additivity. The completion of the first step involves showing that P satisfies condition (d) in Exercise 5.8. For the second step one lets

$$P^*(A) = \inf\{\sum_{n=1}^\infty P(A_n) : A \subset \bigcup_{n=1}^\infty A_n, A_n \in \mathcal{F}\}$$

for all $A \subset \Omega$ and considers the set $\mathcal{H}$ of all $H \subset \Omega$ such that

$$P^*(A) = P^*(H \cap A) + P^*(H^c \cap A)$$

for all $A \in \mathcal{F}_\infty$. It can be shown that $\mathcal{H}$ is a σ-field, that $\mathcal{F} \subset \mathcal{H}$, $P^*(A) = P(A)$ for all $A \in \mathcal{F}_\infty$ and that $(\Omega, \mathcal{H}, P^*)$ is a probability space. We denote the restriction of P^* to $\mathcal{F}$ by P. The required probability space, with sample space Ω, on the infinite product is $(\Omega, \mathcal{F}, P)$.

On this probability space the sequence $(X_n)_{n=1}^\infty$ becomes a sequence of independent random variables, and an application of Example 9.2 shows that $(Y_n)_{n=1}^\infty$ is a martingale on $(\Omega, \mathcal{F}, P)$ adapted to the filtration $(\mathcal{F}_n)_{n=1}^\infty$.

We have considered the unit stake per game case, and one may ask if a player can adopt a *system* or *strategy* which makes the game favorable. For instance a player may decide to quit when a certain amount has been won or lost or to place no bet after three successive wins, etc. A system will consist of betting different amounts on different games with the amount B_n to be placed on the nth game, chosen at any time prior[5] to the start of the nth game and thus with full knowledge of what happened in the $(n-1)$ previous games. This means B_n is $\mathcal{F}_{n-1}$ measurable for $n > 1$. We suppose there is a limit on the amount that can be placed on any one game; that is there exists $M \in \mathbf{R}$ such that $|B_n| \leq M$ for all n. The accumulated winnings W_n at the end of the nth game are given by

$$W_n = B_1 \cdot X_1 + \cdots + B_n \cdot X_n.$$

Since X_i and B_i are $\mathcal{F}_n$ measurable for all $i \leq n$, W_n is $\mathcal{F}_n$ measurable; and as X_i is integrable and B_i is bounded, W_n is integrable. In the following calculation we take out what is known since B_{n+1} and W_n are both $\mathcal{F}_n$ measurable, and independence drops out since X_{n+1} is independent of $\mathcal{F}_n$. We have

$$\begin{aligned}
\mathbb{E}[W_{n+1}|\mathcal{F}_n] &= \mathbb{E}[W_n + B_{n+1} \cdot X_{n+1}|\mathcal{F}_n] \\
&= \mathbb{E}[W_n|\mathcal{F}_n] + \mathbb{E}[B_{n+1} \cdot X_{n+1}|\mathcal{F}_n] \\
&= W_n + B_{n+1} \cdot \mathbb{E}[X_{n+1}|\mathcal{F}_n] \\
&= W_n + B_{n+1} \cdot \mathbb{E}[X_{n+1}] \\
&= W_n
\end{aligned}$$

and $(W_n)_{n=1}^\infty$ is a martingale on $(\Omega, \mathcal{F}, P)$ adapted to the filtration $(\mathcal{F}_n)_{n=1}^\infty$. By Proposition 9.4, $\mathbb{E}[W_n] = \mathbb{E}[W_1] = \mathbb{E}[B_1 \cdot X_1] = B_1 \cdot \mathbb{E}[X_1] = 0$. Hence no system can turn a fair game into a favorable or unfavorable game.

Example 9.6. Let $(X_n)_{n=1}^\infty$ denote a sequence of independent random variables on $(\Omega, \mathcal{F}, P)$ where $\Omega = (\{-1, +1\}, \mathcal{F} = 2^\Omega, P(\{1\}) = P(\{-1\}) = 1/2$ and X_n takes the values ± 1 with probability $1/2$. Clearly, $\mathbb{E}[X_n] = 0$ and $\mathrm{Var}(X_n) = 1$. The sequence is called a symmetric[6] *random walk*. The terminology is appropriate since one can visualize it as a sequence of steps, each being chosen

---

[5]If $(Y_n)_{n=1}^\infty$ is a stochastic process on $(\Omega, \mathcal{F}, P)$, $(\mathcal{F}_n)_{n=1}^\infty$ is a filtration on $(\Omega, \mathcal{F}, P)$ and Y_n is $\mathcal{F}_{n-1}$ measurable for $n > 1$, then the process is said to be *predictable* or *previsible* with respect to the given filtration. The terminology arises since on any path followed by the process, the value taken by the nth random variable Y_n is *known* at the start of the nth period. A gambling strategy is a predictable process. A hedging strategy that covers claims on an option must be predictable since it has to be in place prior to the contingency it is hedging (see Exercise 9.7).

[6]Symmetric because of $1/2$.

at random to the left or right, independent of the previous choices.[7] As in the previous example it is first necessary to construct a probability space $(\Omega, \mathcal{F}, P)$ on which each X_n is defined and such that $(X_n)_{n=1}^{\infty}$ is a sequence of independent random variables. We have $\Omega = 2^{\mathbf{N}}$, $\mathcal{F}$ is the σ-field generated by $(X_n)_{n=1}^{\infty}$ and P is the product measure. Let $Y_n = \sum_{i=1}^{n} X_i$ for n a positive integer. By Example 9.2, $(Y_n)_{n=1}^{\infty}$ is a martingale.

We now consider the sequence $(Z_n)_{n=1}^{\infty}$ where $Z_n = Y_n^2 - n$ for all n. Since $0 \leq Y_n^2 \leq n^2$ the sequence $(Z_n)_{n=1}^{\infty}$ is a stochastic process of bounded, and hence integrable, random variables adapted to the filtration $(\mathcal{F}_n)_{n=1}^{\infty}$. Since $\mathbb{E}[X_n] = 0$ and $\mathbb{E}[X_n^2] = 1$ we have $\mathbb{E}[Y_n] = \sum_i^n \mathbb{E}[X_n] = 0$ and, by Example 7.13, $\mathbb{E}[Y_n^2] = \mathrm{Var}(Y_n) = n$. Hence $\mathbb{E}[Z_n] = \mathbb{E}[Y_n^2] - n = 0$. It is possible, by Proposition 9.4, that the sequence $(Z_n)_{n=1}^{\infty}$ is a martingale. We have

$$
\begin{aligned}
\mathbb{E}[Z_{n+1}|\mathcal{F}_n] &= \mathbb{E}[Y_{n+1}^2|\mathcal{F}_n] - (n+1) \\
&= \mathbb{E}[Y_n^2 + 2Y_n X_{n+1} + X_{n+1}^2|\mathcal{F}_n] - n - 1 \\
&= \mathbb{E}[Y_n^2|\mathcal{F}_n] + 2\mathbb{E}[Y_n X_{n+1}|\mathcal{F}_n] + \mathbb{E}[X_{n+1}^2|\mathcal{F}_n] - n - 1 \\
&= Y_n^2 + 2Y_n\mathbb{E}[X_{n+1}|\mathcal{F}_n] + \mathbb{E}[X_{n+1}^2|\mathcal{F}_n] - n - 1 \\
&\quad \text{(taking out what is known)} \\
&= Y_n^2 + 2Y_n\mathbb{E}[X_{n+1}] + \mathbb{E}[X_{n+1}^2] - n - 1 \\
&\quad \text{(independence drops out)} \\
&= Y_n^2 + 1 - n - 1 = Z_n
\end{aligned}
$$

and $(Z_n)_{n=1}^{\infty}$ is a martingale.

Constructing a probability measure from a given collection of probability measures, as in the two previous examples, is a standard routine in analyzing infinite sets of random variables. Borel considered this problem in 1909 and, as a result, was the first to construct an infinite product of measures.[8] He was interested in the problem of choosing a number at random in $[0, 1]$. He identified a real number X in $[0, 1]$ with its binary[9] expansion

$$
\frac{1}{2} + \sum_{n=1}^{\infty} \frac{X_n}{2^{n+1}}
$$

---

[7]The random fluctuation of share prices can be attributed to similar random up/down choices by investors (see Chapter 10).

[8]Borel's ideas, as usual, were highly original and intuitively sound. His proof, however, was incomplete and only brought up to standard by Hugo Steinhaus in 1923. Incorrect and incomplete *proofs* are occasionally published in mathematics and do not necessarily imply that the *result* is false. If the reputed result is considered sufficiently important, mathematicians will attempt to provide a correct proof or to show the result is false. Either way, this self-correcting procedure helps mathematics.

[9]The binary expansion of a real number is not unique, but fortunately the set of problem points is countable and has probability 0.

where $|X_n| = 1$ for all n and identified choosing X at random in $[0,1]$ with assigning, with probability $1/2$, the values ± 1 to X_n for all n. The process $(X_n/2^{n+1})_{n=1}^\infty$ moves, at the nth step, a distance $1/2^{n+1}$ to the left or right with probability $1/2$, and hence P_X, which appears as the product measure, should show X uniformly distributed[10] over $[0,1]$. This is the fundamental property of Lebesgue measure, and Borel obtained the product probability measure on $\{-1,+1\}^{\mathbf{N}}$ by transferring Lebesgue measure from $[0,1]$ to the infinite product. It is interesting to note that Borel was implicitly using the axioms for a probability space over twenty years before they were formally introduced by Kolmogorov.

This approach to constructing product measures, by establishing a connection with Lebesgue measure, was frequently used in the first quarter of the 20th century, for instance by Norbert Wiener in constructing a probability measure for Brownian motion. In 1918, P. J. Daniell obtained an independent method for constructing infinite products of probability measures from which one can conclude that the above approach of Borel led to an independent proof of the existence of Lebesgue measure. In 1933, Kolmogorov proved his consistency theorem, which deals with an even more general type of product, a *projective system of probability measures*.

9.2. Martingale Convergence

If $(X_n)_{n=1}^\infty$ is a martingale on $(\Omega, \mathcal{F}, P)$ adapted to the filtration $(\mathcal{F}_n)_{n=1}^\infty$, then $(X_n(\omega))_{n=1}^\infty$ is a sample path for each $\omega \in \Omega$. We investigate if this stabilizes with time, that is whether or not $\lim_{n\to\infty} X_n(\omega)$ exists. In addressing this question we identify many examples of martingales covered by Example 9.3.

Our point of departure is a rather novel approach[11] to convergence of sequences of real numbers and an even more novel application to martingales. In Chapter 6 we saw that a sequence of real numbers $(a_n)_{n=1}^\infty$ converges if and only if $-\infty < \liminf_{n\to\infty} a_n = \limsup_{n\to\infty} a_n < +\infty$. Hence the sequence does not converge if and only if there exists a pair of real numbers a and b with $a < b$

---

[10]A random variable X is uniformly distributed over $[0,1]$ if $P(\{x \in [0,1] : X(x) \in [a,b]\}) = b - a$.

[11]All the results in this section are due to Joseph Leo Doob (1910-2004). Doob was born in Cincinnati, Ohio, and wrote his thesis on complex analysis. He graduated in 1932, but because of the difficult employment situation for pure mathematicians in the US at the time, he accepted a Carnegie fellowship to study the applied area of probability theory during the year 1934-35. In 1935 he obtained an academic position at the University of Illinois (Urbana) and remained there until he retired in 1978. Doob made major contributions to complex analysis, potential theory and probability theory, and found fundamental connections between the three areas. He developed the theory of martingales so that it is today one of the most powerful tools available for analyzing stochastic processes. He showed, moreover, that martingales are just about everywhere, and as a result they are now widely used in many different areas of pure and applied mathematics.

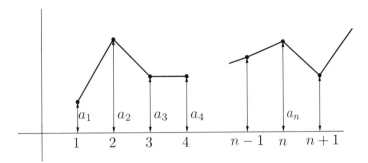

Figure 9.3

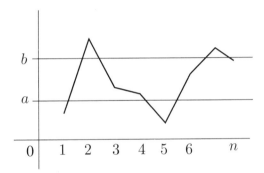

Figure 9.4

such that

(9.3) $$\liminf_{n\to\infty} a_n < a < b < \limsup_{n\to\infty} a_n.$$

We call the set of points obtained by joining (n, a_n) to $(n+1, a_{n+1}), n = 1, 2, \ldots,$ the *graph* of $(a_n)_{n=1}^{\infty}$ (see Figure 9.3).

If (9.3) holds, then the graph contains an infinite number of points above the horizontal line through b and an infinite number of points below the horizontal line through a, and the graph crosses the horizontal strip $[a, b]$ an infinite number of times (see Figure 9.4).

An *upcrossing*[12] occurs when the graph crosses the horizontal strip $[a, b]$ from below to above. We summarize the above.

Lemma 9.7. *A sequence of real numbers converges if and only if $U(a, b)$, the number of upcrossings over $[a, b]$, is finite for every pair of real numbers a and b, $a < b$.*

---

[12]Strictly speaking we should say an $[a, b]$-upcrossing.

We recall, from Definition 6.27, that the space of integrable random variable is denoted by $\mathbf{L}^1(\Omega, \mathcal{F}, P)$. A collection of integrable random variables, $(X_\alpha)_{\alpha \in \Gamma}$ is $\mathbf{L}^1$-*bounded* if

$$\sup_{\alpha \in \Gamma} \mathbb{E}[|X_\alpha|] < \infty.$$

If $(X_n)_{n=1}^\infty$ is a sequence of integrable random variables and there exists an integrable random variable X such that $\lim_{n \to \infty} \mathbb{E}[|X_n - X|] = 0$, then the sequence $(X_n)_{n=1}^\infty$ is said to converge to X in $\mathbf{L}^1(\Omega, \mathcal{F}, P)$. In this case we write $X_n \xrightarrow{\mathbf{L}^1} X$ as $n \longrightarrow \infty$.

Proposition 9.8. *If* $(X_n)_{n=1}^\infty$ *is a martingale*[13] *on* $(\Omega, \mathcal{F}, P)$ *and* $(X_n)_{n=1}^\infty$ *is* $\mathbf{L}^1$ *bounded, then there exists an integrable random variable* X *on* $(\Omega, \mathcal{F}, P)$ *such that* $\lim_{n \to \infty} X_n = X$ *almost surely.*

Proof. Let $A := \{\omega \in \Omega : (X_n(\omega))_{n=1}^\infty \text{ converges}\}$. If $\omega \notin A$, then

$$\liminf_{n \to \infty} X_n(\omega) < \limsup_{n \to \infty} X_n(\omega)$$

and, since the rationals are dense in the real, there exist rational numbers p and q, $p < q$, such that

$$\omega \in A_{p,q} := \{\omega \in \Omega : \liminf_{n \to \infty} X_n(\omega) < p < q < \limsup_{n \longrightarrow \infty} X_n(\omega)\}.$$

Hence, if $P(A_{p,q}) = 0$ for all $p, q \in \mathbf{Q}, p < q$, then, by Exercise 5.2

$$P(A^c) = P(\bigcup_{\{p,q \in \mathbf{Q}, p<q\}} A_{p,q}) \le \sum_{\{p,q \in \mathbf{Q}, p<q\}} P(A_{p,q}) = 0$$

and the sequence $(X_n(\omega))_{n=1}^\infty$ converges almost surely. To complete the proof it suffices to show $P(A_{p,q}) = 0$ for all $p, q \in \mathbf{Q}, p < q$.

For this purpose we consider two players, Sara and Stephen, taking part in a sequence of fair games. We suppose Sara bets one unit on each game. Stephen feels that when Sara's accumulated winnings fall below p her luck will change for the better and that when they rise above q it will change for the worse. His strategy is to observe Sara's accumulated winnings at the end of each game. He places his first bet when her winnings fall below p and keeps betting until her winnings rise above q. He then stops playing and only plays again when her winnings fall below p. He continues with this strategy and always bets one unit. Sara's winnings are given by the martingale $(X_n)_{n=1}^\infty$ where X_n denotes her accumulated winnings at the end of the nth game. If Y_n denotes Stephen's accumulated winnings at the end of the nth game, then $(Y_n)_{n=1}^\infty$ is also a martingale by Example 9.5. Stephen's betting will consist of continuous playing periods followed by waiting periods. We call a *cycle* for Stephen one

---

[13]We assume that the martingale is adapted to the filtration $(\mathcal{F}_n)_{n=1}^\infty$ where $\mathcal{F}_n$ is the σ-field generated by $(X_i)_{i=1}^n$.

full playing period followed by a waiting period. Let U_n denote the number of full cycles that Stephen has completed at the end of the nth game. Since U_n is known by the end of game n, U_n is $\mathcal{F}_n$ measurable and $(U_n)_{n=1}^\infty$ is an *increasing* sequence of random variables. If $U_n = k$, then, over the interval of the first n games we have the following landmarks (Figure 9.5) where u_i is the

Figure 9.5

first game of the ith cycle and v_i is the first game that Stephen does not play in that cycle. Stephen will play the games $\{u_i, \ldots, v_i - 1\}$ and place the same bets as Sara on these games and will not play games $\{v_i, \ldots, u_{i+1} - 1\}$. Since Sara's accumulated winnings are less than p at u_i and greater than q at the beginning of game v_i, Stephen wins at least $(q - p)$ over every completed cycle. We consider the final, possibly uncompleted, cycle. We have two possibilities (see Figure 9.6). In the first case, $u_{k+1} \le n < v_{k+1}$ and Stephen plays all these

Figure 9.6

games. His winnings for these games will match those of Sara and amount to at least $X_n - p$. This may be negative. Hence Stephen's accumulated winnings by the end of game n, Y_n, will be at least $k(q - p) - |X_n - p|$. In the second case we have $v_{k+1} \le n < u_{k+2}$, and Stephen will have completed the playing period of the $(k + 1)^{th}$ cycle. In this case his accumulated winnings will be at least $(k+1)(q-p)$. Since $(k+1)(q-p) \ge k(q-p) - |X_n - p|$ we have, in either case, $Y_n \ge k(q - p) - |X_n - p|$. Hence

$$\mathbb{E}[Y_n] \ge (q - p)\mathbb{E}[U_n] - \mathbb{E}[|X_n - p|].$$

Since $(Y_n)_{n=1}^\infty$ are the winnings on fair games, $\mathbb{E}[Y_n] = 0$, and hence

$$\mathbb{E}[U_n] \le \frac{\mathbb{E}[|X_n - p|]}{q - p} \le \frac{M + |p|}{q - p}$$

where $M = \sup_n \mathbb{E}[|X_n|]$. By the Monotone Convergence Theorem the increasing sequence $(U_n)_{n=1}^\infty$ converges almost surely to an integrable random variable U and $\lim_{n\to\infty} U_n(\omega) < \infty$ almost surely. Since the cycles for Stephen are precisely the $[p, q]$ upcrossings for the sequence $(X_n)_{n=1}^\infty$, we have shown $P(A_{p,q}) = 0$ and hence $\lim_{n\to\infty} X_n = X$ almost surely.

By Fatou's Lemma,[14]

$$\int_\Omega |X|dP = \int_\Omega (\liminf_{n\to\infty} |X_n|)dP \leq \liminf_{n\to\infty} \int_\Omega |X_n|dP \leq M$$

and X is integrable. This completes the proof.   □

The boundedness hypothesis in Proposition 9.8 cannot be removed without some replacement. Let $(X_n)_{n=1}^\infty$ denote a sequence of independent random variables on $(\Omega, \mathcal{F}, P)$ and suppose $P(X_n = n) = P(X_n = -n) = 1/2$ for all n. By Example 9.2, the sequence $(Y_n)_{n=1}^\infty$, $Y_n := \sum_{i=1}^n X_n$, is a martingale. The sequence $(Y_n)_{n=1}^\infty$ does not converge almost surely.

To obtain stronger convergence we place extra conditions on the martingale sequence and at the same time refine Proposition 6.26. For simplicity of notation we write $\{X \geq a\}$ in place of $\{\omega \in \Omega : X(\omega) \geq a\}$.

Lemma 9.9. *Let X denote an integrable random variable on $(\Omega, \mathcal{F}, P)$ and let $(A_n)_{n=1}^\infty \subset \mathcal{F}$. Then*

(a) $\lim_{m\to\infty}(\int_{\{|X|\geq m\}} |X|dP) = 0$;

(b) *if* $\lim_{n\to\infty} P(A_n) = 0$, *then* $\lim_{n\to\infty}(\int_{A_n} |X|dP) = 0$.

Proof. Let $A_m = \{\omega \in \Omega : |X(\omega)| \leq m\}$ and let $X_m = X \cdot \mathbf{1}_{A_m}$ for all m. Then $|X_m| \leq |X|$ and $X_m \to X$ pointwise as $m \to \infty$. By the Dominated Convergence Theorem, $\int_\Omega |X_m|dP \longrightarrow \int_\Omega |X|dP$ as $m \longrightarrow \infty$. Hence

$$0 = \lim_{m\longrightarrow\infty}(\int_\Omega (|X| - |X_m|)dP) = \lim_{m\longrightarrow\infty}(\int_{A_m^c} |X|dP) = \lim_{m\longrightarrow\infty}(\int_{\{|X|>m\}} |X|dP)$$

and this proves[15] (a).

For (b) we first show that for any $\epsilon > 0$ we can find $\delta > 0$ such that,[16] if $A \in \mathcal{F}$ and $P(A) < \delta$, then $\int_A |X|dP < \epsilon$. By (a) we can choose a positive integer m such that $\int_{\{|X|>m\}} |X|dP < \epsilon/2$. Let $\delta = \epsilon/2m$. If $P(A) < \delta$, then $mP(A) < \epsilon/2$ and

$$\begin{aligned}
\int_A |X|dP &= \int_{A\cap\{|X|>m\}} |X|dP + \int_{A\cap\{|X|\leq m\}} |X|dP \\
&\leq (\epsilon/2) + m \cdot P(A) \\
&< \epsilon.
\end{aligned}$$

---

[14]See the proof of Proposition 6.30.

[15]Alternatively, if $\mathbb{E}[|X|] > 0$, let $Q(A) = \int_A |X|dP/\mathbb{E}[|X|]$ for all $A \in \mathcal{F}$. By Proposition 6.26, $(\Omega, \mathcal{F}, Q)$ is a probability space. The sequence $(A_m^c)_{m=1}^\infty$ is decreasing and $\lim_{m\to\infty} A_m^c = \emptyset$. By Proposition 5.3, $\lim_{m\to\infty} Q(A_m^c) = \lim_{m\to\infty} \int_{\{|X|>m\}} |X|dP = 0$.

[16]This property is reminiscent of the definition of uniform continuity, see Proposition 7.7.

If $P(A_n) \longrightarrow 0$ as $n \longrightarrow \infty$, then $P(A_n) < \delta$ and hence $0 \leq \int_{A_n} |X| dP \leq \epsilon$ for all n sufficiently large. Hence $0 \leq \limsup_{n \to \infty} (\int_{A_n} |X| dP) \leq \epsilon$. Since ϵ was arbitrary this proves (b). $\qquad\square$

For our next proposition we require a uniform version of the property established in Lemma 9.9(a).

Definition 9.10. *A set of integrable random variables* $(X_i)_{i \in I}$ *on the probability space* $(\Omega, \mathcal{F}, P)$ *is uniformly integrable if*

$$(9.4) \qquad \lim_{m \longrightarrow \infty} (\sup_{i \in I} \int_{\{|X_i| \geq m\}} |X_i| dP) = 0.$$

Let X denote an integrable random variable on $(\Omega, \mathcal{F}, P)$ and let $(\mathcal{F}_n)_{n=1}^{\infty}$ be a filtration on $(\Omega, \mathcal{F}, P)$. For each positive integer n let $X_n = \mathbb{E}[X|\mathcal{F}_n]$. By Exercise 8.4, $|X_n| \leq \mathbb{E}[|X| \,|\mathcal{F}_n]$ almost surely and for positive integers m and n, $\{\omega \in \Omega : |X_n(\omega)| \geq m\} \in \mathcal{F}_n$. Hence

$$(9.5) \quad mP(|X_n| \geq m) \;\leq\; \int_{\{|X_n| \geq m\}} |X_n| dP \leq \int_{\{|X_n| \geq m\}} \mathbb{E}[\,|X|\,|\mathcal{F}_n] dP$$

$$(9.6) \qquad\qquad\qquad =\; \int_{\{|X_n| \geq m\}} |X| dP \leq \mathbb{E}[|X|].$$

Let ϵ be an arbitrary positive number. By Lemma 9.9 there exists a positive number δ such that $\int_A |X| dP < \epsilon$ whenever $P(A) < \delta$. By (9.5) and (9.6) there exists a positive integer m_0 such that $P(|X_n| \geq m) \leq \mathbb{E}[|X|]/m \leq \delta$ for all $m > m_0$ and all n. Lemma 9.9(b) and further applications of (9.5) and (9.6) show that

$$\int_{\{|X_n| \geq m\}} |X_n| dP \leq \epsilon$$

for all n and all $m > m_0$. Since ϵ was arbitrary this shows that $(X_n)_{n=1}^{\infty}$ is a uniformly integrable sequence of random variables. In the following proposition we prove the converse.

Proposition 9.11. *If* $(X_n)_{n=1}^{\infty}$ *is a martingale on* $(\Omega, \mathcal{F}, P)$ *adapted to the filtration* $(\mathcal{F}_n)_{n=1}^{\infty}$ *and* $(X_n)_{n=1}^{\infty}$ *is uniformly integrable, then there exists an integrable random variable* X *on* $(\Omega, \mathcal{F}, P)$ *such that* $X_n = \mathbb{E}[X|\mathcal{F}_n]$ *almost surely for all* n *and* $X_n \longrightarrow X$ *almost surely and in* $\mathbf{L}^1(\Omega, \mathcal{F}, P)$ *as* $n \longrightarrow \infty$.

Proof. Choose m_1 so that $\int_{\{|X_n| \geq m_1\}} |X_n| dP \leq 1$ for all n. Then

$$\mathbb{E}[|X_n|] = \int_{\{|X_n| \geq m_1\}} |X_n| dP + \int_{\{|X_n| < m_1\}} |X_n| dP \leq 1 + \int_{\Omega} m_1 dP \leq 1 + m_1$$

for all n. Hence $(\mathbb{E}[\,|X_n|\,])_{n=1}^{\infty}$ is bounded and, by Proposition 9.8, $(X_n)_{n=1}^{\infty}$ converges almost surely to an integrable random variable X.

Let $Y_n = |X_n - X|$ for all n. Since $|Y_n| \leq |X_n| + |X|$ for all n the sequence $(Y_n)_{n=1}^{\infty}$ is uniformly integrable. We are required to show that $\mathbb{E}[Y_n] \longrightarrow 0$ as $n \longrightarrow \infty$. Let $\epsilon > 0$ be arbitrary. By uniform integrability we can choose a positive integer m_2 such that $\int_{\{Y_n \geq m_2\}} Y_n dP \leq \epsilon/2$ for all n. Let $A_n := \{\omega \in \Omega : Y_n(\omega) < m_2\}$ and let $Z_n = Y_n \cdot \mathbf{1}_{A_n}$. Then $0 \leq Z_n \leq m_2$ for all n and $(Z_n)_{n=1}^{\infty}$ tends to 0 almost surely as $n \longrightarrow \infty$. By the Dominated Convergence Theorem, $\mathbb{E}[Z_n] \to 0$ as $n \to \infty$. Hence we may choose a positive integer m_3 such that $\mathbb{E}[Z_n] < \epsilon/2$ for all $n \geq m_3$. If $n \geq m_3$, then

$$0 \leq \mathbb{E}[Y_n] = \int_{\{Y_n \geq m_2\}} Y_n dP + \int_{\Omega} Z_n dP \leq \epsilon.$$

Since $\epsilon > 0$ was arbitrary, this proves $X_n \longrightarrow X$ in $\mathbf{L}^1(\Omega, \mathcal{F}, P)$ as $n \longrightarrow \infty$. Let $n \geq m$ and $A \in \mathcal{F}_m$. Since $(X_n)_{n=1}^{\infty}$ is a martingale

$$\int_A \mathbb{E}[X_n | \mathcal{F}_m] dP = \int_A X_m dP,$$

and, by the definition of conditional expectation (see Proposition 8.7),

$$\int_A \mathbb{E}[X_n | \mathcal{F}_m] dP = \int_A X_n dP.$$

Hence

$$\left| \int_A (X_m - X) dP \right| = \left| \int_A (X_n - X) dP \right| \leq \int_{\Omega} |X_n - X| dP.$$

Since $\int_{\Omega} |X_n - X| dP \to 0$ as $n \longrightarrow \infty$ this implies

$$\int_A X_m dP = \int_A X dP$$

for all $A \in \mathcal{F}_m$ and, by Proposition 8.7, $X_m = \mathbb{E}[X | \mathcal{F}_m]$ almost surely. This completes the proof. □

9.3. Continuous Martingales

Continuous martingales are similar to discrete martingales but indexed by intervals.

Definition 9.12. *Let $(\mathcal{F}_t)_{t \in I}$ denote a filtration on $(\Omega, \mathcal{F}, P)$, indexed by an interval I of real numbers, and let $(X_t)_{t \in I}$ denote a set of integrable random variables on $(\Omega, \mathcal{F}, P)$ adapted to the filtration; that is, X_t is $\mathcal{F}_t$ measurable for all $t \in I$. Then $(X_t)_{t \in I}$ is a continuous martingale if $\mathbb{E}[X_t | \mathcal{F}_s] = X_s$ for all $s, t \in I, s \leq t$.*

As in the case of discrete martingales, there is no loss of generality in assuming that $\mathcal{F}_t$ is the σ-field generated by $(X_s)_{s \in I, s \leq t}$. We are interested in two cases $I = [0, T]$, where T is a positive real number, and $I = [0, \infty)$. We can absorb the first case into the second by letting $X_t = X_T$ and $\mathcal{F}_t = \mathcal{F}_T$ for all $t > T$. For this reason we restrict ourselves to continuous martingales over $[0, \infty)$ and use the notation $(X_t)_{t \geq 0}$.

It is helpful to think of I as an interval of time and $\mathcal{F}_t$ as either the history of the process up to time t or as the information available at time t. If $(X_t)_{t \geq 0}$ is a continuous martingale, then $(X_{t_n})_{n=1}^{\infty}$ is a discrete martingale for any strictly increasing sequence of real numbers tending to infinity.

Our first example is similar to Example 9.3 and shows how discrete martingales may be used to interpolate and, as a result, derive results about continuous martingales.

Example 9.13. Let X denote an integrable random variable on $(\Omega, \mathcal{F}, P)$ and let $(\mathcal{F}_t)_{t \geq 0}$ denote a filtration on $(\Omega, \mathcal{F}, P)$. Let $X_t = \mathbb{E}[X | \mathcal{F}_t]$ for all t. If $0 < s < t$, the Tower Law implies

$$\mathbb{E}[X_t | \mathcal{F}_s] = \mathbb{E}[\mathbb{E}[X | \mathcal{F}_t] | \mathcal{F}_s] = \mathbb{E}[X | \mathcal{F}_s] = X_s$$

and $(X_t)_{t \geq 0}$ is a martingale.

Conversely, suppose $(X_t)_{t \geq 0}$ is a martingale adapted to $(\mathcal{F}_t)_{t \geq 0}$ and there exists a strictly increasing sequence of real numbers $(t_n)_{n=1}^{\infty}$, with $t_n \longrightarrow \infty$ as $n \longrightarrow \infty$, such that $(X_{t_n})_{n=1}^{\infty}$ is uniformly integrable. By Proposition 9.11, there exists an integrable random variable X such that $\mathbb{E}[|X_{t_n} - X|] \longrightarrow \infty$ as $n \longrightarrow \infty$ and $\mathbb{E}[X | \mathcal{F}_{t_n}] = X_{t_n}$ for all n. If $t_n > t \geq 0$, the Tower Law and the martingale property imply

$$\mathbb{E}[X | \mathcal{F}_t] = \mathbb{E}[\mathbb{E}[X | \mathcal{F}_{t_n}] | \mathcal{F}_t] = \mathbb{E}[X_{t_n} | \mathcal{F}_t] = X_t.$$

It is now an easy exercise to show that

$$\lim_{t \longrightarrow \infty} \mathbb{E}[|X_t - X|] = 0.$$

This implies[17]

$$\lim_{m \longrightarrow \infty} \left(\sup_{t \geq 0} \int_{\{X_t \geq m\}} |X_t| dP \right) = 0$$

that is, $(X_t)_{t \geq 0}$ is uniformly integrable.

In proving the next proposition, we require the following simple result for normal random variables. The proof relies on completing squares (see Example 7.34). We include it because we use it so often.

---

[17]The proof of the converse shows: if $(X_{t_n})_{n=1}^{\infty}$ is uniformly integrable for *one* sequence $(t_n)_{n=1}^{\infty}$ tending to infinity, then the same is true for *every* sequence tending to infinity.

Lemma 9.14. *If X is an $N(0, \sigma^2)$ random variable, then*

(9.7)
$$\mathbb{E}[e^X] = e^{\frac{1}{2}\sigma^2}.$$

Proof. As X has density $f_X(x) = (\sqrt{2\pi}\sigma)^{-1/2}\exp(-x^2/2\sigma^2)$, Proposition 7.10 implies

$$
\begin{aligned}
\mathbb{E}[e^X] &= \int_{-\infty}^{+\infty} e^x f_X(x)dx = \frac{1}{\sqrt{2\pi}\sigma}\int_{-\infty}^{+\infty} e^x e^{-x^2/2\sigma^2}dx \\
&= \frac{1}{\sqrt{2\pi}\sigma}\int_{-\infty}^{+\infty} e^{-\frac{1}{2\sigma^2}(x^2 - 2x\sigma^2 + \sigma^4) + \sigma^2/2}dx \\
&= \frac{e^{\sigma^2/2}}{\sqrt{2\pi}\sigma}\int_{-\infty}^{+\infty} e^{-\frac{1}{2\sigma^2}(x-\sigma^2)^2}dx \\
&= e^{\sigma^2/2}.
\end{aligned}
$$

This completes the proof. $\qquad\square$

Until now we have taken expected values with respect to a fixed probability measure, but in our next example we use two *different probabilities* on the same measurable space, and it is necessary to introduce notation to distinguish between them. When dealing with measures P and Q on the same measurable space $(\Omega, \mathcal{F})$, we let $\mathbb{E}_P[X]$ and $\mathbb{E}_Q[X]$ denote, respectively, the expected value of the random variable X with respect to the probability measures P and Q, and use similar modified notation for conditional expectations.

The following proposition introduces the process that unravels, in Chapter 10, the stochastic behavior of share prices.

Proposition 9.15. *Let $(W_t)_{t\geq 0}$ denote a collection of random variables on $(\Omega, \mathcal{F}, P)$, and for $t \geq 0$ let $\mathcal{F}_t$ denote the σ-field generated by $(W_s)_{0\leq s\leq t}$. Suppose W_t and $W_t - W_s$ are $N(0,t)$ and $N(0, t-s)$ distributed random variables respectively and $W_t - W_s$ and W_r are independent for all $r, s, t, 0 \leq r \leq s \leq t$. The following hold:*

(a) *$(W_t)_{t\geq 0}$ and $(W_t^2 - t)_{t\geq 0}$ are martingales;*

(b) *if μ and σ are real numbers, then $(e^{\mu t + \sigma W_t})_{t\geq 0}$ is a martingale if and only if $\mu = -\sigma^2/2$;*

(c) *if $\gamma \in \mathbf{R}$, then $(e^{-\frac{1}{2}\gamma^2 t + \gamma W_t})_{t\geq 0}$ is a uniformly integrable set of random variables;*

(d) *if $X_t := e^{-\frac{1}{2}\gamma^2 t + \gamma W_t}$ for $t \geq 0$, then there exists an integrable random variable X_∞ such that $\lim_{n\to\infty} X_{t_n} = X_\infty$ almost surely for any increasing sequence of real numbers $(t_n)_{n=1}^\infty$ which converges to infinity. If $P_\gamma(A) := \int_A X_\infty dP$ when $A \in \mathcal{F}$, then $(\Omega, \mathcal{F}, P_\gamma)$ is a probability* space. If $\mathcal{G}$ is a σ-field on Ω with $\mathcal{G} \subset \mathcal{F}$ and Y is an integrable random variable on $(\Omega, \mathcal{F}, P_\gamma)$, then $\mathbb{E}_{P_\gamma}[Y|\mathcal{G}] = \mathbb{E}_P[X_\infty \cdot Y|\mathcal{G}]$; and if $t \geq s$ and Y is $\mathcal{F}_t$ measurable, then

(9.8)
$$\mathbb{E}_{P_\gamma}[Y|\mathcal{F}_s] = \mathbb{E}_P[X_t \cdot Y|\mathcal{F}_s].$$

Proof. Since W_t is normal both W_t and W_t^2 are integrable for all t (see Exercise 1.3). By our hypotheses $W_t - W_s$ and $(W_t - W_s)^2$ are independent of $\mathcal{F}_s$ for all t and s, $0 \leq s \leq t$. For $0 \leq s \leq t$

$$
\begin{aligned}
\mathbb{E}[W_t|\mathcal{F}_s] &= \mathbb{E}[W_t - W_s|\mathcal{F}_s] + \mathbb{E}[W_s|\mathcal{F}_s] \\
&= \mathbb{E}[W_t - W_s|\mathcal{F}_s] + W_s, \text{ taking out what is known,} \\
&= \mathbb{E}[W_t - W_s] + W_s, \text{ independence drops out,} \\
&= W_s, \text{ since } \mathbb{E}[W_t] = \mathbb{E}[W_s] = 0.
\end{aligned}
$$

Hence $(W_t)_{t \geq 0}$ is a martingale.

For $0 \leq s \leq t$, $W_t^2 = (W_t - W_s)^2 + 2(W_t - W_s)W_s + W_s^2$ and

$$
\begin{aligned}
\mathbb{E}[W_t^2|\mathcal{F}_s] &= \mathbb{E}[(W_t - W_s)^2|\mathcal{F}_s] + 2\mathbb{E}[(W_t - W_s)W_s|\mathcal{F}_s] + \mathbb{E}[W_s^2|\mathcal{F}_s] \\
&= \mathbb{E}[(W_t - W_s)^2|\mathcal{F}_s] + 2W_s\mathbb{E}[W_t - W_s|\mathcal{F}_s] + W_s^2 \\
&\quad \text{(on taking out what is known)} \\
&= \mathbb{E}[(W_t - W_s)^2] + 2W_s\mathbb{E}[W_t - W_s] + W_s^2 \\
&\quad \text{(independence drops out)} \\
&= t - s + 2W_s \cdot 0 + W_s^2 \\
&\quad \text{(since } W_t - W_s \text{ is } N(0, t-s)\text{).}
\end{aligned}
$$

Hence

$$\mathbb{E}[W_t^2 - t|\mathcal{F}_s] = W_s^2 + t - s - t = W_s^2 - s$$

and $(W_t^2 - t)_{t \geq 0}$ is a martingale.[18] This proves (a).

To prove (b) we first suppose that $(e^{\mu t + \sigma W_t})_{t \geq 0}$ is a martingale. From Lemma 9.14, $\mathbb{E}[e^{\mu t + \sigma W_t}] = e^{\mu t} \cdot \mathbb{E}[e^{\sigma W_t}] = e^{(\mu + \sigma^2/2)t}$. Proposition 9.4 easily extends to continuous martingales and implies that $e^{(\mu + \sigma^2/2)t}$ is independent of t. Hence $\mu = -\sigma^2/2$.

---

[18]This proof is very similar to that given in Example 9.6.

Conversely suppose $\mu = -\sigma^2/2$. By Lemma 9.14, $e^{\mu t + \sigma W_t}$ is integrable. If $0 \le s \le t$, then

$$
\begin{aligned}
\mathbb{E}[e^{\sigma W_t} | \mathcal{F}_s] &= \mathbb{E}[e^{\sigma(W_t - W_s)} \cdot e^{\sigma W_s} | \mathcal{F}_s] \\
&= e^{\sigma W_s} \cdot \mathbb{E}[e^{\sigma(W_t - W_s)} | \mathcal{F}_s] \\
&= e^{\sigma W_s} \cdot \mathbb{E}[e^{\sigma(W_t - W_s)}] \\
&= e^{\sigma W_s} \cdot e^{\sigma^2(t-s)/2}
\end{aligned}
$$

and

$$
\begin{aligned}
\mathbb{E}[e^{-\frac{1}{2}\sigma^2 t + \sigma W_t} | \mathcal{F}_s] &= e^{-\sigma^2 t/2} \cdot e^{\sigma^2(t-s)/2} \cdot e^{\sigma W_s} \\
&= e^{-\frac{1}{2}\sigma^2 s + \sigma W_s}.
\end{aligned}
$$

This shows that $(e^{\mu t + \sigma W_t})_{t \ge 0}$ is a martingale if and only if $\mu = -\sigma^2/2$ and proves (b).

We may suppose without loss of generality that $\gamma > 0$. Let m denote a positive number greater than 1. In the following estimate we use the fact that W_t and $\sqrt{t}W_1$ are identically distributed and the fact, easily proved using one variable calculus, that $\min_{t>0}(At^{-1/2} + Bt^{1/2}) = \min_{t>0}(At^{-1} + Bt) = 2\sqrt{AB}$ when A and B are positive. Since W_t and $\sqrt{t}W_1$ are identically distributed

$$
\begin{aligned}
P\Big(\{e^{-\frac{1}{2}\gamma^2 t + \gamma W_t} \ge m\}\Big) &= P\Big(\{W_t \ge \frac{1}{\gamma}\log m + \frac{1}{2}\gamma t\}\Big) \\
&= P\Big(\{W_1 \ge \frac{1}{\gamma\sqrt{t}}\log m + \frac{1}{2}\gamma\sqrt{t}\}\Big) \\
&\le P\Big(\{W_1 \ge \sqrt{2\log m}\}\Big).
\end{aligned}
$$

By Lemma 9.9(a),

$$
\lim_{m \to \infty}\Big(\sup_{t \ge 0} P(\{e^{-\frac{1}{2}\gamma^2 t - \gamma W_t} \ge m\})\Big) \le \lim_{m \to \infty} P\Big(\{W_1 \ge \sqrt{2\log m}\}\Big) = 0
$$

and this proves (c).

By (c), the sequence $(X_{t_n})_{n=1}^{\infty}$ is uniformly integrable and, by Proposition 9.11 and Example 9.13, there exists an integrable random variable X_∞ such that $X_{t_n} \to X_\infty$ almost surely and $\mathbb{E}_P[|X_{t_n} - X_\infty|] \to 0$ as $n \to \infty$. Since $\mathbb{E}[X_{t_n}] = 1$ and $|\mathbb{E}[X_{t_n}] - \mathbb{E}[X_\infty]| \le \mathbb{E}[|X_{t_n} - X_\infty|]$ we have $\mathbb{E}_P[X_\infty] = 1$ and, as $X_{t_n}(\omega) \ge 0$ almost surely for each n, $X_\infty \ge 0$ almost surely. By Proposition 6.26, $P_\gamma(A) := \int_A X_\infty dP$ defines a probability measure on $(\Omega, \mathcal{F})$ and

$$
(9.9) \qquad\qquad \int_A Y dP_\gamma = \int_A X_\infty \cdot Y dP
$$

for all $A \in \mathcal{F}$ and all P_γ integrable random variables Y. By Proposition 8.7, $\mathbb{E}_{P_\gamma}[Y|\mathcal{G}]$ is almost surely the unique $\mathcal{G}$ measurable random variable on Ω satisfying

$$(9.10) \qquad \int_A \mathbb{E}_{P_\gamma}[Y|\mathcal{G}]dP_\gamma \;=\; \int_A Y dP_\gamma$$

and $\mathbb{E}_P[X_\infty \cdot Y|\mathcal{G}]$ is almost surely the unique $\mathcal{G}$ measurable random variable on Ω satisfying

$$(9.11) \qquad \int_A \mathbb{E}_P[X_\infty Y|\mathcal{G}]dP \;=\; \int_A X_\infty Y dP$$

for all $A \in \mathcal{G}$. By (9.9), (9.10) and (9.11), $\mathbb{E}_{P_\gamma}[Y|\mathcal{G}] = \mathbb{E}_P[X_\infty \cdot Y|\mathcal{G}]$ almost surely as random variables on $(\Omega, \mathcal{G}, P)$.

If Y is $\mathcal{F}_t$ measurable and $t \geq s$, then

$$
\begin{aligned}
\mathbb{E}_{P_\gamma}[Y|\mathcal{F}_s] &= \mathbb{E}_P[X_\infty \cdot Y|\mathcal{F}_s] \\
&= \mathbb{E}_P[\mathbb{E}_P[X_\infty \cdot Y|\mathcal{F}_t]|\mathcal{F}_s] \\
&\qquad \text{(by the Tower Law since } \mathcal{F}_s \subset \mathcal{F}_t) \\
&= \mathbb{E}_P[Y \cdot \mathbb{E}_P[X_\infty|\mathcal{F}_t]|\mathcal{F}_s] \\
&\qquad \text{(taking out what is known)} \\
&= \mathbb{E}_P[Y \cdot X_t|\mathcal{F}_s] \\
&\qquad \text{(by Example 9.13, } \mathbb{E}_P[X_\infty|\mathcal{F}_t] = X_t).
\end{aligned}
$$

This proves (9.8) and completes the proof. $\qquad\qquad\qquad\qquad\qquad \square$

9.4. Exercises

(9.1) Let T denote a fixed positive number, let $(\mathcal{F}_t)_{0 \leq t \leq T}$ denote a filtration and let X denote an integrable $\mathcal{F}_T$ measurable random variable on $(\Omega, \mathcal{F}, P)$. For $0 \leq t \leq T$ let $X_t = \mathbb{E}[X|\mathcal{F}_t]$ and for $t \geq T$ let $X_t = X_T$ and $\mathcal{F}_t = \mathcal{F}_T$. Show that $(X_t)_{t \geq 0}$ is a martingale adapted to the filtration $(\mathcal{F}_t)_{t \geq 0}$.

(9.2) Let $(W_t)_{t \geq 0}$ denote a martingale on $(\Omega, \mathcal{F}, P)$ with respect to the filtration $(\mathcal{F}_t)_{t \geq 0}$. If $W_t - W_s$ and W_r are independent and $W_t - W_s$ is $N(0, t - s)$ for all $r, s, t, 0 \leq r \leq s \leq t$, show that $(W_t^3 - 3tW_t)_{t \geq 0}$ is a martingale.

(9.3) If $(X_n)_{n=1}^\infty$ is a martingale on $(\Omega, \mathcal{F}, P)$ adapted to the filtration $(\mathcal{F}_n)_{n=1}^\infty$, show, using Exercise 8.9 or otherwise, that $\mathbb{E}[X_n^2|\mathcal{F}_j] \geq X_j^2$ almost surely for all $n \geq j$.

(9.4) Let $(X_n)_{n=1}^\infty$ denote a martingale on $(\Omega, \mathcal{F}, P)$ adapted to the filtration $(\mathcal{F}_n)_{n=1}^\infty$. For fixed $t > 0$ let $A_j := \{\omega \in \Omega : |X_i(\omega)| \leq t \text{ for } i < j, |X_j(\omega)| > t\}$. Show that $P(\{\omega : \sup_{i \leq n} |X_i(\omega)| > t\}) = \sum_{j=0}^n P(A_j)$. By conditioning on $\mathcal{F}_j$ show that

$$\mathbb{E}[\mathbf{1}_{A_j}|X_n|] \geq \mathbb{E}[\mathbf{1}_{A_j}|X_j|] \geq tP(A_j).$$

Hence deduce the *Doob-Kolmogorov Inequality*:

$$P(\sup_{j \leq n} |X_j| > t) \leq \frac{1}{t}\mathbb{E}[\,|X_n|\,].$$

(9.5) Let $(X_n)_{n=1}^{\infty}$ denote a sequence of independent integrable random variables on the probability space $(\Omega, \mathcal{F}, P)$ and suppose $\mathbb{E}[X_n] = 1$ for all n. If $\mathcal{F}_n$ is the σ-field generated by $(X_i)_{i=1}^{n}$ and $Y_n = X_1 \cdots X_n$, show that $(Y_n)_{n=1}^{\infty}$ is a martingale.

(9.6) Let $(X_n)_{n=1}^{\infty}$ be a sequence of independent random variables on $(\Omega, \mathcal{F}, P)$. If $\theta \in \mathbf{R}$, $\mathcal{F}_n$ is the σ-field generated by $(X_j)_{j=1}^{n}$, $\phi(\theta) = \mathbb{E}[e^{\theta X_n}] < \infty$ and $Y_n = \sum_{j=1}^{n} X_n$, show that $(e^{\theta Y_n}/\phi(\theta)^n)_{n=1}^{\infty}$ is a martingale with respect to the filtration $(\mathcal{F}_n)_{n=1}^{\infty}$.

(9.7) Let $(X_n)_{n=0}^{\infty}$ denote a sequence of integrable random variables on $(\Omega, \mathcal{F}, P)$ adapted to the filtration $(\mathcal{F}_n)_{n=0}^{\infty}$ where $X_0 = 0$ and $\mathcal{F}_0 = \mathcal{F}_\emptyset$. For $n \geq 1$ let $Y_n = \sum_{i=1}^{n} \mathbb{E}[X_i - X_{i-1}|\mathcal{F}_{i-1}]$ and $Z_n = X_n - Y_n$. Show that $(Y_n)_{n=1}^{\infty}$ is a previsible process: that is Y_{n+1} is $\mathcal{F}_n$ measurable for $n \geq 1$, and that $(Z_n)_{n=1}^{\infty}$ is a martingale with respect to the filtration $(\mathcal{F}_n)_{n=1}^{\infty}$.

Chapter 10

The Black-Scholes Formula

Just as the model helped shape the markets, the markets in turn helped shape the evolving model.

Robert Merton

Summary

We examine share prices as random variables and derive the Black-Scholes formula for pricing a call option in two different ways. Brownian motion or Wiener processes are introduced and used in our analysis.

10.1. Share Prices as Random Variables

The main ideas in this section are due to Louis Bachelier (1870-1946), now recognized as the founder of financial mathematics. From La Harvé in France, he defended his thesis *Théorie de la Spéculation* in 1900 in Paris. He had remarkable intuition and insight, and it took mathematicians several decades to make mathematically rigorous his conclusions. Although the most eminent French mathematician at the time, Henri Poincaré, examined and had a high opinion of his thesis, Bachelier's mathematical presentation lacked rigor. As a result his reputation suffered among French academics, and he did not obtain the recognition or the academic positions he deserved. Scholarships, arranged by Borel, and part-time lecturing apparently kept him going during the period 1900-1914. He served as a conscript in the French army during World War I and afterwards moved from one provincial French university to another (Besançon, Dijon, Rennes) until finally returning in 1927 to a permanent position in Besançon.

Bachelier used random walks to show that share prices followed a Brownian motion and proposed a method that gives a good approximation for pricing certain short-term options. He introduced the key differential equations, now called the Chapman-Kolmogorov diffusion equations, used in pricing options. Bachelier's mathematical results made an impact outside France and motivated Kolmogorov in his development of stochastic processes, but he was practically forgotten by the financial world until the American economist, Paul Samuelson[1], read his thesis in the mid-fifties. Samuelson also observed that *geometric Brownian motion*,[2] rather than simple Brownian motion as proposed by Bachelier, gave a more accurate long-term stochastic description of the movement of share prices.

We now know that many other natural phenomena behave in the same erratic way as share prices, e.g. the diffusion of gases, the dispersion of smoke, etc. The common feature in all these phenomena is that change is brought about by a large number of *independent* forces, molecules in the case of gases and investors in the case of share prices, each of which is *individually negligible*. The best-known example is due to Robert Brown,[3] who, in 1827, observed ceaseless and irregular movement within pollen grains suspended in water. This gave rise to the terminology "Brownian movement" or "Brownian motion", as it is now more commonly called[4] by physicists.

We return to our task of pricing a call option. In Chapters 5 and 8 we assumed the share price could achieve only a small finite set of values at a

---

[1]Paul Samuelson (b. 1915) won the Nobel Prize for economics in 1970. He is noted for bringing mathematical and literary clarity to economics, and his undergraduate textbook *Economics: an Introductory Analysis* is the best-selling economics textbook of all time.

[2]Discussed later in this chapter.

[3]Brownian motion was first observed by Antony van Leeuwenhoeck (1632-1723) from Delft (Holland). Leeuwenhoeck had no scientific training and was a draper by trade. His endless curiosity, patience, skill, acute eyesight and sensitivity to shades of lighting led him to many important discoveries in biology, including bacteria, blood cells and Brownian motion. Robert Brown (1773-1858) was a medical doctor and botanist from Scotland who founded and ran the botany section of the British Museum from 1827 until his death. A methodical and thorough scientist, he established, contrary to the belief of many at the time, the non-biological nature of Brownian motion and thus showed, for the first time, the active nature of molecules.

[4]In 1905 Einstein proposed a satisfactory statistical model for the diffusion of gases which turned out to be the same as Bachelier's model for share prices. This was one of three influential papers that Einstein wrote in 1905 while working in isolation and obscurity in a patent office in Bern. The second explained the electromagnetic radiation of light using quantum theory, while the final paper introduced the special theory of relativity. To paraphrase Bill Bryson, *A Short History of Nearly Everything*, Doubleday, London-New York, 2003, *the first showed that atoms existed, the second made television possible while the third merely changed the world.* Albert Einstein (1879-1955) is the most famous theoretical physicist of the 20th century and was awarded the Nobel Prize for physics in 1921.

number of specified future times. To remove this artificial assumption and build a more realistic model, we examine the share price as a random variable.

Consider a company quoted on the stock market with share price X_t at time t where $t = 0$ is the present, $t < 0$ the past and $t > 0$ the future. Our plan is to use the history of the company and the share price to make at time $t = 0$ reasonable assumptions about the future. Since share prices are always positive, we let $X_t = X_0 \cdot e^{A_t}$ where A_t may take any real value. If r is the interest rate and the share price followed this growth rate *exactly*, then $X_t = X_0 \cdot e^{rt}$. However, the value of each company has its own *internal* rate of growth, the *drift μ*, which may well be different from the rate of interest. For simplicity we suppose that the drift is constant; in practice it will be a function of t. Since the share price is a fixed fraction of the perceived *value* of the company, the drift will reflect itself in the share price, but the share price is also subject to a large number of *independent random changes* brought about by investors. We suppose that these independent random changes are *equally likely* to move the share price in either direction, up or down. Let Z_t be the random variable brought about by these independent random changes. Thus we have two components which affect the share price, $e^{\mu t}$ and e^{Z_t}, where $\mathbb{E}[Z_t] = 0$.

Changes in share prices are usually considered as a *proportion* of the current price.[5] This implies

$$X_t = X_0 \cdot e^{\mu t} \cdot e^{Z_t} = X_0 \cdot \exp\left(\mu t + Z_t\right).$$

It is reasonable to suppose that the spread of values taken by Z_t, that is $\mathrm{Var}(Z_t)$, is finite and strictly positive. Different stocks, however, do have different spreads or variances, with the more speculative stocks having share prices with bigger swings. As t increases Z_t has more time to wander, and thus it is safe to suppose that $\mathrm{Var}(Z_t)$ is an increasing function of t. Observations of different share prices over many periods of time suggest that $\mathrm{Var}(Z_t)$ will behave like $tf(t)$ where $f(t)$ is fairly regular, for example continuous and bounded away from both 0 and ∞. For simplicity, we suppose that $f(t)$ is constant and strictly positive. Thus for each stock we have a constant σ such that $\mathrm{Var}(Z_t) = \mathbb{E}[Z_t^2] = \sigma^2 t$. We call σ the *volatility* of the stock.[6] The parameters μ and σ are required in our analysis, but the formula for pricing an option will involve only the volatility.[7]

---

[5]This is normal in any commercial transaction. In buying a car we look for the percentage increase on last year or the percentage discount on offer.

[6]If $\sigma = 0$, then $X_t = X_0 \exp\left(\mu t\right)$ and the share price is non-random.

[7]There is no universally agreed method for calculating volatility and the topic is currently an active research area. One method, used by French traders in the 19th century and known to Bachelier, is to use (*average deviation of the share price over* $[-T, 0])/\sqrt{T}$) as an estimate for σ. It is a surprise that the drift does not appear in the Black-Scholes formula for pricing an option. This is related to the fact that the expected return in a fair game should not drift up or down. The drift is used in the

The case $\sigma = 1$ may be regarded as the unit measure of volatility. We let $Z_t = \sigma W_t$. This implies $\mathbb{E}[W_t] = 0$, $\mathbb{E}[W_t^2] = t$, and

$$X_t = X_0 \cdot \exp\left(\mu t + \sigma W_t\right).$$

The random or probabilistic component of the share price, on which we now concentrate, is encoded in W_t. We make similar assumptions to those already employed in Examples 5.5 and 8.1 and follow the approach used in those examples. Suppose investors act independently over disjoint time intervals and that their behavior over a given time interval depends only on the length of the interval. Fix $t > 0$ and divide the time interval $[0, t]$ into a large number, n, of subintervals of equal length $\Delta t = t/n$. By our assumptions W_t is the limit of equally likely independent up/down discrete jumps of size Δx on each subinterval as $n \longrightarrow \infty$ (Figure 10.1). Let B_j^n denote the random variable which

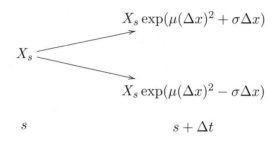

Figure 10.1

records the movement on the jth subinterval. This is similar to the situation for symmetric random walks discussed in Example 9.6. Hence

$$P[B_j^n = \Delta x] = P[B_j^n = -\Delta x] = 1/2,$$

$$\mathbb{E}[B_j^n] = \frac{1}{2}(\Delta x) + \frac{1}{2}(-\Delta x) = 0,$$

$$\mathrm{Var}(B_j^n) = \mathbb{E}[(B_j^n)^2] = \frac{1}{2}(\Delta x)^2 + \frac{1}{2}(-\Delta x)^2 = (\Delta x)^2.$$

The cumulative effect of these independent jumps is $\sum_{j=1}^{n} B_j^n$ and

$$\mathbb{E}[\sum_{j=1}^{n} B_j^n] = \sum_{j=1}^{n} \mathbb{E}[B_j^n] = 0.$$

analysis leading to the Black-Scholes formula. In practise the volatility is usually non-constant and may even be a random variable.

The sequence $(B_j^n)_{j=1}^n$ consists of identically distributed independent random variables and Example 7.13 implies

$$\text{Var}(\sum_{j=1}^n B_j^n) = n \cdot \text{Var}(B_j^n) = n \cdot (\Delta x)^2.$$

Since $\sum_{j=1}^n B_j^n$ tends to W_t as $n \longrightarrow \infty$ it is reasonable to suppose that

$$n \cdot (\Delta x)^2 = \text{Var}(\sum_{j=1}^n B_j^n) \longrightarrow \text{Var}(W_t) = t$$

as $n \longrightarrow \infty$. It is thus convenient, and it can be justified, to let $(\Delta x)^2 = \Delta t = t/n$ or, equivalently, $\sqrt{n}(\Delta x) = \sqrt{\Delta t}$. By the Central Limit Theorem, Proposition 7.19,

$$\lim_{n \longrightarrow \infty} P\Big[\frac{\sum_{j=1}^n B_j^n}{\sqrt{t}} \leq x\Big] = \frac{1}{\sqrt{2\pi}} \int_{-\infty}^{x} e^{-\frac{1}{2}y^2} dy$$

for any real number x. Hence $W_t/\sqrt{t}$ is an $N(0,1)$ distributed random variable and W_t is $N(0,t)$. The following proposition summarizes our progress.

Proposition 10.1. *If $(X_t)_{t\geq 0}$ is the process that gives the share price of a stock at time t, then, under the above assumptions, there exists a constant μ, the drift, and a constant σ, the volatility, such that*

$$X_t = X_0 \exp(\mu t + \sigma W_t)$$

where W_t is a normal random variable with mean 0 and variance t.

An analysis similar to the above shows that the process $(W_t)_{t\geq 0}$ has the following properties:

(a) $W_0 = 0$ almost surely;

(b) W_t is $N(0,t)$ distributed for all $t \geq 0$ (*Gaussian increments*);

(c) for any n and any $\{0 = t_0 < t_1 < \ldots < t_{n+1}\}$, $(W_{t_i} - W_{t_{i-1}})_{i=1}^n$ is a set of independent random variables (*independent increments*);

(d) the probability distribution of $W_t - W_s$ depends only on $t - s$ for $0 \leq s \leq t$ (*stationary increments*).

A stochastic process satisfying the above properties was originally called *Brownian motion*. Processes with stationary independent increments and continuous sample paths (see Chapter 11) were studied by Norbert Wiener and afterwards called *Wiener processes*. It was later shown that Brownian motion and Wiener processes are identical, and as a result both terms are used interchangeably today.[8] If $0 \leq s \leq t$, then (a) and (c) imply $W_t - W_s, W_{t-s} - W_0$ and W_{t-s} are identically distributed random variables and, by (b), $W_t - W_s$ is $N(0, t - s)$.

We are now in a familiar situation;[9] we have a collection of random variables, in fact an uncountable collection, about which we have certain probabilistic information but do not have a probability space $(\Omega, \mathcal{F}, P)$ in which to analyze this information. Wiener constructed a suitable measure in 1923 and completed the process of making mathematically rigorous the work of Bachelier and Einstein. He proved that almost surely paths are continuous and almost surely nowhere differentiable, results that have ramifications in Chapter 11. Because of these contributions, we use the expression Wiener process.

We briefly outline a construction[10] of this measure. For each positive number t, $W_t(x) = x$ for all $x \in \mathbf{R}$ is an $N(0, t)$ distributed random variable on $(\mathbf{R}, \mathcal{B}(\mathbf{R}), P_t)$ where $P_t(A) = (1/\sqrt{2\pi t}) \int_A \exp(-x^2/2t) dx$ for any Borel subset A of $\mathbf{R}$ and any $t > 0$ and $P_0(\{0\}) = 1$. If $(t_i)_{i=0}^n$ is a finite increasing sequence of positive real numbers, with $t_0 = 0$, then $(W_{t_i} - W_{t_{i-1}})_{i=1}^n$ is a set of independent random variables and, as in Propositions 5.16 and 7.32, there exists a product probability measure $P_{\mathbf{t}}$ on $(\mathbf{R}^n, \mathcal{B}(\mathbf{R}^n))$ where[11] $\mathbf{t} = \{t_0, \ldots, t_n\}$ such that

$$P_{\mathbf{t}}(A_1 \times \cdots \times A_n) = P_{t_1 - t_0}(A_1) \times \cdots \times P_{t_n - t_{n-1}}(A_n)$$

for any finite collection, $(A_i)_{i=1}^n$, of Borel subsets of $\mathbf{R}$. If $\mathbf{x} = (x_1, \ldots, x_n) \in \mathbf{R}^n$ and we identify $W_{t_i} - W_{t_{i-1}}$ with the random variable $\mathbf{x} \in \mathbf{R}^n \mapsto (W_{t_i} - W_{t_{i-1}})(x_i)$ for all $i, 1 \leq i \leq n$, then $(W_{t_i} - W_{t_{i-1}})_{i=1}^n$ is a set of independent random variables on the product probability space $(\mathbf{R}^n, \mathcal{B}(\mathbf{R}^n), P_{\mathbf{t}})$ and we have the following consistency condition: if $t_{n+1} \geq t_n$ and $\mathbf{t}' = (\mathbf{t}, t_{n+1})$, then

$$\lim_{x_{n+1} \to +\infty} P_{\mathbf{t}'}(\mathbf{x} \in \mathbf{R}^{n+1} : W_{t_i} \leq x_i, i \leq n+1) = P_{\mathbf{t}}(\mathbf{x} \in \mathbf{R}^n : W_{t_i} \leq x_i, i \leq n).$$

---

[8]Important mathematical results are frequently named after those who discovered them, but sometimes results may be due, independently or in collaboration, to more than one person. This can result in more than one suitable name for the same result, but generally, over time and through usage, one title tends to dominate. For instance the probabilist William Feller called the *Radon-Nikodým Theorem* the *Lebesgue-Nikodým Theorem* and the *Wiener process* the *Bachelier-Wiener process*, and many authors refer to the *Black-Scholes formula* as the *Black-Scholes-Merton formula*. Norbert Wiener (1896-1964) was a child prodigy from Boston who graduated from high school at 11, from university at 14 and received his Ph.D. at 18. He had a wide range of interests: pure and applied mathematics, theoretical physics, communications, and philosophy. Wiener was full of tremendous ideas and great insight and intuition and initiated the subject *cybernetics*. He talked non-stop but was, at least to many people, a poor communicator, and it was said of him: *he spoke many languages but was not easy to understand in any of them.*

[9]See Examples 5.15, 9.5 and 9.6 and Propositions 5.16 and 7.32.

[10]Not the original construction of Wiener, who obtained his results using Lebesgue measure prior to the introduction of the axiomatic approach to probability theory by Kolmogorov.

[11]$\mathcal{B}(\mathbf{R}^n)$ is the Borel σ-field on $\mathbf{R}^n$ generated by the sets $(a_1 - b_1) \times \ldots \times (a_n - b_n)$ where a_i and b_i range over all real numbers, $a_i < b_i, 1 \leq i \leq n$.

Kolmogorov's Consistency Theorem shows that the required probability space exists. The sample space Ω is the uncountable product space $\mathbf{R}^{[0,\infty)}$. A typical point $\omega \in \Omega$ has the form $(\omega_t)_{t \geq 0}$ and may be identified with the function or path $t \in \mathbf{R} \mapsto \omega_t$. Thus Ω is the space of *sample paths*. The σ-field $\mathcal{F}_\infty$ is the smallest σ-field on Ω for which the functions $\omega \in \Omega \mapsto \omega_t \in \mathbf{R}$ are measurable for all $t \geq 0$. We identify W_t with the function $\omega \mapsto \omega_t$; that is $W_t(\omega) = \omega_t$ for all $\omega \in \Omega$ and all $t \geq 0$. We call the measure constructed a *Wiener measure* and denote it by W. If $\mathcal{F}_t$ denotes the σ-field generated by $(W_s)_{0 \leq s \leq t}$, then $(W_t)_{t \geq 0}$ is a stochastic process on the probability space $(\Omega, \mathcal{F}_\infty, W)$ adapted to the filtration $(\mathcal{F}_t)_{t \geq 0}$. The following proposition is an upgrading of Proposition 10.1 incorporating the results of Wiener.

Proposition 10.2. *If $(W_t)_{t \geq 0}$ is a Wiener process, then there exists a probability space $(\mathbf{R}^{[0,\infty)}, \mathcal{F}_\infty, W)$, a filtration on $(\mathbf{R}^{[0,\infty)}, \mathcal{F}_\infty, W)$, $(\mathcal{F}_t)_{t \geq 0}$, such that $(W_t)_{t \geq 0}$ is a stochastic process adapted to the filtration. Moreover, paths of the process are almost surely continuous and almost surely nowhere differentiable[12] with respect to the measure W.*

By Proposition 9.15, $(W_t)_{t \geq 0}$ and $(W_t^2 - t)_{t \geq 0}$ are martingales. Paul Lévy characterized Wiener processes as those processes $(X_t)_{t \geq 0}$ with $X_0 = 0$ and almost surely continuous sample paths such that $(X_t)_{t \geq 0}$ and $(X_t^2 - t)_{t \geq 0}$ are martingales. The ability of Wiener processes to model many different natural phenomena and admit different non-trivial mathematical characterizations is evidence of their intrinsic importance within both pure and applied mathematics.

The process $(\mu t + \sigma W_t)_{t \geq 0}$ is called *Brownian motion with drift*, while the process $(C \exp(\mu t + \sigma W_t))_{t \geq 0}$ is called *geometric or exponential Brownian motion*. If interest is a constant rate r, then the discounted share price

$$(10.1) \qquad\qquad e^{-rt} X_t = X_0 \exp\left((\mu - r)t + \sigma W_t\right)$$

is a random variable on $(\mathbf{R}^{[0,\infty)}, \mathcal{F}_\infty, W)$ and $(e^{-rt} X_t)_{t \geq 0}$ is a stochastic process adapted to the filtration generated by the Wiener process. For a fair price, the buyer requires, by (8.26), the discounted share price to be a martingale. However, by Proposition 9.15(b), this will occur only when $\mu - r = -\sigma^2/2$. This shows that the particular Wiener measure we have constructed is not the required risk neutral probability measure. In the next two sections we rectify this matter.

---

[12]That is there exist $\mathcal{F}_\infty$-measurable subsets A and B of $\mathbf{R}^{[0,\infty)}$, such that $W(A) = W(B) = 1$, and the mappings $t \mapsto \omega_t$ are continuous for all $\omega \in A$ and nowhere differentiable for all $\omega \in B$.

10.2. Call Options 3

We are now ready to present the main result in this book, the *Black-Scholes formula* for pricing a call option. As the history of this formula and the background of the main participants is well documented elsewhere[13] we limit ourselves to a few brief comments. Many attempts were made to find such a formula and many economists came close, but it was two young financial economists, Fisher Black (1938-1995) and Myron Scholes (b. 1941), with important contributions from Robert Merton (b. 1944), who finally put it all together in the early nineteen seventies. Black's undergraduate degree was in physics, and he obtained a Ph.D. from Harvard in applied mathematics. While working as a financial consultant for Arthur D. Little in Cambridge (Mass.) he developed an interest in warrant[14] pricing. Scholes[15] from Ontario (Canada) studied economics as an undergraduate at McMaster University (Hamilton) and wrote his doctoral thesis at the University of Chicago on the role of arbitrage in the securities market. In 1968 he became an assistant professor at M.I.T. (Boston) and during his first year there he met Black. Merton, from New York, studied Engineering Mathematics at Columbia University and obtained a master's degree in applied mathematics at the California Institute of Technology. In 1967 he went to Boston and enrolled as a graduate student in economics at M.I.T., where he progressed rapidly from student to research assistant to collaborator with Paul Samuelson. His interest in dynamic portfolio selection led him to the Itô calculus as the appropriate mathematics to model a hedging strategy (see Chapter 11). In 1969, while being interviewed for a position at M.I.T., Merton met Scholes and the three began collaborating on their common interest, *asset and derivative pricing models.* In their seminal 1973 paper,[16] Black and Scholes gave two derivations of the Black-Scholes formula: one based on the Capital Asset Pricing Model[17] and the other based on hedging ideas due to Merton, who also published an important paper on the same topic in 1973. Robert Merton and Myron Scholes were awarded the Nobel Prize for economics in 1997, and it is

---

[13]For instance in P. Bernstein, *Capital Ideas: The Improbable Origins of Wall Street*, The Free Press, New York; and P. Boyle, F. Boyle, *Derivatives*, Risk Books, 2001.

[14]Basically an option issued by a company on its own stock.

[15]Myron Scholes and Norbert Wiener both had eye problems in their youth which restricted their reading. Both used this handicap to their advantage, in more or less the same way. To quote Scholes *It was difficult to read for extended periods of time. I learned to think abstractly and to conceptualize the solution to problems.*

[16]The fundamental papers are F. Black, M. Scholes, *The Pricing of Options and Corporate Liabilities,* Journal of Political Economy, 81, pp. 637-674, 1973; and R. Merton, *Theory of Rational Option Pricing,* Bell Journal of Economics and Management Science, 4, pp. 141-183, 1973. The first version of the Black-Scholes paper was dated October 1970 and was twice rejected for publication. Merton, who referred in his paper to the Black-Scholes paper, delayed publication so that it would not appear before the Black-Scholes paper. Both papers appeared at practically the same time.

[17]Derived from the basic principle that prices are determined by *supply* and *demand.*

generally agreed that Fisher Black would have received the same honor if he had been alive in 1997.

We now proceed to price a call option so that it represents a fair price for the buyer.[18] Let r, T and k denote, respectively, the interest rate, the maturity date and the strike price of a call option. By our results in Example 8.10, we need to show that there exists a probability measure, call it P_N, on the measurable space $(\mathbf{R}^{[0,\infty)}, \mathcal{F}_\infty)$ such that

$$(10.2) \qquad (e^{-rt}X_t)_{t\geq 0} \text{ is a martingale on } (\mathbf{R}^{[0,\infty)}, \mathcal{F}_\infty, P_N),$$

and afterwards we need to evaluate

$$(10.3) \qquad \mathbb{E}_{P_N}[e^{-rT}(X_T - k)^+|\mathcal{F}_0] \;=\; \mathbb{E}_{P_N}[e^{-rT}(X_T - k)^+].$$

Note that (10.3) holds because $\mathcal{F}_0 = \mathcal{F}_\emptyset$ and gives a fair price for the buyer since $(\mathbb{E}_{P_N}[e^{-rT}(X_T-k)^+|\mathcal{F}_t])_{0\leq t\leq T}$ is a martingale by Example 9.3 and Exercise 9.1. In particular, we do not require an explicit formula for P_N. It is natural, in view of Proposition 5.6 and Example 8.1, to combine the finite binomial approach to risk neutral probabilities developed in Chapters 5 and 8 with the limiting procedure used to derive Proposition 10.1 in order to find P_N.

We assume that the stock has drift μ and strictly positive volatility σ. We partition the interval $[0, t]$ into n adjacent subintervals, each of length $\Delta t = t/n$. As noted in the previous section, the share price changes on each subinterval by a factor $\exp(\mu\Delta t \pm \sigma\Delta x)$ where $(\Delta x)^2 = \Delta t$. To simplify calculations and to avoid square roots and a second variable, we write this in the form $\exp(\mu(\Delta x)^2 \pm \sigma\Delta x)$ and use the approximations $\exp x \approx 1 + x + (x^2/2)$ and $\exp(-x) \approx 1 - x + (x^2/2)$, neglecting higher powers. By Proposition 5.6, the risk neutral probability, p, that the discounted share price rises by Δx over a typical subinterval $[s, s + \Delta t]$ so that a fair price is maintained or equivalently that the martingale property is satisfied (see Figure 10.2), is given by

$$\begin{aligned}
p &= \frac{e^{r(\Delta x)^2} - e^{\mu(\Delta x)^2 - \sigma\Delta x}}{e^{\mu(\Delta x)^2 + \sigma\Delta x} - e^{\mu(\Delta x)^2 - \sigma\Delta x}} \\
&= \frac{e^{(r-\mu)(\Delta x)^2} - e^{-\sigma\Delta x}}{e^{\sigma\Delta x} - e^{-\sigma\Delta x}} \\
&\approx \frac{(r - \mu)(\Delta x)^2 + \sigma\Delta x - \sigma^2(\Delta x)^2/2}{\sigma\Delta x + \sigma^2(\Delta x)^2/2 + \sigma\Delta x - \sigma^2(\Delta x)^2/2} \\
&= \frac{\sigma + (r - \mu - \sigma^2/2)\Delta x}{2\sigma}
\end{aligned}$$

---

[18]A second, independent, approach using martingales is given in the next section. In Chapter 11 we show that there exists a hedging strategy for any claim on the option and thus it is also a fair price for the seller.

$$= \frac{1}{2}\Big(1 + \frac{(r - \mu - \frac{\sigma^2}{2})}{\sigma}\Delta x\Big).$$

The above shows that

(10.4) $$p = \frac{1}{2}(1 + \frac{(r - \mu - \frac{\sigma^2}{2})}{\sigma}\Delta x) + f(\Delta x)$$

where $|f(x)| \leq c|x|^2$ for some constant $c > 0$ and all x close to 0. We neglect the term $f(\Delta x)$ in (10.4) and use instead the approximate value for p in our analysis. It is a simple exercise to show that this also leads to Proposition 10.3.

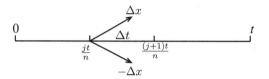

Figure 10.2

Let A_j^n denote the random variable on the jth interval which takes the value $\sigma\Delta x$ with probability p and the value $-\sigma\Delta x$ with probability $1 - p$. The change in the discounted share price over $[0, t]$ is given approximately by the random variable

$$X_0 \cdot \exp\Big((\mu - r)t + \sum_{j=1}^{n} A_j^n\Big).$$

We have

$$
\begin{aligned}
\mathbb{E}[A_j^n] &= p(\sigma\Delta x) + (1 - p)(-\sigma\Delta x) \\
&= (2p - 1) \cdot (\sigma\Delta x) \\
&= (r - \mu - \frac{\sigma^2}{2}) \cdot (\Delta x)^2
\end{aligned}
$$

and

$$
\begin{aligned}
\mathbb{E}[(A_j^n)^2] &= p \cdot (\sigma\Delta x)^2 + (1 - p) \cdot (\sigma\Delta x)^2 \\
&= \sigma^2(\Delta x)^2.
\end{aligned}
$$

Hence

$$\mathrm{Var}(A_j^n) = \mathbb{E}[(A_j^n)^2] - \mathbb{E}[A_j^n]^2 \approx \sigma^2(\Delta x)^2.$$

Since the random variables $(A_j^n)_{j=1}^n$ are independent and identically distributed

$$\mathbb{E}[\sum_{j=1}^{n} A_j^n] = n(r - \mu - \frac{\sigma^2}{2})(\Delta x)^2 = (r - \mu - \frac{\sigma^2}{2})t$$

and[19]

$$\text{Var}(\sum_{j=1}^{n} A_j^n) \approx n\sigma^2(\Delta x)^2 = \sigma^2 t.$$

By the Central Limit Theorem

$$(10.5) \quad \lim_{n \longrightarrow \infty} P\left[\frac{\sum_{j=1}^{n} A_j^n - (r - \mu - \frac{\sigma^2}{2})t}{\sigma\sqrt{t}} \le x\right] = \frac{1}{\sqrt{2\pi}} \int_{-\infty}^{x} e^{-y^2/2} dy$$

for any $x \in \mathbf{R}$. Hence $\sum_{j=1}^{n} A_j^n \xrightarrow{D} (r - \mu - \frac{\sigma^2}{2})t + \sigma \widetilde{W}_t$ as $n \longrightarrow \infty$ for all $t \ge 0$ where $\widetilde{W}_t$ is an $N(0, t)$ distributed random variable. The properties already shown to hold for the process $(W_t)_{t \ge 0}$ can now be shown to hold for the process $(\widetilde{W}_t)_{t \ge 0}$, and, by Kolmogorov's Consistency Theorem, there exists a probability measure on $\mathbf{R}^{[0,\infty)}$, P_N, such that $(\widetilde{W}_t)_{t \ge 0}$ is a Wiener process on the probability space $(\mathbf{R}^{[0,\infty)}, \mathcal{F}_\infty, P_N)$. We call P_N the risk neutral probability measure for the share price. Since

$$\mu t + (r - \mu - \frac{\sigma^2}{2})t + \sigma \widetilde{W}_t = (r - \frac{1}{2}\sigma^2)t + \sigma \widetilde{W}_t$$

we have proved the following result.

Proposition 10.3. *If a stock has drift μ and volatility σ, then there exist two probability measures: W, the Wiener measure, and, P_N, the risk neutral probability measure, on the measurable space $(\mathbf{R}^{[0,\infty)}, \mathcal{F}_\infty)$ such that the share price at time t, X_t has the following properties:*

(a) *under W, $X_t = X_0 \exp(\mu t + \sigma W_t)$, and $(W_t)_{t \ge 0}$ is a Wiener process;*

(b) *under P_N, $e^{-rt} X_t = X_0 \exp(-\frac{\sigma^2}{2}t + \sigma \widetilde{W}_t)$ and $(\widetilde{W}_t)_{t \ge 0}$ is a Wiener process.*

Corollary 10.4. *The discounted share price $(e^{-rt} X_t)_{t \ge 0}$ is a martingale with respect to the risk neutral probability measure P_N.*

Proof. It suffices to combine Propositions 9.15(b) and 10.3(b). □

Let $N(x) = \frac{1}{\sqrt{2\pi}} \int_{-\infty}^{x} e^{-y^2/2} dy$; that is $N(x) = P[X \le x]$ where X is an $N(0, 1)$ distributed random variable. Since the density function for the standardized normal distribution is symmetric about the origin, $N(-x) = 1 - N(x)$ for all $x \in \mathbf{R}$. There is no explicit formula for $N(x)$, but statistical tables and computer approximations are available which give $N(x)$ to any required degree

---

[19]It is easily seen that $\text{Var}(\sum_{j=1}^{n} A_j^n) = \sigma^2 t + g(\Delta x)$ where $|g(x)| \le d|x|^2$ for some constant d and all x close to 0.

of accuracy, or one may use Exercise 1.7. We now present the Black-Scholes formula.

Proposition 10.5. (*Black-Scholes Formula*) *Suppose the share price of a stock with volatility σ is X_0 today. For the buyer*

$$(10.6) \quad X_0 N\left(\frac{\log(\frac{X_0}{k}) + (r + \frac{1}{2}\sigma^2)T}{\sigma\sqrt{T}}\right) - ke^{-rT}N\left(\frac{\log(\frac{X_0}{k}) + (r - \frac{1}{2}\sigma^2)T}{\sigma\sqrt{T}}\right)$$

is a fair price for a call option with maturity date T and strike price k given that r is the risk-free interest rate.

Proof. By Proposition 10.3(b) and Corollary 10.4

$$V_0 = \mathbb{E}_{P_N}[e^{-rT}(X_T - k)^+|\mathcal{F}_0] = \mathbb{E}_{P_N}[e^{-rT}(X_T - k)^+]$$

is the buyer's fair price for the option, and it suffices to show that this reduces to (10.6). By Proposition 10.3,

$$e^{-rT}(X_T - k)^+ = e^{-rT}\left(X_0 \cdot e^{(r-\frac{1}{2}\sigma^2)T + \sigma\sqrt{T}Y} - k\right)^+$$

where Y is an $N(0,1)$ distributed random variable. By Proposition 7.18,

$$V_0 = \frac{1}{\sqrt{2\pi}} \int_{\mathbf{R}} e^{-rT}\left(X_0 e^{(r-\frac{1}{2}\sigma^2)T + \sigma\sqrt{T}x} - k\right)^+ e^{-\frac{1}{2}x^2} dx.$$

Since

$$X_0 e^{(r-\frac{1}{2}\sigma^2)T + \sigma\sqrt{T}x} - k \geq 0 \quad \Leftrightarrow \quad e^{\sigma\sqrt{T}x} \geq \left(\frac{k}{X_0}\right)e^{-(r-\frac{1}{2}\sigma^2)T}$$

$$\Leftrightarrow \quad x \geq \frac{1}{\sigma\sqrt{T}}\left\{\log(\frac{k}{X_0}) - (r - \frac{1}{2}\sigma^2)T\right\} =: T_1$$

we have, using the substitution $y = x - \sigma\sqrt{T}$,

$$\begin{aligned} V_0 &= \frac{X_0 e^{-\frac{1}{2}\sigma^2 T}}{\sqrt{2\pi}} \int_{T_1}^{\infty} e^{\sigma\sqrt{T}x - \frac{1}{2}x^2} dx - \frac{ke^{-rT}}{\sqrt{2\pi}} \int_{T_1}^{\infty} e^{-\frac{1}{2}x^2} dx \\ &= \frac{X_0}{\sqrt{2\pi}} \int_{T_1}^{\infty} e^{-\frac{1}{2}(x-\sigma\sqrt{T})^2} dx - ke^{-rT}(1 - N(T_1)) \\ &= \frac{X_0}{\sqrt{2\pi}} \int_{T_1-\sigma\sqrt{T}}^{\infty} e^{-\frac{1}{2}y^2} dy - ke^{-rT}(1 - N(T_1)) \\ &= X_0(1 - N(T_1 - \sigma\sqrt{T})) - ke^{-rT}(1 - N(T_1)). \end{aligned}$$

Since

$$T_1 - \sigma\sqrt{T} = \frac{1}{\sigma\sqrt{T}}\left(-\log(\frac{X_0}{k}) - (r + \frac{1}{2}\sigma^2)T\right)$$

we have

$$1 - N(T_1 - \sigma\sqrt{T}) = N(-T_1 + \sigma\sqrt{T}) = N\Big(\frac{\log(\frac{X_0}{k}) + (r + \frac{1}{2}\sigma^2)T}{\sigma\sqrt{T}}\Big).$$

Similarly

$$1 - N(T_1) = N\Big(\frac{\log(\frac{X_0}{k}) + (r - \frac{1}{2}\sigma^2)T}{\sigma\sqrt{T}}\Big).$$

Substituting these two formulae into the integral representation for V_0, we obtain the Black-Scholes formula. $\qquad\square$

Example 10.6. We use the Black-Scholes formula to price a call option with strike price \$26, maturity date 6 months, and interest rate 8% given that the stock has volatility 10%, that is $\sigma = .1$, and the share price is \$25 today. The price is

$$25N\Big(\frac{\log(\frac{25}{26}) + (.08 + \frac{1}{2}(.1)^2)\frac{1}{2}}{(.1)\sqrt{.5}}\Big) - 26e^{-.04}N\Big(\frac{\log(\frac{25}{26}) + (.08 - \frac{1}{2}(.1)^2)\frac{1}{2}}{(.1)\sqrt{.5}}\Big).$$

This equals $25N(.0495) - (24.98)N(-.0212) = .51$.

To find the value V_t of the option at time t, $0 \le t \le T$, apply the Black-Scholes formula (10.6) with initial price X_t, strike price k and maturity date $T - t$ (see Proposition 11.24).

Proposition 10.7. *(Call-Put Parity) Suppose the share price of a stock with volatility σ is X_0 today. If C_T and P_T denote, respectively, fair prices for a call option and a put option with maturity date T, strike price k and risk-free interest rate r, then*[20]

$$C_T - P_T = X_0 - ke^{-rt}.$$

Proof. Since $C_T = \mathbb{E}[e^{-rT}(X_T - k)^+]$ and $P_T = \mathbb{E}[e^{-rT}(X_T - k)^-]$, Proposition 10.3 and Lemma 9.14 imply

$$\begin{aligned} C_T - P_T &= \mathbb{E}[e^{-rT}(X_T - k)^+] - \mathbb{E}[e^{-rT}(X_T - k)^-] \\ &= \mathbb{E}[e^{-rT}(X_T - k)] \\ &= X_0 - ke^{-rT}. \end{aligned}$$

This completes the proof. $\qquad\square$

---

[20]This result also follows from financial arguments, as in the proof of Proposition 5.6, and depends only on $\mathbb{E}[e^{-rT}X_T] = X_0$.

10.3. Change of Measure Derivation

In the previous section we followed a first principles approach and obtained the Black-Scholes formula by using a limiting process and finite risk neutral probabilities derived from properties of elementary fair games. In this section, which may be omitted on a first reading, we take a different approach and use the martingale property (9.8) in Proposition 9.15(d).

We need to solve the following problem. Given a probability space $(\Omega, \mathcal{F}, P)$, a filtration $(\mathcal{F}_t)_{t \geq 0}$, a Wiener process $(W_t)_{t \geq 0}$ adapted to the filtration, μ and r real numbers and $\sigma > 0$, show that there exists a probability measure on $(\Omega, \mathcal{F})$ such that $(e^{(\mu-r)t + \sigma W_t})_{t \geq 0}$ is a martingale under this new measure. Once we have found this measure the derivation of the Black-Scholes proceeds as in the final part of the previous section.

Let $Y_t = e^{(\mu-r)t + \sigma W_t}$, and for a fixed $\gamma \in \mathbf{R}$ let $Z_t = e^{-\frac{1}{2}\gamma^2 t + \gamma W_t}$. By Proposition 9.15(d), there exists a positive integrable random variable Z_∞ on $(\Omega, \mathcal{F}, P)$ such that $P_\gamma(A) = \int_A Z_\infty dP$ defines a probability measure P_γ on $(\Omega, \mathcal{F})$ and, moreover, if Y is an $\mathcal{F}_t$ measurable P_γ integrable random variable and $0 \leq s \leq t$, then

$$\mathbb{E}_{P_\gamma}[Y|\mathcal{F}_s] = \mathbb{E}_P[Z_t \cdot Y|\mathcal{F}_s].$$

Since $\mathcal{F}_0 = \mathcal{F}_\emptyset$ this implies $\mathbb{E}_{P_\gamma}[Y] = \mathbb{E}_P[Z_t \cdot Y]$ if Y is $\mathcal{F}_t$ measurable.

If $(Y_t)_{t \geq 0}$ is a martingale on $(\Omega, \mathcal{F}, P_\gamma)$, then the sequence $(\mathbb{E}_{P_\gamma}[Y_t])_{t \geq 0}$ must be independent of t. By Lemma 9.14,

$$\begin{aligned}
\mathbb{E}_{P_\gamma}[Y_t] &= \int_\Omega e^{(\mu-r)t + \sigma W_t} \cdot e^{-\frac{1}{2}\gamma^2 t + \gamma W_t} dP \\
&= e^{(\mu - r - \frac{1}{2}\gamma^2)t} \int_\Omega e^{(\sigma+\gamma)W_t} dP \\
&= e^{(\mu - r - \frac{1}{2}\gamma^2)t + \frac{1}{2}(\sigma+\gamma)^2 t}.
\end{aligned}$$

This means we must have

$$\mu - r - \frac{1}{2}\gamma^2 + \frac{1}{2}(\sigma + \gamma)^2 = \mu - r + \frac{1}{2}\sigma^2 + \sigma\gamma = 0,$$

that is

(10.7)
$$\gamma = \frac{-\mu + r - \frac{1}{2}\sigma^2}{\sigma}.$$

We now examine $(W_t)_{t \geq 0}$ as a stochastic process on $(\Omega, \mathcal{F}, P_\gamma)$ where γ is given by (10.7). Fix $x \in \mathbf{R}$ and $t > 0$ and let $f = \mathbf{1}_{(-\infty,x]}$ and $g(y) = e^{-\frac{1}{2}\gamma^2 t + \gamma y}$ for all $y \in \mathbf{R}$. Then $g(W_t) = Z_t$, and, by the proof of Proposition 5.19, $f(W_t) =$

$\mathbf{1}_{\{W_t \leq x\}}$. Since $f(W_t)$ is $\mathcal{F}_t$ measurable

$$
\begin{aligned}
P_\gamma(\{W_t \leq x\}) &= \int_{\{W_t \leq x\}} dP_\gamma = \int_\Omega \mathbf{1}_{\{W_t \leq x\}} dP_\gamma = \int_\Omega f(W_t) dP_\gamma \\
&= \int_\Omega f(W_t) \cdot g(W_t) dP = \mathbb{E}_P[f(W_t) \cdot g(W_t)],
\end{aligned}
$$

and as W_t is $N(0, t)$ distributed $f_{W_t}(y) = (2\pi t)^{-1/2} \exp\left(-y^2/2t\right)$ for all $y \in \mathbf{R}$. By Proposition 7.10,

$$
\begin{aligned}
\mathbb{E}_P[f(W_t) \cdot g(W_t)] &= \int_\mathbf{R} f(y) g(y) f_{W_t}(y) dy \\
&= \frac{1}{\sqrt{2\pi t}} \int_{-\infty}^x \exp\left(-\frac{1}{2}\gamma^2 t + \gamma y\right) \cdot \exp\left(-\frac{1}{2t} y^2\right) dy \\
&= \frac{1}{\sqrt{2\pi t}} \int_{-\infty}^x \exp\left(-\frac{1}{2t}(y - \gamma t)^2\right) dy.
\end{aligned}
$$

Hence W_t is $N(\gamma t, t)$ distributed and $\widetilde{W}_t := -\gamma t + W_t$ is $N(0, t)$ distributed over $(\Omega, \mathcal{F}, P_\gamma)$. Our choice of γ in (10.7) implies

$$
\begin{aligned}
Y_t = \exp\left\{(\mu - r)t + \sigma(\gamma t + \widetilde{W}_t)\right\} &= \exp\left\{(\mu - r + \gamma\sigma)t + \sigma \widetilde{W}_t\right\} \\
&= \exp\left\{-\frac{1}{2}\sigma^2 t + \sigma \widetilde{W}_t\right\}
\end{aligned}
$$

on $(\Omega, \mathcal{F}, P_\gamma)$. To show that $(\widetilde{W}_t)_{t \geq 0}$ is a Wiener process on $(\Omega, \mathcal{F}, P_\gamma)$ we must show that it has independent, stationary and Gaussian increments. In our next set of calculations we use Proposition 7.9, Lemma 9.14 and the fact that $W_t - W_s$ is an $N(0, t - s)$ distributed random variable on $(\Omega, \mathcal{F}, P)$. For $0 \leq s \leq t$ an argument similar to the above implies

$$
\begin{aligned}
P_\gamma(\{W_t - W_s \leq x\}) &= \int_\Omega \mathbf{1}_{\{W_t - W_s \leq x\}} Z_t dP \\
&= \int_\Omega f(W_t - W_s) e^{-\frac{1}{2}\gamma^2 t + \gamma(W_t - W_s)} e^{\gamma W_s} dP \\
&= \mathbb{E}_P[f(W_t - W_s) g(W_t - W_s) e^{\gamma W_s}] \\
&= \mathbb{E}_P[f(W_t - W_s) g(W_t - W_s)] \cdot \mathbb{E}_P[e^{\gamma W_s}] \\
&\quad (\text{as } W_t - W_s \text{ and } W_s \text{ are independent on } (\Omega, \mathcal{F}, P)) \\
&= \frac{e^{\frac{1}{2}\gamma^2 s}}{\sqrt{2\pi(t - s)}} \int_{-\infty}^x f(y) g(y) \exp\left(-\frac{y^2}{2(t - s)}\right) dy
\end{aligned}
$$

by Lemma 9.14 and since $W_t - W_s$ is $N(0, t-s)$. Hence

$$P_\gamma(\{W_t - W_s \le x\}) = \frac{e^{\frac{1}{2}\gamma^2 s}}{\sqrt{2\pi(t-s)}} \int_{-\infty}^x \exp\left(-\frac{1}{2}\gamma^2 t + \gamma y - \frac{y^2}{2(t-s)}\right) dy$$

$$= \frac{1}{\sqrt{2\pi(t-s)}} \int_{-\infty}^x \exp\left(-\frac{1}{2(t-s)}(y - (t-s)\gamma)^2\right) dy.$$

This shows that $W_t - W_s$ is an $N((t-s)\gamma, t-s)$ distributed random variable on the space $(\Omega, \mathcal{F}, P_\gamma)$ and, as $\widetilde{W}_t - \widetilde{W}_s = -\gamma(t-s) + (W_t - W_s)$, $\widetilde{W}_t - \widetilde{W}_s$ has an $N(0, t-s)$ distribution over $(\Omega, \mathcal{F}, P_\gamma)$. We have shown that the stochastic process $(\widetilde{W}_t)_{t\ge 0}$ on $(\Omega, \mathcal{F}, P_\gamma)$ has Gaussian and stationary increments (see Proposition 10.2). It remains to show that it has independent increments. We again use Proposition 7.9, and to avoid lengthy calculations we just show that $\widetilde{W}_t - \widetilde{W}_s$ and $\widetilde{W}_s$ are independent when $0 \le s \le t$. Let h and l denote real-valued bounded Borel measurable functions on $\mathbf{R}$. Since $W_t - W_s$ and W_s are independent $\mathcal{F}_t$ measurable random variables on $(\Omega, \mathcal{F}, P)$, Proposition 9.15(d) implies

$$\mathbb{E}_{P_\gamma}[h(\widetilde{W}_t - \widetilde{W}_s) \cdot l(\widetilde{W}_s)] = \mathbb{E}_P[h(W_t - W_s - \gamma(t-s))e^{-\frac{1}{2}\gamma^2(t-s)+\gamma(W_t-W_s)}$$

$$\cdot l(W_s - \gamma s) \cdot e^{-\frac{1}{2}\gamma^2 s + \gamma W_s}]$$

$$= \mathbb{E}_P[h(W_t - W_s - \gamma(t-s))e^{-\frac{1}{2}\gamma^2(t-s)+\gamma(W_t-W_s)}]$$

$$\cdot \mathbb{E}_P[l(W_s - \gamma s) \cdot e^{-\frac{1}{2}\gamma^2 s + W_s}]$$

$$= \mathbb{E}_{P_\gamma}[h(\widetilde{W}_t - \widetilde{W}_s)] \cdot \mathbb{E}_{P_\gamma}[l(\widetilde{W}_s)].$$

By Proposition 7.9, $\widetilde{W}_t - \widetilde{W}_s$ and $\widetilde{W}_s$ are independent random variables on $(\Omega, \mathcal{F}, P_\gamma)$. We have proved the following proposition.

Proposition 10.8. *Let $(W_t)_{t\ge 0}$ denote a Wiener process on $(\Omega, \mathcal{F}, P)$ and let $Y_t = e^{(\mu-r)t+\sigma W_t}$ for $t \ge 0$ where $\mu, r, \sigma \in \mathbf{R}$ and $\sigma > 0$. If*

$$\gamma = \frac{-\mu + r - \frac{1}{2}\sigma^2}{\sigma},$$

then on the probability space $(\Omega, \mathcal{F}, P_\gamma)$

$$Y_t = \exp\left(-\frac{1}{2}\sigma^2 t + \sigma \widetilde{W}_t\right),$$

where $\widetilde{W}_t = -\gamma t + W_t$ and $(\widetilde{W}_t)_{t\ge 0}$ is a Wiener process. Moreover, $(Y_t)_{t\ge 0}$ is a martingale.

By Propositions 10.3(b) and 10.7 the discounted share price has the same distribution under P_N and P_γ, γ as above, and hence both give the same formula, the Black-Scholes formula, for a call option. We now show that $P_N = P_\gamma$ on $(\Omega, \mathcal{F}_\infty)$ where $\mathcal{F}_\infty$ is the σ-field generated by $(X_t)_{t \geq 0}$.

If A is an $\mathcal{F}_t$ measurable subset of Ω, then, as above, $\mathbf{1}_A = f(\widetilde{W}_t)$ where f is a bounded Borel measurable function on $\mathbf{R}$. Since $\widetilde{W}_t$ has the same distribution under P_γ and P_N and $(\widetilde{W}_s)_{0 \leq s \leq t}$ generates the σ-field $\mathcal{F}_t$, we have

$$P_\gamma(A) = \mathbb{E}_{P_\gamma}[\mathbf{1}_A] = \mathbb{E}_{P_\gamma}[f(\widetilde{W}_t)] = \mathbb{E}_{P_N}[f(\widetilde{W}_t)] = P_N(A).$$

Hence $P_\gamma = P_N$ on $\bigcup_{t \geq 0} \mathcal{F}_t$ and hence on $\mathcal{F}_\infty$ (see Exercise 10.1).

10.4. Exercises

(10.1) Let P_1 and P_2 denote two probability measures on the measurable space $(\Omega, \mathcal{F})$ and let $\mathcal{G}$ denote a collection of subsets of Ω which is closed under the operations of taking finite unions and complements. If $\mathcal{F}(\mathcal{G}) = \mathcal{F}$ and $P_1(A) = P_2(A)$ for all $A \in \mathcal{G}$, show that $P_1 = P_2$.

(10.2) If $(W_t)_{t \geq 0}$ is a Wiener process over $(\Omega, \mathcal{F}, P)$ and $c > 0$, show that $(\frac{1}{c} W_{c^2 t})_{t \geq 0}$ is also a Wiener process over $(\Omega, \mathcal{F}, P)$. Hence show that

$$P(|W_t| \leq \sqrt{c}t, t \in [0, 1/c])$$

does not depend on c.

(10.3) If $(W_t)_{t \geq 0}$ is a Wiener process over $(\Omega, \mathcal{F}, P)$, find $\mathbb{E}[(W_t - W_s)^2 \cdot W_t]$ for (a) $t \geq s$ and (b) $t \leq s$.

(10.4) Use the Black-Scholes formula to price a call option for a stock whose share price today is 16 when the interest rate is 4%, the maturity date is 6 months, the strike price is 17.5 and the volatility is 20%. Find the price of the option half way to maturity if the share price at that time is 17.

(10.5) If $(W_t)_{t \geq 0}$ is a Weiner process, find $P\left[\max_{0 \leq t \leq T} W_t \geq a\right]$.

Chapter 11

Stochastic Integration

I finally devised stochastic differential equations,
after painstaking solitary endeavors.

Kiyoshi Itô

Summary

We define the stochastic Riemann and Itô integrals of a continuous process and prove Itô's formula. Stochastic integral equations are used to hedge a call option.

11.1. Riemann Sums

The complexity of our investigations has been gradually increasing. In Chapters 3 to 5 we introduced and studied directly basic concepts such as *probability spaces* and *random variables*. In Chapter 6 we introduced *expected values* and, after overcoming some technical difficulties, obtained fundamental *convergence results*. Chapters 8 to 10 involved new ideas defined using earlier concepts, such as *conditional expectations*, *martingales* and *Brownian motion*. At all times we were motivated to find an *arbitrage free price* for a call option and reached our goal, the *Black-Scholes formula*, in Chapter 10. To convince the seller that this is so, we must show that it is possible to hedge any claim on the option.

A direct approach in Section 8.3, using small finite models, led to Riemann sums of random variables and to *two* new types of integrals in (8.42). The greater part of this chapter is devoted to giving a rigorous meaning to these integrals. Since the Riemann sums in (8.41) are random variables, it is natural to take limits using one or other of the modes of convergence introduced for random variables and to look to our experience with the Lebesgue integral for technical guidance. We carry out this procedure; it will involve a number of unexpected twists, with contributions from all previous chapters, and deliver more than we might expect.

To understand why certain technical arrangements must be in place, we look briefly at how one might define the Riemann integral $\int_0^1 f \, dg$ where f and g are real-valued functions. The Riemann sum corresponding to a partition of $[a, b]$ into adjacent subintervals $([t_i, t_{i+1}))_{i=0}^{n-1}$ has the form

$$\sum_{i=0}^{n-1} f(t_i^*) \cdot (g(t_{i+1}) - g(t_i))$$

where $t_i \leq t_i^* < t_{i+1}$. If f is *continuous* and g is *continuously differentiable* on $[a, b]$, then, by the Mean Value Theorem (Proposition 1.8), the above sum equals

$$\sum_{i=0}^{n-1} f(t_i^*) \cdot g'(t_i^{**}) \cdot (t_{i+1} - t_i)$$

where $t_i \leq t_i^{**} < t_{i+1}$. Continuity of f and g' imply, by Proposition 7.7, that the Riemann sums converge, as we take finer and finer partitions, to

$$\int_a^b f(x) g'(x) dx.$$

There are four components in the above construction: conditions on f, conditions on g, admissible Riemann sums and a limiting procedure. The conditions on f and g may be relaxed somewhat, but the above illustrates an essential gap, imposed by their respective roles, between natural hypotheses that are usually placed on the two functions. For the Itô integral the choice of *evaluation point* in each subinterval determines which Riemann sums are allowed (see Example 11.18). The Riemann sums for stochastic integrals show the degree of regularity needed for a simple construction, and when this is not present the only option left is to modify the final ingredient, *the limiting process*. Some flexibility is possible as the Riemann sums involved are random variables, and these, as we have already seen, converge in different ways. In the next section, we prove the convergence results required to obtain examples of Itô integrable random variables.

Another, less obvious, consideration may help orient us through the technical constructions ahead. In Chapter 10 we showed that the share price $(X_t)_{t \geq 0}$ could be written as $(f(t, W_t))_{t \geq 0}$ where $(W_t)_{t \geq 0}$ is a Wiener process and f is a well-behaved function of two variables. The Wiener process gave rise to the probability space $(\mathbf{R}^{[0,\infty)}, \mathcal{F}_\infty, W)$ where W is Wiener measure. The measure W contains all information on the process since the coordinate evaluation, that is the mapping $\omega := (\omega_s)_{s \in [0,\infty)} \mapsto \omega_t$, gives us W_t, and by letting t range over $[0, \infty)$ we recover the process. However, under W, $(X_t)_{t \geq 0}$ is not a martingale, and it was necessary to change to the risk neutral measure, P_N, to obtain a martingale. Under P_N, $X_t = g(t, \widetilde{W}_t)$, where $(\widetilde{W}_t)_{t \geq 0}$ is another Wiener process and g is a well-behaved function of two variables. Mathematical coincidences, such as the appearance of *two* Wiener processes, frequently suggest the existence of a more general underlying principle at work. It turns out that many important stochastic processes can be expressed as a function of the *deterministic*[1] time variable t and the random variable[2] W_t, just as many distribution functions can be expressed as the integral of a density function with respect to Lebesgue measure. Certain distinct, but comparable, properties of Lebesgue measure and the Wiener process point to the similarities and differences that will appear as we proceed. We display these and a special case of Itô's Lemma, the stochastic analogue of the Fundamental Theorem of Calculus, in the following table.

Lebesgue Measure $\mathbf{m}$	Wiener Process $(W_t)_{t \geq 0}$
$\mathbf{m}([s, t]) = t - s$	$\mathbb{E}[(W_t - W_s)^2] = t - s$
$\mathbf{m}(\bigcup_{i=1}^n [s_i, t_i]) = \sum_{i=1}^n (t_i - s_i)$ (for disjoint intervals by (5.4))	$\mathbb{E}\left[\left(\sum_{i=1}^n (W_{t_i} - W_{s_i})\right)^2\right] = \sum_{i=1}^n (t_i - s_i)$ (for disjoint intervals by independence)
$f(T) - f(0) = \int_0^T f'(t)dt$ (f continuously differentiable)	$f(W_T) - f(W_0) =$ $\int_0^T f'(W_t)dW_t + \frac{1}{2}\int_0^T f''(W_t)dt$ (f twice continuously differentiable)

As we saw in Chapters 6, 7 and 9, existence and convergence results for integrable random variables revolve about almost sure convergence, $\mathbb{E}[\,|X|\,] = \int_\Omega |X| dP$ and the space $\mathbf{L}^1(\Omega, \mathcal{F}, P)$. The above table suggests that $\mathbb{E}[X^2] = \int_\Omega |X|^2 dP$ and $\mathbf{L}^2(\Omega, \mathcal{F}, P)$ will play a more dominant role in constructing stochastic integrals.

---

[1] That is non-random.

[2] Now finally behaving like a variable.

11.2. Convergence of Random Variables

Unfortunately, the Riemann sums involved in constructing the Itô integral do not appear to converge almost surely, and we are obliged to consider a weaker form of convergence, *convergence in measure*, which involves almost sure convergence of *subsequences*. To prepare for this definition, we provide yet another characterization of convergent sequences of real numbers.

Lemma 11.1. *A sequence of real numbers $(a_n)_{n=1}^{\infty}$ converges to the real number a if and only if every subsequence of $(a_n)_{n=1}^{\infty}$ contains a subsequence which converges[3] to a.*

Proof. Every convergent sequence is easily seen to have the subsequence property. Conversely suppose every subsequence of $(a_n)_{n=1}^{\infty}$ contains a subsequence which converges to a. If the sequence does not converge to a, then there exists $\epsilon > 0$ and an increasing sequence of positive integers $(n_j)_{j=1}^{\infty}$ such that $|a_{n_j} - a| \geq \epsilon$ for all j. Since every term in *any* subsequence of $(a_{n_j})_{j=1}^{\infty}$ is at least ϵ away from a, it cannot converge to a. This contradicts our hypothesis and hence $(a_n)_{n=1}^{\infty}$ converges to a. This completes the proof. □

Similar characterizations hold for pointwise convergence and convergence in $\mathbf{L}^i(\Omega, \mathcal{F}, P), i = 1, 2$, but *do not* hold[4] for almost sure convergence (see Exercise 11.3). We include the following proposition because (b) is the usual definition of convergence in measure whereas we use (c) *exclusively* in constructing the Itô integral.

Proposition 11.2. *Let $(X_n)_{n=1}^{\infty}$ and X denote random variables on a probability space $(\Omega, \mathcal{F}, P)$. The following conditions are equivalent:*

(a) $\lim_{n \to \infty} \int_{\Omega} \frac{|X_n - X|}{1 + |X_n - X|} dP = 0$;

(b) $\lim_{n \to \infty} P(\{\omega \in \Omega : |X_n(\omega) - X(\omega)| > \epsilon\}) = 0$ *for every $\epsilon > 0$;*

(c) *every subsequence of $(X_n)_{n=1}^{\infty}$ contains a subsequence which converges almost surely to X.*

If these equivalent conditions are satisfied, the sequence $(X_n)_{n=1}^{\infty}$ converges in measure[5] to X.

---

[3]The sequence $a_n = (-1)^n$ shows that we cannot drop the assumption that all subsequences converge to the *same* limit.

[4]Basically because the number of subsequences of a given sequence may be uncountable, and the uncountable union of sets of measure 0 may not, even if measurable, have measure 0.

[5]The expression *convergence in probability* is also used. Convergence in measure is the natural convergence to associate with almost sure convergence to obtain (c) in Proposition 11.2.

Proof. (a) $\implies$ (b). Let $\epsilon > 0$ be arbitrary, $A_n := \{\omega \in \Omega : |X_n(\omega) - X(\omega)| \geq \epsilon\}$ and
$$B_n := \{\omega \in \Omega : \frac{|X_n(\omega) - X(\omega)|}{1 + |X_n(\omega) - X(\omega)|} \geq \frac{\epsilon}{1 + \epsilon}\}.$$
Since $f(x) = x/(1+x)$ is increasing on $[0, \infty)$, $A_n \subset B_n$. Hence
$$P(\{\omega : |X_n(\omega) - X(\omega)| \geq \epsilon\}) \leq \frac{1 + \epsilon}{\epsilon} \int_{B_n} \frac{\epsilon}{1 + \epsilon} dP$$
$$\leq \frac{1 + \epsilon}{\epsilon} \int_\Omega \frac{|X_n - X|}{1 + |X_n - X|} dP$$
which tends to 0 as n tends to infinity and (a) $\implies$ (b).

(b) $\implies$ (c). If $(X_n)_{n=1}^\infty$ satisfies (b), then clearly every subsequence of $(X_n)_{n=1}^\infty$ satisfies (b) and it suffices to show that $(X_n)_{n=1}^\infty$ contains a subsequence which converges almost surely to X. For each positive integer k, choose a positive integer n_k such that
$$P(\{\omega \in \Omega : |X_n(\omega) - X(\omega)| \leq \frac{1}{2^k}\}) \geq 1 - \frac{1}{2^k}$$
for all $n \geq n_k$. Let $C_k := \{\omega \in \Omega : |X_{n_k}(\omega) - X(\omega)| \leq \frac{1}{2^k}\}$ and let $m_k = n_1 + n_2 + \cdots + n_k$ for all k. The sequence $(m_k)_{k=1}^\infty$ is strictly increasing. If $\omega \in D_k := \bigcap_{l \geq k} C_l$, then $X_{m_k}(\omega) \longrightarrow X(\omega)$ as $k \longrightarrow \infty$. By Exercise 5.2,
$$P(D_k^c) = P(\bigcup_{l \geq k} C_l^c) \leq \sum_{l=k}^\infty P(C_l^c) \leq \sum_{l=k}^\infty 2^{-l} = 2^{-k+1}.$$
If $\omega \in D := \bigcup_{k \geq 1} D_k$, then $X_{m_k}(\omega) \longrightarrow X(\omega)$ as $k \longrightarrow \infty$ and $P(D) \geq P(D_{k+1}) \geq 1 - \frac{1}{2^k}$ for all k. Hence $P(D) = 1$ and $X_{m_k} \longrightarrow X$ almost surely as $k \longrightarrow \infty$. This shows (b) $\implies$ (c).

(c) $\implies$ (a). Let $Y_n = \frac{|X_n - X|}{1 + |X_n - X|}$ and $a_n = \int_\Omega \frac{|X_n - X|}{1 + |X_n - X|} dP$ for all n. Then $|Y_n(\omega)| \leq 1$ for all n and ω. Given any subsequence $(Y_{n_j})_{j=1}^\infty$ of $(Y_n)_{n=1}^\infty$ we can, by (c), choose a subsequence of $(Y_{n_j})_{j=1}^\infty$, $(Y_{n_{j_k}})_{k=1}^\infty$, which converges almost surely to 0. By the Dominated Convergence Theorem, $(a_{n_{j_k}})_{k=1}^\infty$ converges to 0 and, by Lemma 11.1, the sequence $(a_n)_{n=1}^\infty$ converges to 0. Hence (c) implies (a) and this completes the proof. $\square$

We now list a number of elementary properties of convergence in measure that follow easily from Proposition 11.2(c).

(a) If $(X_n)_{n=1}^\infty$ converges in measure to both X and Y, then $X = Y$ almost surely.

(b) If $(X_n)_{n=1}^\infty$ converges in measure to X, then every subsequence of $(X_n)_{n=1}^\infty$ converges in measure to X.

(c) Almost sure convergence implies convergence in measure.

(d) *If every subsequence of $(X_n)_{n=1}^\infty$ contains a subsequence which converges in measure and any two such limits are almost surely equal, then the sequence $(X_n)_{n=1}^\infty$ converges in measure.*

(e) *If $(X_n)_{n=1}^\infty$ and $(Y_n)_{n=1}^\infty$ converge in measure to X and Y, respectively, and $a, b \in \mathbf{R}$, then $(aX_n + bY_n)_{n=1}^\infty$ converges in measure to $aX + bY$.*

We now recall some definitions from Chapters 6 and 7 and discuss convergence in $\mathbf{L}^i(\Omega, \mathcal{F}, P), i = 1, 2$. If $X \in \mathbf{L}^1(\Omega, \mathcal{F}, P)$,

$$(11.1) \qquad \|X\|_1 = \mathbb{E}[|X|] = \int_\Omega |X| dP$$

and, if $X \in \mathbf{L}^2(\Omega, \mathcal{F}, P)$,

$$(11.2) \qquad \|X\|_2 = (\mathbb{E}[|X|^2])^{1/2} = \left(\int_\Omega X^2 dP \right)^{1/2}.$$

Note that $\|X\|_2^2 := (\|X\|_2)^2 = \mathbb{E}[X^2] = \int_\Omega X^2 dP$. We have *three* expressions for the same object and each has its uses: the notation $\|\cdot\|_i, i = 1, 2$ helps with convergence, $\mathbb{E}[\cdot]$ allows a probabilistic interpretation and the integral notation reminds us of the underlying construction. A rephrasing of the definition given prior to Proposition 9.8 states that

$$X_n \xrightarrow{\mathbf{L}^1} X \text{ as } n \longrightarrow \infty \quad \text{if} \quad \|X_n - X\|_1 \longrightarrow 0 \text{ as } n \longrightarrow \infty.$$

We introduce a similar notion in $\mathbf{L}^2(\Omega, \mathcal{F}, P)$.

Definition 11.3. *Let $(\Omega, \mathcal{F}, P)$ denote a probability space. If $(X_n)_{n=1}^\infty \subset \mathbf{L}^2(\Omega, \mathcal{F}, P)$ and $X \in \mathbf{L}^2(\Omega, \mathcal{F}, P)$, then*

$$X_n \xrightarrow{\mathbf{L}^2} X \text{ as } n \longrightarrow \infty \quad \text{if} \quad \|X_n - X\|_2 \longrightarrow 0 \text{ as } n \longrightarrow \infty.$$

Proposition 11.4. *If $X, Y \in \mathbf{L}^2(\Omega, \mathcal{F}, P)$, then*

(a) $\|X \cdot Y\|_1 \le \|X\|_2 \cdot \|Y\|_2$,

(b) $\|X + Y\|_2 \le \|X\|_2 + \|Y\|_2$,

(c) $\|X\|_1 \le \|X\|_2$.

Proof. If $x > 0$, then $(X \pm xY)^2 = X^2 \pm 2xX \cdot Y + x^2Y^2 \ge 0$ and hence $|X \cdot Y| \le (X^2 + x^2Y^2)/2x$. By Proposition 6.28(d), $X \cdot Y$ is integrable and hence $\mathbb{E}[X^2] + 2x\mathbb{E}[X \cdot Y] + x^2\mathbb{E}[Y^2] \ge 0$ for any real number x. Replacing X by $|X|$ and Y by $|Y|$ we obtain

$$\mathbb{E}[X^2] + 2x\mathbb{E}[|X \cdot Y|] + x^2\mathbb{E}[Y^2] = \|X\|_2^2 + 2x\|X \cdot Y\|_1 + x^2\|Y\|_2^2 \ge 0$$

and this proves[6] (a). Since $\mathbb{E}[(X+Y)^2] = \mathbb{E}[X^2] + 2\mathbb{E}[X \cdot Y] + \mathbb{E}[Y^2]$, $\|X+Y\|_2^2 \leq \|X\|_2^2 + 2\mathbb{E}[|X \cdot Y|] + \|Y\|_2^2$ and an application of (a) completes the proof of (b). The result in (c) follows from letting $Y = \mathbf{1}_\Omega$ in (a) or from Jensen's Inequality (Proposition 7.29) with $\phi(x) = x^2$. □

Proposition 11.4(a) is known as the *Cauchy-Schwarz inequality* and in integral notation has the following form:

$$(11.3) \qquad \int_\Omega |X \cdot Y| dP \;\leq\; \left(\int_\Omega X^2 dP \right)^{1/2} \cdot \left(\int_\Omega Y^2 dP \right)^{1/2}.$$

The spaces $\mathbf{L}^1(\Omega, \mathcal{F}, \mu)$ and $\mathbf{L}^2(\Omega, \mathcal{F}, \mu)$ can be defined for arbitrary measures (see Definition 7.14) and the analogues of Proposition 11.4(a) and (b) are still valid. As the proofs are routine we leave them as an exercise. We require later the Cauchy-Schwarz inequality for Lebesgue measure on $[0, T]$. Proposition 11.4(b) is known as *the triangle inequality*. Proposition 11.4(c) requires a probability measure.

Motivated by the definition of Cauchy sequences in $\mathbf{R}$ (see Section 6.4) we introduce Cauchy sequences in $\mathbf{L}^i(\Omega, \mathcal{F}, P), i = 1, 2$.

Definition 11.5. *A sequence* $(X_n)_{n=1}^\infty$ *in* $\mathbf{L}^i(\Omega, \mathcal{F}, P), i = 1, 2$, *is a Cauchy sequence if* $\lim_{n,m \to \infty} \|X_n - X_m\|_i = 0$.

Proposition 11.4(b) implies that every convergent sequence in $\mathbf{L}^2(\Omega, \mathcal{F}, P)$ is Cauchy and the same result for $\mathbf{L}^1(\Omega, \mathcal{F}, P)$ follows from Proposition 6.31. Our next proposition looks at the converse.

Proposition 11.6. *If* $(X_n)_{n=1}^\infty$ *is a Cauchy sequence in* $\mathbf{L}^i(\Omega, \mathcal{F}, P), i = 1, 2$, *then there exists* $X \in \mathbf{L}^i(\Omega, \mathcal{F}, P)$ *such that* $\|X_n - X\|_i \longrightarrow 0$ *and* $X_n \longrightarrow X$ *in measure as* $n \longrightarrow \infty$.

Proof. The proof for $i = 1$ is practically included in the $i = 2$ case, and we confine the proof to $i = 2$.

For each positive integer j choose a positive integer n_j such that $\|X_n - X_m\|_2 \leq 2^{-j}$ for all $n, m \geq n_j$. We may suppose, without loss of generality, that $(n_j)_{j=1}^\infty$ is strictly increasing. By Proposition 11.4(c)

$$(11.4) \qquad \sum_{j=1}^\infty \|X_{n_{j+1}} - X_{n_j}\|_1 \;\leq\; \sum_{j=1}^\infty \|X_{n_{j+1}} - X_{n_j}\|_2 \leq \sum_{j=1}^\infty \frac{1}{2^j} < \infty.$$

---

[6]It suffices to apply the following well-known elementary result obtained by completing squares. The non-constant real-valued quadratic $ax^2 + bx + c$ is positive for all $x \in \mathbf{R}$ if and only if $a > 0$ and $b^2 - 4ac \leq 0$.

For any positive integer k let $Y_k = \sum_{j=1}^{k} |X_{n_{j+1}} - X_{n_j}|$. Then $(Y_k)_{k=1}^{\infty}$ is an increasing sequence of positive integrable random variables and for all k

$$\|Y_k\|_1 \leq \sum_{j=1}^{k} \|X_{n_{j+1}} - X_{n_j}\|_1 \leq \sum_{j=1}^{\infty} \frac{1}{2^n}.$$

By the Monotone Convergence Theorem (Proposition 6.23), $\sum_{j=1}^{\infty} |X_{n_{j+1}}(\omega) - X_{n_j}(\omega)| < \infty$ almost surely and

$$(11.5) \quad X(\omega) := X_{n_1}(\omega) + \sum_{j=1}^{\infty} (X_{n_{j+1}}(\omega) - X_{n_j}(\omega)) = \lim_{j \to \infty} X_{n_j}(\omega)$$

defines almost surely an integrable random variable on $(\Omega, \mathcal{F}, P)$. If j is a positive integer and $m \geq n_j$, then, by Fatou's Lemma, (6.23),

$$\int_{\Omega} \left(\liminf_{k \to \infty} |X_{n_k} - X_m|^2 \right) dP \leq \liminf_{k \to \infty} \int_{\Omega} |X_{n_k} - X_m|^2 dP \leq \frac{1}{2^j}.$$

Since

$$\liminf_{k \to \infty} |X_{n_k} - X_m| = \lim_{k \to \infty} |X_{n_k} - X_m| = |X - X_m|$$

almost surely this implies $(X - X_m) \in \mathbf{L}^2(\Omega, \mathcal{F}, P)$ and, for every j and all $m \geq n_j$, $\|X - X_m\|_2 \leq 2^{-j}$. By Proposition 11.4(b), $X \in \mathbf{L}^2(\Omega, \mathcal{F}, P)$ and $\|X_n - X\|_2 \to 0$ as $n \to \infty$.

By (11.5), $(X_n)_{n=1}^{\infty}$ contains a subsequence which converges almost surely to X. If $(X_{n_k})_{k=1}^{\infty}$ is any subsequence of $(X_n)_{n=1}^{\infty}$, then $\|X_{n_k} - X\|_2 \to 0$ as $k \to \infty$. Hence $(X_{n_k})_{k=1}^{\infty}$ contains a subsequence which converges almost surely to X. By Proposition 11.2 the sequence $(X_n)_{n=1}^{\infty}$ converges in measure to X and this completes the proof. $\square$

We complete this section by comparing the different ways a sequence of random variables $(X_n)_{n=1}^{\infty}$ on $(\Omega, \mathcal{F}, P)$ may converge to the random variable X. By Propositions 11.4(c) and 11.6,

$\mathbf{L}^2$ convergence $\implies \mathbf{L}^1$ convergence $\implies$ convergence in measure.

Suppose $(X_n)_{n=1}^{\infty}$ converges in measure to X and $x \in \mathbf{R}$ is a point of continuity of F_X, the distribution function of X. By Proposition 11.2, any subsequence of $(X_n)_{n=1}^{\infty}$ contains a subsequence which converges almost surely to X. By Proposition 7.21 any subsequence of the sequence of real numbers $(F_{X_n}(x))_{n=1}^{\infty}$ contains a subsequence which converges to $F_X(x)$. This implies $F_{X_n}(x) \to F_X(x)$ as $n \to \infty$ and $(X_n)_{n=1}^{\infty}$ converges in distribution to X as $n \to \infty$. This completes the picture and we have

almost sure convergence $\implies$ convergence in measure

$\implies$ convergence in distribution.

11.3. The Stochastic Riemann Integral

In this section we define, using almost sure convergence, the stochastic Riemann integral of a stochastic process and give conditions under which it is integrable. Let $X := (X_t)_{t \geq 0}$ denote a stochastic process on $(\Omega, \mathcal{F}, P)$ adapted to a filtration $(\mathcal{F}_t)_{t \geq 0}$. For each $t \geq 0$ we have the random variable X_t

$$\omega \in \Omega \mapsto X_t(\omega) \in \mathbf{R}$$

and for each $\omega \in \Omega$ we obtain the path

$$t \in [0, \infty) \mapsto X_t(\omega) \in \mathbf{R}.$$

We may also consider X as a function from $\Omega \times [0, T]$ into $\mathbf{R}$, that is

$$X : (\omega, t) \in \Omega \times [0, T] \mapsto X(t, \omega) := X_t(\omega).$$

Definition 11.7. *A stochastic process $X = (X_t)_{t \geq 0}$ on $(\Omega, \mathcal{F}, P)$ is continuous if there exists an $\mathcal{F}$ measurable set $A \subset \Omega$ with $P(A) = 1$ such that the mapping*

(11.6) $$t \in [0, +\infty) \mapsto X_t(\omega)$$

is continuous[7] for all $\omega \in A$.

A path $\omega \in \Omega$ is called X-continuous if the mapping in (11.6) is continuous. We have noted, but did not prove, in Chapter 10 that any Wiener process is continuous. In view of our discussion prior to Proposition 10.2, we let $(\mathbf{R}^{[0,\infty)}, \mathcal{F}_\infty, W)$ denote the probability space for a Wiener process $(W_t)_{t \geq 0}$, where $\mathcal{F}_\infty$ is the σ-field on Ω generated by $(W_t)_{t \geq 0}$, and let $\mathcal{F}_t$ denote the σ-field on Ω generated by $(W_s)_{0 \leq s \leq t}$ for all $t \geq 0$. Since $W_t(\omega) = \omega_t$ when $\omega = (\omega_t)_{t \geq 0} \in \mathbf{R}^{[0,\infty)}$, W-continuity coincides with the usual notion of continuity. For the sake of clarity, we sometimes use the notation W-continuous.

Let $B : [0, +\infty) \longrightarrow \mathbf{R}$ denote a continuously differentiable function. To define $\int_0^T X_t dB(t), 0 < T < +\infty$, we begin by considering the Riemann sum corresponding to the partition of $[0, T)$, given by $\{0 = t_0, t_1, \ldots, t_n = T\}$,

(11.7) $$\sum_{i=0}^{n-1} X_{t_i} \cdot (B(t_{i+1}) - B(t_i)).$$

By the Mean Value Theorem there exists for all i, t_i^*, $t_i < t_i^* < t_{i+1}$, such that $B(t_{i+1}) - B(t_i) = B'(t_i^*)(t_{i+1} - t_i)$. On substituting this into (11.7) and evaluating the sum at $\omega \in \Omega$ we obtain the Riemann sum

$$\sum_{i=0}^{n} X_{t_i}(\omega) B'(t_i^*)(t_{i+1} - t_i)$$

---

[7]Note we assume only that there are sufficiently many X-continuous paths to form a measurable set of probability 1. In particular, we do not require that the collection of *all* X-continuous paths is measurable.

of the function $t \mapsto X_t(\omega) \cdot B'(t)$. If the mapping $t \mapsto X_t(\omega)$ is continuous, the Riemann sums converge, by Proposition 7.7, as we take finer and finer partitions to $\int_0^T X_t(\omega) B'(t) dt$. If $(X_t)_{t \geq 0}$ is a continuous process, then the mapping

$$\omega \mapsto \left(\int_0^T X_t dB(t) \right)(\omega) =: \int_0^T X_t(\omega) B'(t) dt$$

is the almost sure limit of a *sequence* of measurable Riemann sums and may be regarded, with the convention we have been following,[8] as a random variable that we denote by $\int_0^T X_t dB(t)$, on $(\Omega, \mathcal{F}, P)$. The same convention allows us to consider $\left(\int_0^T X_t dB(t) \right)_{T \geq 0}$ as a stochastic process.

If $(X_t)_{t \geq 0}$ is a continuous process and B is a continuously differentiable function, then $(X_t B'(t))_{t \geq 0}$ is also a continuous process and

$$\int_0^T X_t dB(t) = \int_0^T (X_t B'(t)) dt.$$

For this reason we confine ourselves to the case $B(t) = t$.

Proposition 11.8. *If $X := (X_t)_{t \geq 0}$ is a continuous process on $(\Omega, \mathcal{F}, P)$ adapted to the filtration $(\mathcal{F}_t)_{t \geq 0}$, then $\left(\int_0^T X_t dt \right)_{T \geq 0}$ is a continuous process on $(\Omega, \mathcal{F}, P)$ adapted to the filtration $(\mathcal{F}_t)_{t \geq 0}$.*

Proof. The Riemann sums for $\int_0^T X_t dt$ are $\mathcal{F}_T$ measurable and, as the integral along each X-continuous path is the limit of a sequence of Riemann sums, $\int_0^T X_t dt$ is $\mathcal{F}_T$ measurable.

If ω is X-continuous and $\epsilon \in \mathbf{R}$ is arbitrary, then

$$\left| \int_0^{T+\epsilon} X_t(\omega) dt - \int_0^T X_t(\omega) dt \right| \leq |\epsilon| \cdot \max\{|X_t(\omega)| : T - |\epsilon| \leq t \leq T + |\epsilon|\}.$$

By continuity, $\max\{|X_t(\omega)| : T - |\epsilon| \leq t \leq T + |\epsilon|\} \longrightarrow |X_T(\omega)|$ as $\epsilon \longrightarrow 0$. This completes the proof. $\qquad \square$

To show that the stochastic process $\left(\int_0^T X_t dt \right)_{T \geq 0}$ is integrable and to define, in the next section, the Itô integral we introduce *step processes*. We use these to approximate an arbitrary continuous process in much the same way that we approximated, when constructing the Lebesgue integral, a positive bounded random variable by a sequence of simple random variables.

---

[8]The Riemann Stochastic Integral is defined using almost sure convergence and the Itô Integral using convergence in measure. These are not, unless one chooses a particular almost sure limit, defined at points on the sample space. See the remarks after Definition 6.20.

Definition 11.9. *A step process on* $(\Omega, \mathcal{F}, P)$ *adapted to the filtration* $(\mathcal{F}_t)_{t \geq 0}$ *is a stochastic process* X *of the form*

(11.8)
$$X = \sum_{i=0}^{k-1} X_{t_i} \mathbf{1}_{[t_i, t_{i+1})}$$

where X_{t_i} *is an* $\mathcal{F}_{t_i}$ *measurable random variable for all* i *and* $0 = t_0 < t_1 < \ldots < t_k$.

A step process is not usually a continuous process. However, it is Riemann integrable over *all* finite intervals along *all* paths.

For $T > 0$, we have the product measure space $(\Omega \times [0, T), \mathcal{F} \times \mathcal{B}_T, P \times \mathbf{m})$ where $\mathcal{B}_T$ is the Borel field on $[0, T)$.[9] If $X = X_{t_i} \mathbf{1}_{[t_i, t_{i+1})}$, then

$$X(t, \omega) = \begin{cases} X_{t_i}(\omega) & \text{if } t_i \leq t < t_{i+1}, \\ 0 & \text{otherwise;} \end{cases}$$

and if $B \in \mathcal{B}(\mathbf{R})$, then

$$X^{-1}(B) = \begin{cases} X_{t_i}^{-1}(B) \times [t_i, t_{i+1}) & \text{if } 0 \notin B, \\ \left(X_{t_i}^{-1}(B) \times [t_i, t_{i+1})\right) \bigcup (\Omega \times ([0, t_i) \cup [t_{i+1}, T)) & \text{if } 0 \in B. \end{cases}$$

This shows that X is $\mathcal{F} \times \mathcal{B}_T$ measurable and, on taking finite sums, every step process is $\mathcal{F} \times \mathcal{B}_T$ measurable for all $T \geq 0$.

If $X := (X_t)_{t \geq 0}$ is a stochastic process on $(\Omega, \mathcal{F}, P)$ adapted to the filtration $(\mathcal{F}_t)_{t \geq 0}$ and $(t_i^n)_{i=0}^{k_n}$ is an increasing sequence with $t_0^n = 0$, then $\{[t_i^n, t_{i+1}^n)\}_{i=0}^{k_n-1}$ partitions $[0, t_{k_n}^n)$ into a finite number of non-overlapping adjacent intervals. We let

(11.9)
$$X^n = \sum_{i=0}^{k_n-1} X_{t_i^n} \mathbf{1}_{[t_i^n, t_{i+1}^n)}$$

and maintain this notation[10] for the rest of this chapter.

Lemma 11.10. *Let* $X := (X_t)_{t \geq 0}$ *denote a continuous stochastic process on* $(\Omega, \mathcal{F}, P)$ *adapted to the filtration* $(\mathcal{F}_t)_{t \geq 0}$ *and let* $T > 0$. *Then* X *is an* $\mathcal{F} \times \mathcal{B}_T$ *measurable function.*

---

[9]Thus $A \in \mathcal{B}_T$ if and only if $A = [0, T) \cap B$ where $B \in \mathcal{B}(\mathbf{R})$. Note that this is a probability space if and only if $T = 1$. However, it is always a finite measure space, and the results we have proved for probability spaces extend, with obvious modifications, except for probabilistic interpretations. See the comments after Definition 7.15.

[10]We should write something like $X\{(t_n)_{i=0}^{k_n})\}$ to denote the dependence of X^n on $(t_i^n)_{i=0}^{k_n}$, but this notation is cumbersome and we always use X^n with the above meaning. This should not cause any confusion.

Proof. We choose $(t_i^n)_{i=0}^{k_n}$ and X_n as above and suppose $t_{k_n}^n = T$ and $\sup\{|t_{i+1}^n - t_i^n| : 1 \leq i < k_n\} \leq 1/n$. Since each X^n is a step process, the sequence $(X^n)_{n=1}^\infty$ consists of $\mathcal{F} \times \mathcal{B}_T$ measurable functions. Suppose all paths in A are X-continuous where $\mathsf{A} \in \mathcal{F}$ and $P(\mathsf{A}) = 1$. If $\omega \in \mathsf{A}$ and $t \in [0, T]$ are fixed, then, for each n, there exists a unique t_i^n, $|t - t_i^n| \leq 1/n$, such that $X^n(t, \omega) = X_t^n(\omega) = X_{t_i^n}(\omega)$. By continuity,

$$X_t^n(\omega) = X_{t_i^n}(\omega) \longrightarrow X_t(\omega) \quad \text{as} \quad n \longrightarrow \infty$$

for all $\omega \in A$ and all $t, 0 \leq t \leq T$. Since

$$P \times \mathbf{m}(\mathsf{A} \times [0, T)) = P(\mathsf{A}) \times \mathbf{m}([0, T)) = T$$

the sequence $(X^n)_{n=1}^\infty$ converges almost everywhere to X on the measure space $(\Omega, \times [0, T), \mathcal{F} \times \mathcal{B}, P \times \mathbf{m})$ and, as each X^n is $\mathcal{F} \times \mathcal{B}_T$ measurable, this completes the proof. $\qquad\qquad\square$

We now call on Fubini's Theorem, Proposition 7.33. We proved this result for a product of two probability measures, but the result extends, with a similar proof, to the product of two σ-finite measures and applies, in particular, to the product of a probability measure and Lebesgue measure on $\mathbf{R}$. For convenience we recall the result we require. If X is a measurable function on $(\Omega \times [0, T), \mathcal{F} \times \mathcal{B}, P \times \mathbf{m})$, then X is integrable if and only if all three of the following integrals are well-defined[11] and finite:

$$\int_{\Omega \times [0,T)} |X| d(P \times \mathbf{m}) = \int_\Omega \left\{ \int_{[0,T)} |X(\cdot, \omega)| d\mathbf{m} \right\} dP$$

$$= \int_{[0,T)} \left\{ \int_\Omega |X(t, \cdot)| dP \right\} d\mathbf{m}.$$

When X is integrable

$$\int_{\Omega \times [0,T)} X d(P \times \mathbf{m}) = \int_\Omega \left\{ \int_{[0,T)} X(\cdot, \omega) d\mathbf{m} \right\} dP$$

$$= \int_{[0,T)} \left\{ \int_\Omega X(t, \cdot) dP \right\} d\mathbf{m}.$$

Our final result in this section is a simple criterion which guarantees that the Riemann stochastic integral of a continuous process is an integrable random variable.

Proposition 11.11. *If* $X := (X_t)_{t \geq 0}$ *is a continuous process on* $(\Omega, \mathcal{F}, P)$, *then* $\int_0^T |X_t| dt$ *is an integrable random variable if and*[12] *only if* $\int_0^T \mathbb{E}[|X_t|] dt < \infty$. *If*

---

[11]That is unambiguously.

[12]Strictly speaking we should write $\int_0^T \mathbb{E}[X_t] d\mathbf{m}$ and not $\int_0^T \mathbb{E}[X_t] dt$ as Fubini's Theorem only shows that the mapping $t \in [0, T) \longrightarrow \mathbb{E}[X_t]$ is integrable with respect to Lebesgue measure and does not tell us if it is Riemann integrable. This incorrect use of notation will not cause any difficulties and is helpful in other ways. We use the same convention in Propositions 11.15 and 11.16 for the

$\int_0^T |X_t| dt$ *is integrable, then* $\int_0^T X_t dt$ *is integrable and*

$$\mathbb{E}[\int_0^T X_t dt] = \int_0^T \mathbb{E}[X_t] dt.$$

Proof. By Fubini's Theorem

$$\int_\Omega \left\{ \int_0^T |X_t| dt \right\} dP = \int_0^T \left\{ \int_\Omega |X_t| dP \right\} dt = \int_0^T \mathbb{E}[|X_t|] dt.$$

The left-hand side is finite if and only if the random variable $\omega \mapsto \int_0^T |X_t(\omega)| dt$ is integrable. Since $|\int_0^T X_t(\omega) dt| \leq \int_0^T |X_t(\omega)| dt$ for all X-continuous paths, Proposition 6.28(d) implies that $\int_0^T X_t dt$ is integrable whenever $\int_0^T |X_t| dt$ is integrable, and a further application of Fubini's Theorem completes the proof. $\square$

11.4. The Itô Integral

To define the Itô integral of one process with respect to another, $\int_0^T X_t dY_t$, we use the Riemann stochastic integral from the previous section and a mixture of ideas, used in constructing both the Lebesgue and Riemann integrals. In particular, we proceed from step processes to bounded processes to continuous processes. We are mainly interested in $Y_t = f(W_t)$ where $(W_t)_{t \geq 0}$ is a Wiener process. In this section we discuss the case $Y_t = W_t$.

Before proceeding, we consider informally some properties of the Wiener process. Our aim is to indicate why it should be possible to carry out certain constructions and why other approaches look unpromising.

Since $W_t - W_s$ is $N(0, t - s)$ for positive real numbers t and s, $t \neq s$, we have

$$\mathbb{E}[(W_t - W_s)^2] = |t - s| \longrightarrow 0$$

and hence

$$\mathbb{E}[(\frac{W_t - W_s}{t - s})^2] = \frac{1}{|t - s|} \longrightarrow \infty$$

as $s \longrightarrow t$. The first of these suggests that the *average* path is continuous, while the second suggests that the *average* path is nowhere differentiable. However, the average path *does not exist* and the above says nothing definite about the existence of certain types of paths. It merely suggests. However, it can be shown, although we will not prove it, that the following hold: if $0 < \alpha < 1/2 <$

---

real-valued function of a real variable $t \longrightarrow \mathbb{E}[X_t^2]$. Note, however, that the random variable $\int_0^T X_t dt$, as the almost sure limit of Riemann sums, is a Riemann integral.

β, then almost surely for s close to t and for some t^*, which depends on ω and s, with $|t - t^*| < |t - s|$,

$$(11.10) \qquad\qquad |W_t(\omega) - W_s(\omega)| < |t - s|^\alpha,$$
$$(11.11) \qquad\qquad |W_t(\omega) - W_{t^*}(\omega)| > |t - t^*|^\beta.$$

By (11.10) the process is almost surely continuous at t and by (11.11) it is almost surely non-differentiable at t. We assume *without proof* an even stronger result: *the Wiener process is a continuous process and almost surely paths are nowhere differentiable.* In the previous section limits of Riemann sums were used to define the Riemann stochastic integral. If we attempt to define $\int_0^T X_t dW_t$ by considering the limit of the Riemann sums

$$\sum_{i=0}^{k_n-1} X_{t_i^n}(\omega) \cdot (W_{t_{i+1}^n}(\omega) - W_{t_i^n}(\omega))$$

along different paths, we run into difficulties because the process lacks sufficiently many differentiable paths. To proceed we replace almost sure convergence by convergence in measure.

Definition 11.12. *Let $X = (X_t)_{t\geq 0}$ and $Y = (Y_t)_{t\geq 0}$ denote two continuous processes on the probability space $(\Omega, \mathcal{F}, P)$ both adapted to the filtration $(\mathcal{F}_t)_{t\geq 0}$. If $0 \leq S \leq T$ and there exists a random variable that we denote by $\int_S^T X_t dY_t$ such that for any sequence of partitions of $[S, T]$, $\mathcal{P}_n := (t_i^{k_n})_{i=0}^{k_n}$,*

$$\sum_{i=0}^{k_n-1} X_{t_i^n} \cdot (Y_{t_{i+1}^n} - Y_{t_i^n}) \longrightarrow \int_S^T X_t dY_t$$

in measure as $mesh(\mathcal{P}_n) \longrightarrow 0$, then we say that X is Itô integrable with respect to Y and call $\int_S^T X_t dY_t$ the[13] Itô integral of X with respect to Y.

The Itô integral, if it exists, is only defined almost surely and thus is not unique. Nevertheless, we talk about *the* Itô integral and adopt the same conventions as we did with conditional expectation.

Definition 11.12 may be difficult to verify directly as it requires initially that we identify $\int_S^T X_t dY_t$. However, by using the "*ordering*" of partitions of intervals, we can simplify the process. Suppose every sequence of Riemann

---

[13]Kiyoshi Itô was born in Hokusei-cho (Japan) in 1915. He graduated in mathematics from the Imperial University of Tokyo in 1938. While working at the Cabinet Statistics Bureau between 1938 and 1943 he continued studying probability, and in an effort to make precise, in the sense of the axiomatic approach of Kolmogorov, the intuitive results of Lévy he developed the stochastic differential and integral calculus. His first paper on this subject appeared in 1942. In 1943 he obtained an academic position at Nagoya Imperial University and in 1952 moved to Kyoto University. The Itô stochastic calculus, as it is now called, is used today in mathematics, physics, statistics, genetics, control theory, economics, financial mathematics and many other sciences and is regarded as one of the most fundamental mathematical theories developed during the 20th century.

sums with meshes tending to zero converges in measure. If $(U_n)_n$ and $(V_n)_n$ are two sequences of Riemann sums, then, letting $T_{2n} = U_n$ and $T_{2n+1} = V_n$, we obtain a further sequence of Riemann sums $(T_n)_{n=1}^{\infty}$. If the meshes of the original partitions tend to zero as $n \longrightarrow \infty$, then so does the mesh of $(T_n)_{n=1}^{\infty}$. The sequences $(U_n)_n$ and $(V_n)_n$ are both subsequences of $(T_n)_n$ and, as $(T_n)_n$ converges in measure, $(U_n)_n$ and $(V_n)_n$ converge in measure to the *same limit*. Because of this, we see that the Itô integral exists *if and only if* any sequence of Riemann sums with meshes tending to 0 has a subsequence which converges in measure. In other words, if we know that *all* sequences of Riemann sums converge in measure, then we also know that *any* limits of *any* two sequences of Riemann sums are equal almost surely.

It is important in the above Riemann sums that the process being integrated is evaluated at the *left* endpoint of *each* subinterval in the partition of $[0, T]$. A different choice would lead to a different type of integral (see Example 11.18). Since $\int_0^S X_t dW_t + \int_S^T X_t dW_t = \int_0^T X_t dW_t$ we restrict our study to integrals over $[0, T]$.

Lemma 11.13. *Let* $X := (X_t)_{t \geq 0} = \sum_{i=0}^{k-1} X_{t_i} \mathbf{1}_{[t_i, t_{i+1})}$ *be a step process on the probability space* $(\mathbf{R}^{[0,\infty)}, \mathcal{F}_\infty, W)$ *adapted to the filtration* $(\mathcal{F}_t)_{t \geq 0}$ *and suppose* $0 < t_k < T$. *Then*[14]

(a)
$$\int_0^T X_t dW_t = \sum_{i=0}^{k-1} X_{t_i}(W_{t_{i+1}} - W_{t_i});$$

(b) *if* $\mathbb{E}[|X_{t_i}|] < \infty$ *for all* i, *then* $\int_0^T X_t dW_t$ *is integrable and*
$$\mathbb{E}[\int_0^T X_t dW_t] = 0;$$

(c) *if* $\mathbb{E}[X_{t_i}^2] < \infty$ *for all* i, *then*
$$\mathbb{E}[|\int_0^T X_t dW_t|^2] = \mathbb{E}[\int_0^T X_t^2 dt] = \int_0^T \mathbb{E}[X_t^2] dt.$$

Proof. (a) By linearity we may suppose $X = X_r \mathbf{1}_{[r,s)}$ where $0 \leq r < s \leq T$. Let $\mathcal{P}_n$ denote the partition of $[0, T)$ determined by $(t_i^n)_{i=0}^{k_n}$ and suppose $t_j^n < r \leq t_{j+1}^n \leq t_l^n < s \leq t_{l+1}^n$ (we can always find j and l when the mesh of the partition is sufficiently small). The Riemann sum for X with respect to $\mathcal{P}_n$ is $\sum_{i=j+1}^l X_r(W_{t_{i+1}^n} - W_{t_i^n}) = X_r(W_{t_{l+1}^n} - W_{t_{j+1}^n})$. Since $|r - t_{j+1}^n| \leq mesh(\mathcal{P}_n)$ and $|s - t_{l+1}^n| \leq mesh(\mathcal{P}_n)$, the Riemann sums converge, as $mesh(\mathcal{P}_n) \longrightarrow 0$,

---

[14] It is necessary to carefully distinguish between dW and dW_t: dW refers to the Wiener measure W from the probability space $(\mathbf{R}^{[0,\infty)}, \mathcal{F}_\infty, W)$, while dW_t refers to the Itô integral with respect to the Wiener process $(W_t)_{t \geq 0}$.

along all W-continuous paths and hence almost surely, to $X_r(W_s - W_r)$. This proves (a).

(b) Since $X := (X_t)_{t \geq 0}$ is adapted to the filtration $(\mathcal{F}_t)_{t \geq 0}$, X_{t_i} is $\mathcal{F}_{t_i}$ measurable. Hence X_{t_i} and $W_{t_{i+1}} - W_{t_i}$ are independent random variables and, by Proposition 7.8, $\mathbb{E}[X_{t_i} \cdot (W_{t_{i+1}} - W_{t_i})] = \mathbb{E}[X_{t_i}] \cdot \mathbb{E}[W_{t_{i+1}} - W_{t_i}] = 0$. An application of (a) now completes the proof of (b).

Since $\mathbb{E}[(W_{t_{i+1}} - W_{t_i})^2] = t_{i+1} - t_i$ and $X_{t_i} X_{t_j}(W_{t_{i+1}} - W_{t_i})$ and $(W_{t_{j+1}} - W_{t_j})$ are independent random variables when $i < j$,

$$
\mathbb{E}[|\int_0^T X_t dW_t|^2] = \sum_{i=0}^{k-1} \mathbb{E}[X_{t_i}^2 (W_{t_{i+1}} - W_{t_i})^2]
$$
$$
+ \sum_{0 \leq i \neq j \leq k-1} \mathbb{E}[X_{t_i} X_{t_j}(W_{t_{i+1}} - W_{t_i})(W_{t_{j+1}} - W_{t_j})]
$$

$$
= \sum_{i=0}^{k-1} \mathbb{E}[X_{t_i}^2] \cdot \mathbb{E}[(W_{t_{i+1}} - W_{t_i})^2]
$$
$$
+ 2 \sum_{0 \leq i < j \leq k-1} \mathbb{E}[X_{t_i} X_{t_j}(W_{t_{i+1}} - W_{t_i})] \cdot \mathbb{E}[(W_{t_{j+1}} - W_{t_j})]
$$
$$
= \sum_{i=0}^{k-1} \mathbb{E}[X_{t_i}^2] \cdot (t_{i+1} - t_i) = \int_0^T \mathbb{E}[X_t^2] dt
$$
$$
= \mathbb{E}[\int_0^T X_t^2 dt], \text{ by Proposition 11.11.}
$$

This completes the proof. $\square$

Proposition 11.14. *If $X := (X_t)_{t \geq 0}$ is a continuous stochastic process on the probability space $(\mathbf{R}^{[0,\infty)}, \mathcal{F}_\infty, W)$ adapted to the filtration $(\mathcal{F}_t)_{t \geq 0}$, then X is Itô integrable with respect to the Wiener process $(W_t)_{t \geq 0}$.*

Proof. We first suppose the process is bounded; that is there exists $M > 0$ such that $|X_t(\omega)| \leq M$ for all t and ω. For each n, let $\mathcal{P}_n$ denote the partition of $[0, T)$ into adjacent subintervals given by $(t_i^n)_{i=0}^{k_n}$ and suppose $mesh(\mathcal{P}_n) \longrightarrow 0$ as $n \longrightarrow \infty$. If $X^n = \sum_{i=0}^{k_n-1} X_{t_i^n} \cdot \mathbf{1}_{[t_i^n, t_{i+1}^n)}$, then, by Lemma 11.13(a),

$$
\mathcal{R}(X, \mathcal{P}_n) := \sum_{i=0}^{k_n-1} X_{t_i^n} \cdot (W_{t_{i+1}^n} - W_{t_i^n}) = \int_0^T X_t^n dW_t
$$

is the Riemann sum for X with respect to $\mathcal{P}_n$. By Lemma 11.13(c)

$$
(11.12) \quad \left\| \int_0^T X_t^n dW_t - \int_0^T X_t^m dW_t \right\|_2^2 = \int_{\mathbf{R}^{[0,\infty)}} \int_0^T |X^n - X^m|^2 dt dW.
$$

For any pair (t, ω) and positive integers n and m

$$|X^n - X^m|^2(t, \omega) = |X_t^n - X_t^m|^2(\omega) = |X_{t_i^n}(\omega) - X_{t_j^m}(\omega)|^2 \leq 4M^2$$

for some i and j where $|t - t_i^n| \leq |t_{i+1}^n - t_i^n|$ and $|t - t_j^m| \leq |t_{j+1}^m - t_j^m|$. Hence, if ω is an X-continuous path, $|X^n - X^m|^2 \longrightarrow 0$ almost everywhere as $n, m \longrightarrow \infty$ on the product measure space $(\mathbf{R}^{[0,\infty)} \times [0, T], \mathcal{F}_\infty \times \mathcal{B}_T, W \times \mathbf{m})$. Let $(n_j)_{j=1}^\infty$ denote a strictly increasing sequence of positive integers. The Dominated Convergence Theorem and (11.12) imply $\|X^{n_{j+1}} - X^{n_j}\|_2 \longrightarrow 0$ as $j \longrightarrow \infty$ and, by Exercise 11.4, $(X^n)_{n=1}^\infty$ is an $\mathbf{L}^2$ Cauchy, and hence convergent, sequence in the product measure space. By (11.12) and Proposition 11.6, X is Itô integrable with respect to the Wiener process. This completes the proof for any continuous bounded process and shows, moreover, that

$$(11.13) \qquad \left\| \int_0^T X_t^n dW_t - \int_0^T X_t dW_t \right\|_2 \longrightarrow 0 \text{ as } n \longrightarrow \infty$$

We now remove the boundedness hypothesis. For each positive integer m let $\phi_m : \mathbf{R} \longrightarrow \mathbf{R}$ denote the continuous function with the following properties: $\phi_m(x) = x$ for $|x| \leq m$, $\phi_m(x) = 0$ for $|x| \geq m + 1$, and $\phi_m(x)$ is linear on the intervals $[-m - 1, -m]$ and $[m, m + 1]$.

Since ϕ_m is continuous, $(\phi_m(X_t))_{t \geq 0}$ is a continuous bounded, and hence integrable, process[15] on $(\mathbf{R}^{[0,\infty)}, \mathcal{F}_\infty, W)$ adapted to the filtration $(\mathcal{F}_t)_{t \geq 0}$. For each m let Y_m denote a random variable on $(\mathbf{R}^{[0,\infty)}, \mathcal{F}_\infty, W)$ such that

$$\mathcal{R}(\phi_m(X), \mathcal{P}_n) \longrightarrow Y_m$$

in measure as $n \longrightarrow \infty$. Now choose inductively a sequence of measurable sets $(\mathsf{A}_m)_{m=1}^\infty$, consisting of X-continuous paths such that $W(\mathsf{A}_m) = 1$ for all m and a sequence of subsequences[16] of $(\mathcal{P}_n)_{n=1}^\infty$, $(\mathcal{P}_{(n,m)})_{n=1}^\infty, m = 1, 2, \ldots$, such that for all integers m:

(a) $(\mathcal{P}_{(n,m+1)})_{n=1}^\infty$ is a subsequence of $(\mathcal{P}_{(n,m)})_{n=1}^\infty$,

(b) $\mathcal{R}(\phi_m(X), \mathcal{P}_{(n,m)}) \longrightarrow Y_m$ pointwise on A_m as $n \longrightarrow \infty$.

Let $\mathsf{A} := \bigcap_{m=1}^\infty \mathsf{A}_m$. Then

$$W(\mathsf{A}^c) = W\left(\bigcup_{m=1}^\infty \mathsf{A}_m^c \right) \leq \sum_{m=1}^\infty W(\mathsf{A}_m^c) = 0$$

and $W(\mathsf{A}) = 1$. Fix $\omega \in \mathsf{A}$. By path continuity there exists an integer l such that $|X_t(\omega)| \leq l$ for all $t \in [0, T]$. For $m > k > l$, $\phi_m(X)(\omega) = X(\omega) = \phi_k(X)(\omega)$ on

---

[15]If $\omega \in \mathbf{R}^{[0,\infty)}$, then $(\phi_m(X_t))(\omega) = \phi_m(X_t(\omega))$. The notation $(\phi_m(X))_t$ may be used in place of $\phi_m(X_t)$.

[16]We are using a *diagonal process*; see Proposition 3.1.

$[0, T]$. Hence

$$\mathcal{R}(\phi_m(X), \mathcal{P}_n)(\omega) = \mathcal{R}(X, \mathcal{P}_n)(\omega) = \mathcal{R}(\phi_k(X), \mathcal{P}_n)(\omega)$$

for all n and

$$\begin{aligned} Y_m(\omega) &= \lim_{n \longrightarrow \infty} \mathcal{R}(\phi_m(X), \mathcal{P}_{(n,m)})(\omega) \\ &= \lim_{n \longrightarrow \infty} \mathcal{R}(\phi_k(X), \mathcal{P}_{(n,k)})(\omega) \\ &= Y_k(\omega) \end{aligned}$$

and the sequence $(Y_m)_{m=1}^{\infty}$ converges pointwise to a finite limit on A. Since $(\mathcal{P}_{(n,n)})_{n=m}^{\infty}$ is a subsequence of $(\mathcal{P}_{n,m})_{n=1}^{\infty}$ for all m and

$$\lim_{n \longrightarrow \infty} \mathcal{R}(X, \mathcal{P}_{(n,n)}) = \lim_{m \longrightarrow \infty} Y_m$$

almost surely, this means that *any* sequence of Riemann sums for $(X_t)_{t \geq 0}$ contains a subsequence which converges almost surely to $\lim_{m \to \infty} Y_m$ and, as $\lim_{m \to \infty} Y_m$ is the same for *all choices* of Riemann sums, the Riemann sums converge in measure and $\int_0^T X_t dW_t$ exists. This completes the proof. $\qquad\square$

The above proof shows that

$$(11.14) \qquad \int_0^T \phi_m(X_t) dW_t = \int_0^T (\phi_m(X))_t dW_t \longrightarrow \int_0^T X_t dW_t$$

almost surely as $m \longrightarrow \infty$.

In the remainder of this section we discuss the process $\left(\int_0^T X_t dW_t \right)_{T \geq 0}$. If $(X_t)_{t \geq 0}$ is a continuous process, then it does not follow that the process $\left(\int_0^T X_t dW_t \right)_{T \geq 0}$ is continuous. This inconvenience can be circumvented by changing the process slightly so that continuity is achieved and all essential features preserved. A *modification* of a stochastic process $(X_t)_{t \geq 0}$ on $(\Omega, \mathcal{F}, P)$ adapted to the filtration $(\mathcal{F}_t)_{t \geq 0}$ is a stochastic process $(Y_t)_{t \geq 0}$, adapted to the same filtration, for which

$$P\{\omega \in \Omega : X_t(\omega) = Y_t(\omega)\} = 1$$

for all $t \geq 0$. If $(X_t)_{t \geq 0}$ is a continuous process, then $\left(\int_0^T X_t dW_t \right)_{T \geq 0}$ admits a continuous modification.[17]

---

[17] We have frequently seen how random variables which are almost surely equal can be treated as identical for practical purposes. A modification plays an analogous, but more delicate, role for stochastic processes.

Proposition 11.15. *Let* $(X_t)_{t\geq 0}$ *denote a continuous stochastic process on* $(\mathbf{R}^{[0,\infty)}, \mathcal{F}_\infty, W)$ *adapted to the filtration* $(\mathcal{F}_t)_{t\geq 0}$. *If* $\int_0^T \mathbb{E}[|X_t|^2]dt < \infty$, *then*

$$\mathbb{E}[|\int_0^T X_t dW_t|^2] = \int_0^T \mathbb{E}[|X_t|^2]dt = \mathbb{E}[\int_0^T |X_t|^2 dt]$$

and there exists a sequence of step processes $(X_t^n)_{t\geq 0}$ *with* $\mathbb{E}[|X_t^n|^2] < \infty$ *for all* n *and* t *such that*

$$\left\| \int_0^T X_t^n dW_t - \int_0^T X_t dW_t \right\|_2 \longrightarrow 0 \ as \ n \longrightarrow \infty.$$

Proof. By Fubini's Theorem

$$(11.15) \quad \int_0^T \mathbb{E}[|X_t|^2]dt = \int_{\mathbf{R}^{[0,\infty)}} \int_0^T |X|^2 dt dW = \mathbb{E}[\int_0^T |X_t|^2 dt].$$

First suppose the process is bounded. By (11.13) there is a sequence of Riemann sums $\left(\int_0^T X_t^{n_j} dW_t \right)_{j=1}^\infty$ which converges to $\int_0^T X_t dW_t$ in $\mathbf{L}^2(\mathbf{R}^{[0,\infty)}, \mathcal{F}_\infty, W)$ as $j \longrightarrow \infty$. If $|X_t(\omega)| \leq M$ for all t and all paths ω, then $|X_t^{n_j}(\omega)| \leq M$ for all j and all ω. Since $|X_t^{n_j}(\omega) - X_t(\omega)| \longrightarrow 0$ almost surely as $j \longrightarrow \infty$ the Dominated Convergence Theorem and Lemma 11.13(c) imply

$$\mathbb{E}[|\int_0^T X_t dW_t|^2] = \lim_{j \longrightarrow \infty} \mathbb{E}[|\int_0^T X_t^{n_j} dW_t|^2]$$

$$= \lim_{j \longrightarrow \infty} \mathbb{E}[\int_0^T |X_t^{n_j}|^2 dt]$$

$$= \lim_{j \longrightarrow \infty} \int_{\mathbf{R}^{[0,\infty)}} \int_0^T |X^{n_j}|^2 dt dW$$

$$= \int_{\mathbf{R}^{[0,\infty)}} \int_0^T |X|^2 dt dW.$$

By (11.15) this establishes the proposition for a continuous bounded process.

For an arbitrary process $(X_t)_{t\geq 0}$ let ϕ_m denote the function used in the previous proposition. By (11.14), $\int_0^T \phi_m(X_t)dW_t \to \int_0^T X_t dW_t$ almost surely as $m \to \infty$. Since $|(\phi_m(X_t))(\omega)| \leq |X_t(\omega)|$ and $|(\phi_m(X_t))(\omega) - (\phi_n(X_t))(\omega)| \to 0$ almost surely as $m, n \to \infty$, (11.15) and the Dominated Convergence Theorem imply

$$\left\| \int_0^T \phi_m(X_t)dW_t - \int_0^T \phi_n(X_t)dW_t \right\|_2 = \int_{\mathbf{R}^{[0,\infty)}} \int_0^T |\phi_m(X) - \phi_n(X)|^2 dt dW$$

$$\longrightarrow 0 \ as \ n, m \longrightarrow \infty.$$

By Proposition 11.6, the sequence $(\int_0^T \phi_m(X_t)dW_t)_{m=1}^\infty$ converges to some $Y \in \mathbf{L}^2(\mathbf{R}^{[0,\infty)}, \mathcal{F}_\infty, W)$, and, as it also converges almost surely to $\int_0^T X_t dW_t$, we have $\int_0^T X_t dW_t \in \mathbf{L}^2(\mathbf{R}^{[0,\infty)}, \mathcal{F}_\infty, W)$. Hence

$$
\text{(11.16)} \qquad
\begin{aligned}
\mathbb{E}[|\int_0^T X_t dW_t|^2] &= \lim_{m \to \infty} \mathbb{E}[|\int_0^T \phi_m(X_t) dW_t|^2] \\
&= \lim_{m \to \infty} \int_{\mathbf{R}^{[0,\infty)}} \int_0^T |\phi_m(X)|^2 dt \, dW \\
&= \int_{\mathbf{R}^{[0,\infty)}} \int_0^T |X|^2 dt \, dW.
\end{aligned}
$$

To complete the proof it suffices to combine (11.15) and (11.16). $\square$

Proposition 11.16. *Let $(X_t)_{t \geq 0}$ denote a continuous stochastic process on $(\mathbf{R}^{[0,+\infty)}, \mathcal{F}_\infty, W)$ adapted to the filtration $(\mathcal{F}_t)_{t \geq 0}$. If $\int_0^T \mathbb{E}[|X_t|^2] dt < \infty$ for all $T > 0$, then $\left(\int_0^T X_t dW_t \right)_{T \geq 0}$ is a martingale.*

Proof. Since $\int_0^T X_t dW_t$ is an almost sure limit of Riemann sums which are $\mathcal{F}_T$ measurable, it is $\mathcal{F}_T$ measurable and, by Propositions 11.4(c) and 11.15, it is integrable. It remains to show, for $0 \leq S \leq T$, that

$$
\mathbb{E}[\int_0^T X_t dW_t | \mathcal{F}_S] = \int_0^S X_t dW_t.
$$

By linearity

$$
\mathbb{E}[\int_0^T X_t dW_t | \mathcal{F}_S] = \mathbb{E}[\int_0^S X_t dW_t | \mathcal{F}_S] + \mathbb{E}[\int_S^T X_t dW_t | \mathcal{F}_S].
$$

Since $\int_0^S X_t dW_t$ is $\mathcal{F}_S$ measurable we obtain, on taking out what is known, $\mathbb{E}[\int_0^S X_t dW_t | \mathcal{F}_S] = \int_0^S X_t dW_t$.

Let $(X_t^n)_{t \geq 0}$ denote the sequence of step processes given in Proposition 11.15. If $t_i^n \geq S$ then, by Proposition 8.8(a),(b) and (c),

$$
\begin{aligned}
\mathbb{E}[X_{t_i^n}(W_{t_{i+1}^n} - W_{t_i^n}) | \mathcal{F}_S] &= \mathbb{E}[\mathbb{E}[X_{t_i^n}(W_{t_{i+1}^n} - W_{t_i^n}) | \mathcal{F}_{t_i^n}] | \mathcal{F}_S] \\
&= \mathbb{E}[X_{t_i^n} \mathbb{E}[(W_{t_{i+1}^n} - W_{t_i^n}) | \mathcal{F}_{t_i^n}] | \mathcal{F}_S] \\
&= \mathbb{E}[X_{t_i^n} \mathbb{E}[W_{t_{i+1}^n} - W_{t_i^n}] | \mathcal{F}_S] \\
&= \mathbb{E}[W_{t_{i+1}^n} - W_{t_i^n}] \cdot \mathbb{E}[X_{t_i^n} | \mathcal{F}_S] \\
&= 0.
\end{aligned}
$$

By linearity, $\mathbb{E}[\int_S^T X_t^n dW_t | \mathcal{F}_s] = 0$. If $\int_0^T \mathbb{E}[|X_t|^2] dt < \infty$, Exercise 8.4, Proposition 11.15 and Lemma 11.4(c), imply

$$
\begin{aligned}
\mathbb{E}[\,|\mathbb{E}[\int_S^T X_t dW_t | \mathcal{F}_S]|\,] &= \mathbb{E}[\,|\mathbb{E}[\int_S^T (X_t - X_t^n) dW_t | \mathcal{F}_S]|\,] \\
&\leq \mathbb{E}[\,|\int_S^T (X_t - X_t^n) dW_t|\,] \\
&= \left\| \int_S^T (X_t - X_t^n) dW_t \right\|_1 \\
&\leq \left\| \int_S^T (X_t - X_t^n) dW_t \right\|_2 \\
&\longrightarrow 0 \text{ as } n \longrightarrow \infty.
\end{aligned}
$$

Hence $\mathbb{E}[\int_S^T X_t dW_t | \mathcal{F}_S] = 0$ almost surely, and this completes the proof. $\square$

11.5. Itô's Lemma

We have now defined $\int_0^T X_t dW_t$ for a continuous process $(X_t)_{t \geq 0}$, but if we look to our original motivation in Sections 8.4 and 10.1, we see that our interest lies in $\int_0^T X_t df(t, W_t)$ where $f(t, s) = ce^{\mu t + \sigma s} = ce^{\mu t} e^{\sigma s} =: g(t) h(s)$ and g and h are well-behaved one variable real-valued functions. As a first step in analysing this integral consider $\int_0^T X_t df(W_t)$ where $f : \mathbf{R} \mapsto \mathbf{R}$ is sufficiently regular. The non-random analogue considered earlier

$$
(11.17) \qquad \int_0^T g(x) df(x) = \int_0^T g(x) f'(x) dx
$$

suggests that $\int_o^T X_t f'(W_t) dW_t$ will appear in the answer.

We require two preliminary results. As (11.17) is proved using the *Mean Value Theorem* it should not be a surprise that an extended version is used here. We could just quote the result required, but for completeness include the details. Suppose $f : \mathbf{R} \longrightarrow \mathbf{R}$ has continuous first and second derivatives. The Mean Value Theorem applied to f' on $[a, x]$, $a < x < b$, implies

$$
(11.18) \qquad f'(x) = f'(a) + (x - a) f''(\theta_x)
$$

where $a < \theta_x < x$. On integrating (11.18) and applying the *Fundamental Theorem of Calculus* we obtain

$$
f(b) - f(a) = \int_a^b f'(x) dx = f'(a) \int_a^b dx + \int_a^b (x - a) f''(\theta_x) dx.
$$

If $m = \min\{f''(x) : a \leq x \leq b\}$ and $M = \max\{f''(x) : a \leq x \leq b\}$, then

$$
\int_a^b (x - a) m \, dx \leq \int_a^b (x - a) f''(\theta_x) dx \leq \int_a^b (x - a) M \, dx
$$

and

$$\frac{m}{2}(b-a)^2 \le \int_a^b (x-a)f''(\theta_x)dx \le \frac{M}{2}(b-a)^2.$$

Hence $\int_a^b (x-a)f''(\theta_x)dx = \alpha(b-a)^2/2$ where $m \le \alpha \le M$. By the *Intermediate Value Theorem*, Proposition 7.3, f'' achieves all values between m and M on $[a, b]$. Hence there exists $c, a \le c \le b$, such that $f''(c) = \alpha$ and

$$f(b) - f(a) = f'(a)(b-a) + \frac{1}{2}f''(c)(b-a)^2.$$

Our second preliminary result isolates a technical aspect of our main proof. We maintain our previous notation and for each positive integer n let $(t_i^n)_{i=0}^{k_n}$ denote a finite set of points which partitions $[0, T)$ into k_n adjacent subintervals. The points t_{i*}^n and t_{i**}^n, in the following proof, are arbitrarily chosen to satisfy $t_i^n \le t_{i*}^n, t_{i**}^n < t_{i+1}^n$.

Proposition 11.17. *Let $(X_t)_{t\ge 0}$ and $(Y_t)_{t\ge 0}$ denote continuous processes on $(\mathbf{R}^{[0,\infty)}, \mathcal{F}_\infty, W)$, adapted to the filtration $(\mathcal{F}_t)_{t\ge 0}$. Then*

$$(11.19) \qquad S_n := \sum_{i=0}^{k_n-1} \left| (W_{t_{i+1}^n} - W_{t_i^n})^2 - (t_{i+1}^n - t_i^n) \right| \longrightarrow 0$$

and

$$(11.20) \qquad \sum_{i=0}^{k_n-1} X_{t_{i*}^n} Y_{t_{i**}^n} (W_{t_{i+1}^n} - W_{t_i^n})^2 \longrightarrow \int_0^T X_t Y_t dt$$

in measure as $\sup_{0\le i<k_n} |t_{i+1}^n - t_i^n| \longrightarrow 0$.

Proof. The random variable

$$(W_{t_{i+1}^n} - W_{t_i^n})^2 - (t_{i+1}^n - t_i^n)$$

has a $(t_{i+1}^n - t_i^n) \cdot (X^2 - 1)$ distribution where X is $N(0, 1)$. Using independent increments in the Wiener process, Proposition 7.8 and Lemma 9.14, we obtain

$$\mathbb{E}\left[\left[\sum_{i=0}^{k_n-1} \left| (W_{t_{i+1}^n} - W_{t_i^n})^2 - (t_{i+1}^n - t_i^n) \right| \right]^2 \right] = \sum_{i=0}^{k_n-1} (t_{i+1}^n - t_i^n)^2 \cdot \mathbb{E}[(X^2 - 1)^2].$$

By Exercise 1.3 and Proposition 7.18,

$$\mathbb{E}[(X^2 - 1)^2] = (1/2\pi)^{-1/2} \int_{-\infty}^{\infty} (x^2 - 1)^2 e^{-x^2/2} dx < \infty.$$

Since

$$\sum_{i=0}^{k_n-1} (t_{i+1}^n - t_i^n)^2 \le \sup_{0\le i<k_n} |t_{i+1}^n - t_i^n| \cdot \sum_{i=0}^{k_n-1} (t_{i+1}^n - t_i^n) = T \sup_{0\le i<k_n} |t_{i+1}^n - t_i^n|$$

tends to 0 as $\sup_{0 \leq i < k_n} |t^n_{i+1} - t^n_i| \longrightarrow 0$ this proves

$$\mathbb{E}[S^2_n] = \mathbb{E}\Big[\big[\sum_{i=0}^{k_n-1} |(W_{t^n_{i+1}} - W_{t^n_i})^2 - (t^n_{i+1} - t^n_i)|\big]^2\Big] \longrightarrow 0$$

as $\sup_{0 \leq i < k_n} |t^n_{i+1} - t^n_i| \longrightarrow 0$ and (11.19) follows from Proposition 11.6.

If ω is a continuous path for both $(X_t)_{t \geq 0}$ and $(Y_t)_{t \geq 0}$, then there exists M_ω such that $|X_t(\omega)| \leq M_\omega$ and $|Y_t(\omega)| \leq M_\omega$ for all $t \in [0, T]$. Hence

$$
\begin{aligned}
T_n(\omega) : \ &= \ \Big| \sum_{i=0}^{k_n-1} X_{t^n_{i*}}(\omega) Y_{t^n_{i**}}(\omega) \big((W_{t^n_{i+1}}(\omega) - W_{t^n_i}(\omega))^2 - (t^n_{i+1} - t^n_i)\big)\Big| \\
&\leq \ M^2_\omega \sum_{i=0}^{k_n-1} \big|(W_{t^n_{i+1}}(\omega) - W_{t^n_i}(\omega))^2 - (t^n_{i+1} - t^n_i))\big| \\
&= \ M^2_\omega |S_n(\omega)|.
\end{aligned}
$$

By (11.19), every subsequence $(S_{n_j})^\infty_{j=1}$ of $(S_n)^\infty_{n=1}$ contains a subsequence $(S_{n_{j_k}})^\infty_{k=1}$ which converges almost surely to 0. This implies $(T_{n_{j_k}})^\infty_{k=1}$ converges almost surely to 0. Hence

$$\sum_{i=0}^{k_n-1} X_{t^n_{i*}} Y_{t^n_{i**}} \big((W_{t^n_{i+1}} - W_{t^n_i})^2 - (t^n_{i+1} - t^n_i)\big) \longrightarrow 0$$

in measure as $\sup_{0 \leq i < k_n} |t^n_{i+1} - t^n_i| \longrightarrow 0$. By Proposition 7.7

$$\sum_{i=0}^{k_n-1} X_{t^n_{i*}} Y_{t^n_{i**}} (t^n_{i+1} - t^n_i) \longrightarrow \int_0^T X_t Y_t dt$$

almost surely as $\sup_{0 \leq i < k_n} |t^n_{i+1} - t^n_i| \longrightarrow 0$, and this completes the proof. $\qquad \square$

Example 11.18. Before proceeding to our main results we use the above lemma to show the difference between evaluating the process at the left, as we did, and the right-hand endpoints of intervals in Riemann sums. The difference, when $(X_t)_{t \geq 0} = (W_t)_{t \geq 0}$, in the notation of Proposition 11.17, is

$$\sum_{i=0}^{k_n-1} W_{t^n_{i+1}}(W_{t^n_{i+1}} - W_{t^n_i}) - \sum_{i=0}^{k_n-1} W_{t^n_i}(W_{t^n_{i+1}} - W_{t^n_i}) \ = \ \sum_{i=0}^{k_n-1}(W_{t^n_{i+1}} - W_{t^n_i})^2$$

and, by (11.20), this converges in measure to T. This shows that

$$\sum_{i=0}^{k_n-1} W_{t^n_{i+1}}(W_{t^n_{i+1}} - W_{t^n_i}) \not\longrightarrow \int_0^T W_t dW_t$$

in measure as $\sup_{0 \leq i < k_n} |t^n_{i+1} - t^n_i| \longrightarrow 0$.

Equation (11.20) plays a fundamental role in proving all versions of Itô's Lemma and may be written symbolically as

$$(dW_t)^2 = dt.$$

Moreover, by taking limits of the Riemann sums

$$\sum_{i=0}^{k_n-1} (t_{i+1}^n - t_i^n)^2 \quad \text{and} \quad \sum_{i=0}^{k_n-1} (t_{i+1}^n - t_i^n) \cdot (W_{t_{i+1}^n} - W_{t_i^n})$$

we obtain the further symbolic formulae

$$(dt)^2 = 0 \quad \text{and} \quad dt \cdot dW_t = dW_t \cdot dt = 0.$$

Now suppose $f : \mathbf{R} \mapsto \mathbf{R}$ has continuous first and second derivatives. Let ω denote a W-continuous path and let $0 \leq i < k_n$. On applying the extended Mean Value Theorem to the function f on the interval $[W_{t_i^n}(\omega), W_{t_{i+1}^n}(\omega)]$ we obtain $\alpha \in [W_{t_i^n}(\omega), W_{t_{i+1}^n}(\omega)]$ such that

$$\begin{aligned}
f(W_{t_{i+1}^n}(\omega)) - f(W_{t_i^n}(\omega)) &= f'(W_{t_i^n}(\omega)) \cdot (W_{t_{i+1}^n}(\omega) - W_{t_i^n}(\omega)) \\
&\quad + \frac{1}{2} f''(\alpha) \cdot (W_{t_{i+1}^n}(\omega) - W_{t_i^n}(\omega))^2.
\end{aligned}$$

Since the function $t \longrightarrow W_t(\omega)$ is continuous on $[t_i^n, t_{i+1}^n]$, the *Intermediate Value Theorem* implies that there exists $t_i^* \in [t_i^n, t_{i+1}^n]$, which depends on ω, i and n, such that $\alpha = W_{t_i^*}(\omega)$.

Let $X := (X_t)_{t \geq 0}$ denote a continuous process on $(\mathbf{R}^{[0,\infty)}, \mathcal{F}_\infty, W)$, adapted to the filtration $(\mathcal{F}_t)_{t \geq 0}$. Let A denote an $\mathcal{F}_\infty$ measurable subset of $\mathbf{R}^{[0,\infty)}$, with $W(\mathsf{A}) = 1$, consisting of paths which are both X and W continuous. For all $\omega \in \mathsf{A}$ we have

$$(11.21) \qquad \sum_{i=0}^{k_n-1} X_{t_i^n}(\omega)\Big(f(W_{t_{i+1}^n}(\omega)) - f(W_{t_i^n}(\omega))\Big)$$

$$(11.22) \qquad = \sum_{i=0}^{k_n-1} X_{t_i^n}(\omega) \cdot f'(W_{t_i^n}(\omega))\big(W_{t_{i+1}^n}(\omega) - W_{t_i^n}(\omega)\big)$$

$$(11.23) \qquad + \frac{1}{2} \sum_{i=0}^{k_n-1} X_{t_i^n}(\omega) \cdot f''(W_{t_i^*}(\omega))\big(W_{t_{i+1}^n}(\omega) - W_{t_i^n}(\omega)\big)^2.$$

By Propositions 11.14 and 11.17 the series in (11.22) and (11.23) converge in measure to $\int_0^T X_t f'(W_t) dW_t$ and $\frac{1}{2} \int_0^T X_t f''(W_t) dt$, respectively, as $\sup_{0 \leq i < k_n} |t_{i+1}^n - t_i^n| \longrightarrow 0$. Hence the sequence in (11.21) converges in measure as $\sup_{0 \leq i < k_n} |t_{i+1}^n - t_i^n| \longrightarrow 0$ and $\int_0^T X_t df(W_t)$ is well defined. We have proved the following stochastic version of the *Fundamental Theorem of Calculus*.

Proposition 11.19. *If $f : \mathbf{R} \longrightarrow \mathbf{R}$ has continuous first and second derivatives and $(X_t)_{t\geq 0}$ is a continuous process on $(\mathbf{R}^{[0,\infty)}, \mathcal{F}_\infty, W)$ adapted to the filtration $(\mathcal{F}_t)_{t\geq 0}$, then*

$$(11.24) \quad \int_0^T X_t df(W_t) = \int_0^T X_t f'(W_t) dW_t + \frac{1}{2} \int_0^T X_t f''(W_t) dt.$$

The result in Proposition 11.19 is a special case of Itô's Lemma. The above techniques allow us, as we shall soon see, to generalize easily this result and prove rigorously another special case of Itô's Lemma, Proposition 11.20. A rigorous proof of the usual version of Itô's Lemma (Proposition 11.23) uses, in a general sort of way the methods we have developed, but as it is more complicated and technical we confine ourselves to a non-rigorous symbolic proof. For this purpose we have already introduced *symbolic differential notation*, and now rewrite (11.24) in this fashion as

$$(11.25) \qquad df(W_t) = f'(W_t) dW_t + \frac{1}{2} f''(W_t) dt.$$

We now integrate with respect to the process $(g(t)f(W_t))_{t\geq 0}$ where $f, g : \mathbf{R} \longrightarrow \mathbf{R}$. The following calculation is standard and used to obtain product rules when differentiating:

$$g(t_{i+1}^n) f(W_{t_{i+1}^n}) - g(t_i^n) f(W_{t_i^n})$$
$$= \big(g(t_{i+1}^n) f(W_{t_{i+1}^n}) - g(t_i^n) f(W_{t_{i+1}^n})\big) \quad + \quad \big(g(t_i^n) f(W_{t_{i+1}^n}) - g(t_i^n) f(W_{t_i^n})\big)$$
$$= f(W_{t_{i+1}^n})(g(t_{i+1}^n) - g(t_i^n)) \quad + \quad g(t_i^n)(f(W_{t_{i+1}^n}) - f(W_{t_i^n})).$$

If g is continuously differentiable and f is twice continuously differentiable, then Proposition 11.19 and results in Section 11.3 show that the Riemann sums for the continuous adapted process $(X_t)_{t\geq 0}$ with respect to $(g(t)f(W_t))_{t\geq 0}$ converges in measure as we take finer and finer partitions and we obtain:

$$d(g(t)f(W_t)) \quad = \quad f(W_t)g'(t)dt + g(t)df(W_t)$$
$$= \quad f(W_t)g'(t)dt + g(t)f'(W_t)dW_t + \frac{1}{2}g(t)f''(W_t)dt.$$

Formally we have the following proposition.

Proposition 11.20. *If $f, g : \mathbf{R} \mapsto \mathbf{R}$ where g is continuously differentiable and f is twice continuously differentiable, then for any continuous process $(X_t)_{t\geq 0}$ on $(\mathbf{R}^{[0,\infty)}, \mathcal{F}_\infty, W)$ adapted to the filtration $(\mathcal{F}_t)_{t\geq 0}$*

$$\int_0^T X_t d(g(t)f(W_t)) \quad = \quad \int_0^T X_t \big(f(W_t)g'(t) + \frac{1}{2}g(t)f''(W_t)\big) dt$$
$$+ \quad \int_0^T X_t g(t) f'(W_t) dW_t.$$

Example 11.21. (a) If $(X_t)_{t\geq 0}$ is any continuous process, then it is easily seen, by examining Riemann sums, that $\int_0^T dX_t = X_T - X_0$.

(b) Let $f(t) = t^2$ for all $t \in \mathbf{R}$. Since $f'(t) = 2t$ and $f''(t) = 2$, Proposition 11.19 and (a) imply

$$W_T^2 = \int_0^T d(W_t^2) = 2\int_0^T W_t dW_t + \frac{1}{2}\int_0^T 2dt = 2\int_0^T W_t dW_t + T.$$

By Proposition 11.16, $(W_t^2 - t)_{t\geq 0}$ is a martingale, and we recover Proposition 9.15(a).

(c) In Proposition 10.1 we showed, under reasonable assumptions, that the share price X_t satisfied $X_t = X_0 \exp(\mu t + \sigma W_t)$ for all $t \geq 0$. We apply Proposition 11.20 with $f(t) = X_0 \exp(\sigma t)$ and $g(t) = \exp(\mu t)$ and obtain, using the above symbolic notation,

$$
\begin{aligned}
dX_t &= g'(t)f(W_t)dt + g(t)f'(W_t)dW_t + \frac{1}{2}g(t)f''(W_t)dt \\
&= \mu e^{\mu t}X_0 e^{\sigma W_t}dt + e^{\mu t}\sigma X_0 e^{\sigma W_t}dW_t + \frac{1}{2}e^{\mu t}\sigma^2 X_0 e^{\sigma W_t}dt \\
&= \left(\mu + \frac{1}{2}\sigma^2\right)X_0 \exp(\mu t + \sigma W_t)dt + \sigma X_0 \exp(\mu t + \sigma W_t)dW_t \\
&= \left(\mu + \frac{1}{2}\sigma^2\right)X_t dt + \sigma X_t dW_t.
\end{aligned}
$$

Hence

$$(11.26) \quad X_T - X_0 = \int_0^T dX_t = \int_0^T \left(\mu + \frac{1}{2}\sigma^2\right)X_t dt + \int_0^T \sigma X_t dW_t.$$

By Proposition 11.16, $(X_t)_{t\geq 0}$ is a martingale if $\mu = -\sigma^2/2$, a result we already proved in Proposition 9.15(b). In Proposition 10.7 we showed that an appropriate *change of measure* turned $(X_t)_{t\geq 0}$ into a martingale, and using this result and the above we obtain

$$X_T - X_0 = \int_0^T \sigma X_t d\widetilde{W}_t$$

where $(\widetilde{W}_t)_{t\geq 0}$ is a Wiener process. Informally $dX_t = \sigma X_t d\widetilde{W}_t$.

(d) Let $X_t = \sigma e^{-\alpha t}\int_0^t e^{\alpha s}dW_s$. The process $(X_t)_{t\geq 0}$ is called an *Ornstein-Uhlenbeck Process*. If $Y_t := \int_0^t e^{\alpha s}dW_s$; then $dY_t = e^{\alpha t}dW_t$, and if $g(t) = \sigma e^{-\alpha t}$, then $X_t = g(t)Y_t$. Hence

$$
\begin{aligned}
dX_t &= g'(t)Y_t dt + g(t)dY_t \\
&= -\alpha\sigma e^{-\alpha t}Y_t dt + \sigma e^{-\alpha t}e^{\alpha t}dW_t \\
&= -\alpha X_t dt + \sigma dW_t
\end{aligned}
$$

and, on using (a),

$$(11.27) \quad X_T = -\alpha \int_0^T X_t dt + \sigma \int_0^T dW_t = -\alpha \int_0^T X_t dt + \sigma W_T.$$

Equations (11.26) and (11.27) are stochastic integral equations. In the above examples we started with a process and showed it satisfied a certain stochastic integral equation. In the next section we meet the more usual situation and need to solve a given stochastic integral equation.

Stochastic processes which admit a special integral representation, such as those in Propositions 11.19 and 11.20 and in (11.26) and (11.27), are called *Itô processes*.

Definition 11.22. *A stochastic process* $(X_t)_{t\geq0}$ *is called an Itô process if there exist continuous processes* $(Y_t)_{t\geq0}$ *and* $(Z_t)_{t\geq0}$ *on* $(\mathbf{R}^{[0,\infty)}, \mathcal{F}_\infty, W)$ *adapted to the filtration* $(\mathcal{F}_t)_{t\geq0}$ *such that for all* $t \geq 0$, $\int_0^t |Y_s| ds < \infty$, $\int_0^t \mathbb{E}[Z_s^2] ds < \infty$, *and*

$$(11.28) \qquad X_t - X_0 = \int_0^t Y_s ds + \int_0^t Z_s dW_s.$$

Informally we write

$$dX_t = Y_t dt + Z_t dW_t.$$

Itô processes have a particularly useful *uniqueness* property. If

$$\int_0^t Y_s ds + \int_0^t Z_s dW_s = \int_0^t U_s ds + \int_0^t V_s dW_s$$

for all t, then $Y_t = U_t$ and $Z_t = V_t$ almost surely as random variables for all t.

The most popular version of Itô's Lemma, Proposition 11.23, gives an explicit formula for $(u(t, X_t))_{t\geq0}$, as an Itô process, when $(X_t)_{t\geq0}$ is an Itô process and $u : \mathbf{R}^2 \mapsto \mathbf{R}$ has continuous first and second order *partial derivatives*. If u is a function of (t, s), let $u_1 = \frac{\partial u}{\partial t}$, $u_2 = \frac{\partial u}{\partial s}$, $u_{11} = \frac{\partial^2 u}{\partial t^2}$, $u_{12} = \frac{\partial^2 u}{\partial t \partial s}$, etc.

Proposition 11.23. *(Itô's Lemma) Let* $u : \mathbf{R}^2 \longrightarrow \mathbf{R}$ *have continuous first and second order partial derivatives and let* $(X_t)_{t\geq0}$ *denote an Itô process with representation* (11.28). *A modified version of* $(u(t, X_t))_{t\geq0}$ *is an Itô process with representation*

$$u(t, X_t) - u(0, X_0) = \int_0^t \left(u_1(s, X_s) + u_2(s, X_s) Y_s + \frac{1}{2} u_{22}(s, X_s) Z_s^2 \right) ds$$

$$+ \int_0^t u_2(s, X_s) Z_s dW_s.$$

To derive the formula in Proposition 11.23 *symbolically* we use Taylor series expansions in *two* variables:

$$u(t + \Delta t, s + \Delta s) - u(t, s) \approx u_1(t, s)\Delta t + u_2(t, s)\Delta s + \frac{1}{2}u_{11}(t, s)(\Delta t)^2$$

$$+ \ u_{12}(t, s)\Delta t \Delta s + \frac{1}{2}u_{22}(t, s)(\Delta s)^2.$$

Since $dX_t = Y_t dt + Z_t W_t$ we have

$$\begin{aligned} dt \cdot X_t &= dt(Y_t dt + Z_t dW_t) \\ &= Y_t(dt)^2 + Z_t(dt \cdot W_t) \\ &= 0 \end{aligned}$$

and

$$\begin{aligned} (dX_t)^2 &= (Y_t dt + Z_t W_t)^2 \\ &= Y_t^2(dt)^2 + 2Y_t Z_t(dt \cdot W_t) + Z_t^2(dW_t)^2 \\ &= Z_t^2 dt. \end{aligned}$$

Using the Taylor series expansion we obtain

$$du(t, X_t) = u_1(t, X_t)dt + u_2(t, X_t)dX_t + \frac{1}{2}u_{11}(t, X_t)(dt)^2 + u_{12}(t, X_t)dt \cdot dX_t$$

$$+ \frac{1}{2}u_{22}(t, X_t)(dX_t)^2$$

$$= u_1(t, X_t)dt + u_2(t, X_t)(Y_t dt + Z_t dW_t) + \frac{1}{2}u_{22}(t, X_t)Z_t^2 dt$$

$$= \left(u_1(t, X_t) + u_2(t, X_t)Y_t + \frac{1}{2}u_{22}(t, X_t)Z_t^2\right)dt + u_2(t, X_t)Z_t^2 dW_t.$$

Symbolic manipulations, such as the above, are one of the techniques employed daily by research mathematicians when seeking new results. These often lead, especially when guided by a good intuitive understanding of the subject area, to correct results which must afterwards be proved rigorously. The ancient Greeks used infinity in this way.

11.6. Call Options 4

We return to the problem, left over from Chapters 8 and 10, of hedging any claim on a call option. We recall that $X_t := X_0 e^{\mu t + \sigma W_t}$ denotes the share price at time $t \geq 0$, r is the interest rate, k is the strike price and T is the maturity date on the option. For convenience we let $c := \mu + \frac{1}{2}\sigma^2$. If V_t is the value of the option at time t, then $V_T = (X_T - k)^+$. To hedge any claim on the option, as usual for one share, a portfolio of θ_t shares and β_t units of a riskless bond are held at time t. We suppose that one unit of the bond is worth $B(t) = e^{rt}$ at time t. Hence $dB(t) = B'(t)dt = re^{rt}dt$. This provides a hedge if

$$(11.29) \qquad V_t = \theta_t X_t + e^{rt}\beta_t$$

for all t, $0 \le t \le T$. By (8.42)

$$(11.30) \qquad \int_0^t \theta_s dX_s + \int_0^t re^{rs}\beta_s ds = \int_0^t dV_s = V_t - V_0$$

and hence, by Example 11.21(c),

$$(11.31) \qquad V_t - V_0 = \int_0^t (c\theta_s X_s + re^{rs}\beta_s)ds + \int_0^t \sigma\theta_s X_s dW_s$$

for $0 \le t \le T$. By (11.29), $\beta_s = e^{-rs}(V_s - \theta_s X_s)$, and substituting this into (11.31) we obtain

$$\begin{aligned} V_t - V_0 &= \int_0^t \left(c\theta_s X_s + re^{rs}(e^{-rs}(V_s - \theta_s X_s)) \right)ds + \int_0^t \sigma\theta_s X_s dW_s \\ &= \int_0^t \left((c-r)\theta_s X_s + rV_s \right)ds + \int_0^t \sigma\theta_s X_s dW_s. \end{aligned}$$

Now suppose $V_t = u(t, X_t)$ where $u : \mathbf{R}^2 \longrightarrow \mathbf{R}$ is twice continuously differentiable. To determine the hedging strategy we must find u. The seller's price will then be $u(0, X_0)$. To complete our programme we must show that this coincides with the price given in Proposition 10.5. By Itô's Lemma (Proposition 11.23)

$$\begin{aligned} V_t - V_0 &= \int_0^t \left(u_1(s, X_s) + cX_s u_2(s, X_s) + \frac{\sigma^2}{2}X_s^2 u_{22}(s, X_s) \right)ds \\ &\quad + \int_0^t \sigma X_s u_2(s, X_s)dW_s. \end{aligned}$$

We now have two Itô representations for the process $(V_t)_{t \ge 0}$. By uniqueness, $\sigma X_t \theta_t = \sigma X_t u_2(t, X_t)$, and since $X_t > 0$ for all t, this implies $\theta_t = u_2(t, X_t)$. Moreover,

$$\begin{aligned} (c-r)\theta_t X_t + rV_t &= (c-r)X_t u_2(t, X_t) + ru(t, X_t) \\ &= u_1(t, X_t) + cX_t u_2(t, X_t) + \frac{\sigma^2}{2}X_t^2 u_{22}(t, X_t) \end{aligned}$$

and hence

$$(11.32) \qquad ru(t, X_t) = u_1(t, X_t) + rX_t u_2(t, X_t) + \frac{\sigma^2}{2}X_t^2 u_{22}(t, X_t)$$

almost surely as random variables. Given any positive real number x and any $t > 0$ we can choose a path ω such that $X_t(\omega) = x$. Evaluating (11.32) at ω we obtain

$$(11.33) \qquad ru(t, x) = u_1(t, x) + rxu_2(t, x) + \frac{\sigma^2}{2}x^2 u_{22}(t, x).$$

This is a *partial differential equation.*[18] The conditions on the option mean that our solution to (11.33) must satisfy the boundary condition $u(T, x) = (x - k)^+$. It is generally quite difficult, and often impossible, to obtain explicit solutions for partial differential equations. In this particular case we know, from Proposition 10.5, the only solution that will achieve our final goal of hedging any claim on the option. It is thus a matter of verifying that it satisfies (11.33). We recall that $N(x) = (2\pi)^{-1/2} \int_{-\infty}^{x} \exp(-y^2/2) dy$ and let $n(x) := N'(x) = e^{-x^2/2}/\sqrt{2\pi}$.

Proposition 11.24. *The portfolio consisting of*

$$(11.34) \qquad \theta_t = N\left(\frac{\log(\frac{X_t}{k}) + (r + \frac{1}{2}\sigma^2)(T - t)}{\sigma\sqrt{T - t}}\right)$$

shares and

$$(11.35) \qquad \beta_t = -ke^{-rT}N\left(\frac{\log(\frac{X_t}{k}) + (r - \frac{1}{2}\sigma^2)(T - t)}{\sigma\sqrt{T - t}}\right)$$

riskless bonds at time t, $0 \le t \le T$, hedges any claim on an option for one share with strike price k, maturity date T, given that $X_t = X_0 e^{\mu t + \sigma W_t}$ is the share price at time t, the interest rate r is fixed for the duration of the option and σ, the volatility, is constant. Moreover, the value V_t of the option at time t is given by

$$V_t = \theta_t X_t + \beta_t e^{rt}.$$

Proof. We need to show that $u(t, x)$ given by

$$xN\left(\frac{\log(\frac{x}{k}) + (r + \frac{1}{2}\sigma^2)(T - t)}{\sigma\sqrt{T - t}}\right) - ke^{-r(T-t)}N\left(\frac{\log(\frac{x}{k}) + (r - \frac{1}{2}\sigma^2)(T - t)}{\sigma\sqrt{T - t}}\right)$$

solves (11.33) and satisfies the above boundary condition. If $x > k$ and $t < T$, then

$$\lim_{t \longrightarrow T} N\left(\frac{\log(\frac{x}{k}) + (r \pm \frac{1}{2}\sigma^2)(T - t)}{\sigma\sqrt{T - t}}\right) = N(+\infty) = 1,$$

while if $x < k$ and $t < T$, then

$$\lim_{t \longrightarrow T} N\left(\frac{\log(\frac{x}{k}) + (r \pm \frac{1}{2}\sigma^2)(T - t)}{\sigma\sqrt{T - t}}\right) = N(-\infty) = 0.$$

This implies

$$u(T, x) = \lim_{t \to T} u(t, x) = \begin{cases} x - k & \text{if } x \ge k \\ 0 & \text{if } x \le k \end{cases} = (x - k)^+$$

---

[18]Equation (11.33) does not involve the drift μ and hence the solution will also be independent of the drift. If we had known this when we obtained Propositions 10.1 and 10.2, we could have let $\mu = -\sigma^2/2$ and obtained the required martingale immediately without the analysis in Section 10.2. Equation (11.32) is sometimes called the *Black-Scholes equation.*

and u satisfies the required boundary condition at $t = T$. Moreover, when $t = 0$ we recover the Black-Scholes formula.

To verify that u is a solution for (11.33) is routine but tedious. It consists of taking partial derivatives and substituting them into (11.33). The following substitutions help:

$$g(t,x) := \frac{\log(\frac{x}{k}) + (r + \frac{1}{2}\sigma^2)(T - t)}{\sigma\sqrt{T - t}} \quad , \quad h(t,x) := g(t,x) - \sigma\sqrt{T - t}.$$

Using this notation we have

$$\sqrt{2\pi}n(g(t,x)) = \exp\left\{-\frac{1}{2}\left(h(t,x) + \sigma\sqrt{T - t}\right)^2\right\}$$

$$= \exp\left\{-\frac{1}{2}h(t,x)^2\right\} \cdot \exp\left(-\sigma h(t,x)\sqrt{T - t} - \frac{1}{2}\sigma^2(T - t)\right)$$

$$= \sqrt{2\pi}n(h(t,x)) \exp\left(\log(k/x) - (r - \frac{\sigma^2}{2})(T - t) - \frac{\sigma^2}{2}(T - t)\right)$$

$$= \sqrt{2\pi}n(h(t,x))\frac{k}{x}e^{-r(T-t)}$$

and hence

(11.36) $$xn(g(t,x)) = ke^{-r(T-t)}n(h(t,x)).$$

On taking partial derivatives and substituting (11.36) we obtain

$$g_1(t,x) = \frac{\log(x/k)}{2\sigma(T - t)^{3/2}} - \frac{(r + \frac{1}{2}\sigma^2)}{2\sigma\sqrt{T - t}},$$

$$h_1(t,x) = g_1(t,x) + \frac{\sigma}{2\sqrt{T - t}},$$

$$g_2(t,x) = h_2(t,x) = \frac{1}{x\sigma\sqrt{T - t}},$$

$$u(t,x) = xN(g(t,x)) - ke^{-r(T-t)}N(h(t,x)),$$

$$u_1(t,x) = -\frac{x\sigma n(g(t,x))}{2\sqrt{T - t}} - rke^{-r(T-t)}N(h(t,x)),$$

$$u_2(t,x) = N(g(t,x))$$

and

$$u_{22}(t,x) = \frac{n(g(t,x))}{x\sigma\sqrt{T - t}}.$$

Hence

$$u_1(t,x) + rxu_2(t,x) + \frac{1}{2}\sigma^2x^2u_{22}(t,x) = rxN(g(t,x)) - rke^{-r(T-t)}N(h(t,x))$$

$$= ru(t,x)$$

as required. Since we have already observed that $\theta_t = u_2(t, X_t) = N(g(t, X_t))$, and as

$$\begin{aligned}
\beta_t &= e^{-rt}(V_t - \theta_t X_t) \\
&= e^{-rt}(u(t, X_t) - u_2(t, X_t)X_t) \\
&= -ke^{-rT}N(h(t, X_t)),
\end{aligned}$$

the formulae for a hedging portfolio are now readily available. On substituting we obtain (11.34) and (11.35). This completes the proof. $\qquad\square$

Since $0 \leq N(x) \leq 1$ the amount of shares in the portfolio will always be less than 1 and the borrowings will never exceed the strike price k. It can be shown that the agreed fair price for a call option, obtained in Propositions 9.5 and 11.24, is an *arbitrage-free price*.

11.7. Summary

Now that we have completed our programme and achieved our goal it is time to briefly summarize the situation. A number of questions, mathematical and financial, are appropriate. How realistic is the Black-Scholes model? What role does the Black-Scholes model play today in pricing options? How advanced and useful are the mathematics we have developed?

The model we have developed is, perhaps, the simplest available showing the fundamental ideas, financial and mathematical, which arise in this complex area of applied mathematics. It is only a model and no model is a perfect representation of the real world. A model can be judged only in comparison with the alternatives. The Black-Scholes model was a *big improvement* on what preceded it. Since 1973 a large amount of research has appeared, devoted to refining this model, and more realistic models are now available. All, however, involve the probabilistic methods of the stochastic calculus and it could not be otherwise, as any attempt to predict future events must involve a random component. Consider the Black-Scholes model a first, rather than a final, approximation to the real world of option pricing.

The jury is still out on the long-term role of the Black-Scholes model. Key assumptions in the model are that share prices change continuously, that re-balancing the hedging portfolio is continuous and costless, that there are no transaction costs, that the interest rate is constant, that *all* information on the history of the stock up to time t is reflected in the share price X_t and that the discrete approximation converges to the correct (normal) limit. Traders freely admit that the overall combination is unrealistic. On the other hand, it is possible to use market prices for options and the Black-Scholes formula to estimate *volatility*, and the formula is used by some companies to calculate employee options as operating expenses. It is quite likely that many further uses will be found for this remarkable model.

Mathematically we have taken a direct route to the Black-Scholes formula, and the reader who goes further will find that the methods we have used in this book are indeed basic. Moreover, we have not proved all the results that we used, for example; continuity of Wiener processes, the Central Limit Theorem, and the final version of Itô's Lemma (Proposition 11.23). The interested reader may wish to consult the literature on these topics. This will expose the reader to more advanced tools, such as Hilbert spaces, characteristic functions, stopping times, etc., and lead to a more streamlined approach and a deeper understanding of the material in this book. It will also be more demanding and lead to still further questions. If you keep going you will eventually come to problems and questions which have not been asked, or if asked, have not been answered in the literature. This is the frontier of knowledge, and those who struggle seeking answers to these questions are engaged in *research*.

In the meantime, as the main results in this book have been extended, and as we are now sufficiently advanced to understand and appreciate some of these, we conclude by mentioning two particularly important results.

In Example 11.21(c) we saw that the share price satisfied the stochastic differential equation

$$dX_t = (\mu + \frac{1}{2}\sigma^2)X_t dt + \sigma X_t dW_t$$

and that, by an appropriate change of measure, it satisfied

$$dX_t = \sigma X_t d\widetilde{W}_t$$

where $(W_t)_{t\geq 0}$ and $(\widetilde{W}_t)_{t\geq 0}$ are Wiener processes. By Proposition 11.16 this change of measure turned the share price into a martingale. More generally, given a stochastic differential equation

$$dX_t = f(X_t)dt + \sigma(X_t)dW_t$$

and a function g, then under fairly general conditions on f, g and σ, the *Girsanov Theorem* gives an explicit change of measure formula which shows that $(X_t)_{t\geq 0}$ satisfies the stochastic differential equation

$$dX_t = g(X_t)dt + \sigma(X_t)d\widetilde{W}_t.$$

Proposition 11.24 was obtained by solving the partial differential equation (11.33) which we derived from the stochastic equation (11.32). This is a special case of the following proposition which connects partial and stochastic differential equations.

Proposition 11.25. (*Feymann-Kac Formula*)[19] *If $r \in \mathbf{R}$, μ, σ and ϕ are sufficiently smooth functions of one real variable, then the solution of the partial differential equation*

$$ru(t,x) = u_1(t,x) + \mu(x)u_2(t,x) + \frac{\sigma^2(x)}{2}u_{22}(t,x)$$

with boundary condition $u(T,x) = \phi(x)$ is given by

$$u(t,x) = e^{-r(T-t)}\mathbb{E}[\phi(X_T)|X_t = x]$$

where $(X_t)_{t \geq 0}$ satisfies the stochastic differential equation

$$dX_t = \mu(X_t)dt + \sigma(X_t)dW_t$$

and $(W_t)_{t \geq 0}$ is a Wiener process adapted to the filtration $(\mathcal{F}_t)_{t \geq 0}$.

11.8. Exercises

(11.1) If $X_n \longrightarrow X$ and $Y_n \longrightarrow Y$ in measure as $n \longrightarrow \infty$ and $a, b \in \mathbf{R}$, show that $aX_n + bY_n \longrightarrow aX + bY$ in measure as $n \longrightarrow \infty$.

(11.2) Let $(X_n)_{n=1}^{\infty}$ and $(Y_n)_{n=1}^{\infty}$ denote sequences of random variables on the probability space $(\Omega, \mathcal{F}, P)$. If $X_n \longrightarrow 0$ in measure as $n \longrightarrow \infty$ and $(Y_n)_{n=1}^{\infty}$ is almost surely bounded, that is there exists an $\mathcal{F}$ measurable set $A \subset \Omega, P(A) = 1$ and for all $\omega \in A$, $\sup\{|Y_n(\omega)| : n = 1, 2 \ldots\} < \infty$, show that $X_n \cdot Y_n \longrightarrow 0$ in measure as $n \longrightarrow \infty$.

(11.3) Show that every Cauchy sequence in $\mathbf{L}^1(\Omega, \mathcal{F}, P)$ converges and contains an almost surely convergent subsequence. Construct an example showing that a convergent sequence in $\mathbf{L}^1(\Omega, \mathcal{F}, P)$ is not always almost surely convergent.

(11.4) Show that a sequence $(X_n)_{n=1}^{\infty}$ in $\mathbf{L}^i(\Omega, \mathcal{F}, P), i = 1, 2$, is a Cauchy sequence if and only if for any strictly increasing sequence of positive integers $(n_j)_{j=1}^{\infty}$, $\lim_{j \longrightarrow \infty} \|X_{n_{j+1}} - X_{n_j}\|_i = 0$.

---

[19]Richard Phillips Feynman (1918-1988) was born in Far Rockaway, New York. He studied theoretical physics as an undergraduate at MIT and as a graduate student at Princeton. During World War II he worked on the Manhattan Project and at Los Alamos. After the war he held professorships at Cornell and Caltech and was awarded the Nobel Prize for physics in 1965 for his contributions to quantum electrodynamics. He was a popular lecturer and wrote many articles and books aimed at communicating the nature of physics and scientific creativity. We strongly recommend his highly entertaining best selling autobiography *Surely, you're joking, Mr. Feynman*. Marc Kac (1914-1984) was born in Krzemieniec (Poland) and educated at the University of Lvov. Hugo Steinhaus was one of his teachers. In 1938 he emigrated to the USA, where he subsequently held academic positions at Cornell, Rockfeller University (New York) and the University of Southern California. He made fundamental contributions to probability theory and its application to statistical mechanics and number theory. An important tool in quantum mechanics is the *Feynman-Kac line integral*. Kac won many awards for his expository articles on pure and applied mathematics, including the Chauvenet Prize in 1968 from the Mathematical Association of America for his article *Can one hear the shape of a drum?*.

(11.5) Show that there exists a continuous function $f : \mathbf{R} \mapsto \mathbf{R}$ and a Wiener process $(W_t)_{t \geq 0}$ such that $\int_0^1 \mathbb{E}[f(W_t)^2] dt = \infty$.

(11.6) Use Proposition 11.19 with $f(t) = t^3$ and $X_t = 1$ and Proposition 11.20 with $f(t) = g(t) = t$ and $X_t = 1$ to prove the result in Exercise 9.3.

(11.7) Find the expected values and the variances of the random variables $\int_0^T t dW_t$ and $\int_0^T W_t dt$. Are these random variables independent?

(11.8) Let $(W_t)_{t \geq 0}$ denote a Wiener process and let $\mathcal{F}_t$ denote the σ-field generated by $(\mathcal{F}_s)_{0 \leq s \leq t}$. If $X = \sum_{i=0}^k X_i \mathbf{1}_{[t_i, t_{i+1})}$ where $0 \leq t_0 < t_1 < \ldots t_{k+1}$ and X_i is $\mathcal{F}_{t_i}$ measurable, find $\int_0^T X_t dW_t$ when $0 < T < t_{k+1}$.

(11.9) Let X and $(X_n)_{n=1}^\infty$ denote integrable random variables on $(\Omega, \mathcal{F}, P)$. Show that $X_n \longrightarrow X$ in $\mathbf{L}^1(\Omega, \mathcal{F}, P)$ as $n \longrightarrow \infty$ if and only if $X_n \longrightarrow X$ in measure as $n \longrightarrow \infty$ and $(X_n)_{n=1}^\infty$ is a uniformly integrable sequence.

(11.10) Suppose the share price $(X_t)_{t \geq 0}$ of a continuously traded stock is a continuous stochastic process. If the share price has precisely the same value at the beginning and end of a given month, show that almost surely there is a 24-hour period during the month such that the share price is the same at the beginning and end of this period.

(11.11) Describe a portfolio which hedges any claim on the option in Exercise 10.4.

(11.12) Suppose $f : [a, b] \mapsto [c, d]$ is continuous and bijective. Use Lemma 11.1 to show that the inverse function $f^{-1} : [c, d] \mapsto [a, b]$ is continuous.

Solutions

That I have been able to accomplish anything in mathematics is really due to the fact that I have always found it so difficult. When I read, or when I am told about something, it nearly always seems so difficult, and practically impossible to understand; and then I cannot help wondering if it might not be simpler. And on several occasions it turned out that it really was more simple.

David Hilbert, 1862-1943

Chapter 1

(1.1) $e^{a+b} - e^b = e^b \cdot (e^a - 1) = e^a$ and $b = \log(\frac{e^a}{e^a - 1})$. This is only defined if $e^a > 1$, that is $a > 0$.

(1.2) $e^{x^2/2} = \sum_{n=0}^{\infty} (x^2)^n / 2^n n! \geq x^{2n+2}/2^{n+1}(n+1)!$ and therefore $e^{-x^2/2} \leq 2^{n+1}(n+1)!/x^{2n+2}$. Hence $|x|^n \exp(-x^2/2) \leq 2^{n+1}(n+1)!/|x|^{n+2} \to 0$ as $|x| \to +\infty$.

(1.3) Choose k such that $|x^{n+2} e^{-x^2/2}| \leq 1$ for all $|x| > k$. Then $|x^n e^{-x^2/2}| \leq 1/x^2$ for $|x| > k$. Since $\int_k^{\infty} dx/x^2 = \lim_{n \to \infty} (\frac{-1}{x}]_k^n = 1/k$ the integral exists. Let $I_n = \int_{-\infty}^{+\infty} x^n e^{-x^2/2} dx$. Clearly $I_n = 0$ if n is odd and $\int_{-\infty}^{+\infty} x^n e^{-x^2/2} dx = 2 \int_0^{+\infty} x^n e^{-x^2/2} dx$ if n is even. If $n = 2m$, $\int_0^t x^{2m} e^{-x^2/2} dx = \int_0^t (-x^{2m-1}) \cdot \frac{d}{dx}(e^{-x^2/2}) dx = -x^{2m-1} e^{-x^2/2}]_0^t - \int_0^t (-(2m-1)x^{2m-2} e^{-x^2/2}) dx$. This implies $I_{2m} = (2m-1)I_{2m-2} = (2m-1)(2m-3) \cdots 5 \cdot 3 \cdot 1 \cdot I_0$ and $I_{2m} = \frac{2m!\sqrt{2\pi}}{2^m m!}$.

(1.4) Let $S_n = \sum_{j=1}^n jr^j$, $(1-r)S_n = \frac{r(1-r^n)}{1-r} - nr^{n+1}$ and $S_n = \frac{r-(n+1)r^{n+1}+nr^{n+2}}{(1-r)^2}$. $\lim_{n \to \infty} S_n = \sum_{j=1}^{\infty} jr^j = r/(1-r)^2$.

(1.5) $1,041; $1,720; $412,800.

(1.6) Interest rate is 6.5%, (a) −$1,919, (b) $2,176.

(1.7) $\frac{d}{dx}(e^{-x^2/2}x^{-1}) = -e^{-x^2/2}(1 + x^{-2})$ and, by the Fundamental Theorem of Calculus, $\frac{d}{dx}(\int_x^\infty e^{-y^2/2}(1 + \frac{1}{y^2})dy) = -e^{-x^2/2}(1 + x^{-2})$. By Corollary 1.9 and, as both tend to 0 as $n \to +\infty$, this proves the identity. In the same way one can show

$$e^{-x^2/2}\Big(\frac{1}{x} - \frac{1}{x^3}\Big) = \int_x^\infty e^{-y^2/2}\Big(1 - \frac{3}{y^4}\Big)dy.$$

Now use $1 - (3/y^4) \leq 1 \leq 1 + (1/y^2)$. This gives a good approximation to the normal distribution when x is large (see Proposition 10.5 and Example 10.6).

(1.8) Let A be the rate per year deposited and let $A(t)$ denote the amount accumulated by time t. Then $A(0) = 0$ and $A(5) = 10,000$, $A(t + \Delta t) - A(t) \approx A\Delta t e^{r(5-t)}$ and $A'(t) = Ae^{.06(5-t)}$. Hence $10,000 = Ae^{.3}\int_0^5 e^{-.06t}dt$ and $A = \$1,715$ per year.

Chapter 2

(2.1) 7 to 2, 2 to 1 and 4 to 5. $x = 54$. Profit $6.

(2.3) If Mary bets $x on a home win at 2 to 1 and $(50 − x)$ on an away win at 5 to 4 and her return is independent of who wins, then $3x = 9(50 - x)/4$ and $x = \$21.43$. Her return is $64.29 and the guaranteed profit is $14.29.

Chapter 3

(3.3) Let $A_n = \{\alpha \in \Gamma : a_\alpha \geq (1/n)$. If $|A_n|$ is the number of elements in A_n, then $|A_n|/n \leq \sum_{\alpha \in A_n} a_\alpha \leq \sum_{\alpha \in \Gamma} a_\alpha < \infty$ and hence $|A_n|$ is finite. Since $\{\alpha \in \Gamma : a_\alpha \neq 0\} = \bigcup_{n=1}^\infty A_n$, an application of Exercise 3.2(b) completes the proof.

(3.4) By (3.2)(a), $f(A)$ is countable. Let $f(A) = (x_n)_{n=1}^\infty$. For each n let $f(y_n) = x_n$ (since f is injective there is only one y_n satisfying $f(y_n) = x_n$). Then $B = (y_n)_{n=1}^\infty$ is countable. Let $C = (z_n)_{n=1}^\infty$. Since g is surjective, $D = (g(z_n))_{n=1}^\infty$ is countable.

(3.5) $f(n,m) = f(p,q) \Leftrightarrow 2^n \cdot 3^m = 2^p \cdot 3^q \Leftrightarrow 2^{n-p} = 3^{q-m}$. If $n \neq p$ then 2^{n-p} or 2^{p-n} is even and 3^{q-m} or 3^{m-q} is odd— impossible. Hence $n = p$ and $m = q$. This implies f is injective. By Exercise 3.4, $\mathbf{N} \times \mathbf{N}$ is countable. g maps onto the strictly positive rationals $\mathbf{Q}^+$ and $h(n,m) := -n/m$ maps onto the strictly negative rationals. By Exercise 3.4 both of these are countable.

(3.6) Apply Exercise 3.4 to $A \times B$. Use the first part and induction for finite products.

(3.7) Ω_n, the set of subsets of Ω with n elements, can be identified with Ω^n the n-fold product of Ω with itself n times. By Exercises 3.6, Ω_n is countable. The set of all finite subsets of Ω equals $\bigcup_{n=1}^\infty \Omega_n$ and this is countable by Exercise 3.2(b). If $\Omega = \{x_n\}_{n=1}^\infty$, we identify the set of all subsets of Ω with the set of all sequences of zeros and ones where A is identified with $(y_n)_{n=1}^\infty$ where $y_n = 1$ if $x_n \in A$ and $y_n = 0$ if $x_n \notin A$. To complete the proof use a diagonal process (see Proposition 3.1).

(3.8) Clearly if $\mathcal{A}$ is a σ-field, then $\bigcup_{n=1}^{\infty} A_n \in \mathcal{A}$ for any increasing sequence of subsets in $\mathcal{A}$. Conversely, if this condition is satisfied and $(A_n)_{n=1}^{\infty} \subset \mathcal{A}$, let $B_n = \bigcup_{i=1}^{n} A_n$. Then $B_n \in \mathcal{A}$ and $(B_n)_{n=1}^{\infty}$ is increasing and $\bigcup_{n=1}^{\infty} A_n = \bigcup_{n=1}^{\infty} B_n \in \mathcal{A}$.

(3.9) All least upper bounds are also upper bounds. Let m_1 and m_2 denote 2 least upper bounds for the set A. Since m_1 is a least upper bound and m_2 is an upper bound, $m_1 \leq m_2$. Since m_2 is a least upper bound and m_1 is an upper bound, $m_2 \leq m_1$. Hence $m_1 = m_2$. Because of this result we may talk about *the* least upper bound.

(3.11) If $a_n = n^2 + n$, then $(a_n)_{n=1}^{\infty}$ is easily seen to be increasing and not bounded above. Hence $\lim_{n \to \infty} 1/(n^2 + n) = 0$.

(3.14) A point x belongs to $\bigcup_{n=1}^{\infty} B_n$, (respectively $\bigcap_{n=1}^{\infty} B_n$) if and only if $x \in B_n$ for some (respectively all) n. Hence $x \in \bigcup_{n=1}^{\infty} (\bigcap_{m \geq n}^{\infty} A_m)$ if and only if $x \in \bigcap_{m \geq n}^{\infty} A_m$ for some n, that is if and only if, for some $n, x \in A_m$ for all $m \geq n$. We have $x \in \bigcap_{n=1}^{\infty} (\bigcup_{m \geq n}^{\infty} A_m)$ if and only if $x \in \bigcup_{m \geq n}^{\infty} A_m$ for all n. Hence for all n, we have $x \in A_m$ for some $m \geq n$; that means $x \in A_m$ for an infinite number of A_m.

(3.15) $\{\{1\}, \{2\}, \{3\}, \{4\}, \{5\}, \{6, 7, 8, 10\}, \{9\}\}$.

(3.16) $\Omega = \{1, 2, 3\}$, $\mathcal{F}_1 = \{\emptyset, \{1\}, \{2, 3\}, \Omega\}$ and $\mathcal{F}_2 = \{\emptyset, \{2\}, \{1, 3\}, \Omega\}$. $\mathcal{F}_1 \cup \mathcal{F}_2 = \{\emptyset, \{1\}, \{2\}, \{1, 3\}, \{2, 3\}, \Omega\}$. Since $\{1, 2\} \notin \mathcal{F}_1 \cup \mathcal{F}_2$, $\mathcal{F}_1 \cup \mathcal{F}_2$ is not a σ-field.

(3.17) $\Omega = \{1, 2, 3\}$, $\mathcal{F}_1 = \{\emptyset, \{1\}, \{2, 3\}, \Omega\}$ and $\mathcal{F}_2 = \{\emptyset, \{2\}, \{1, 3\}, \Omega\}$.

(3.18) If $B \in \mathcal{F}, \emptyset \neq B \neq \Omega$, then we have 4 sets in $\mathcal{F}$, $\{\emptyset, B, B^c, \Omega\}$. If A is another set not equal to any of these, then A^c will also not be equal to any of these and so we have the 6 sets in $\mathcal{F}$. We have $A \cap B \neq \emptyset$ or $A \cap B^c \neq \emptyset$. If $A \cap B \neq \emptyset$, then, since $A \cap B = (B^c \cup A^c)^c \in \mathcal{F}$, we have $A \cap B \in \{\emptyset, A, A^c, B, B^c, \Omega\}$. Since $A \cap B \neq A^c$ or B^c and $A \cap B \subset A \neq \Omega$ we have $A \cap B = A$ or B. If $A \cap B = A$, then $A \subset B$, and since $A \neq B$ we have $\emptyset \neq B \backslash A \subset B \neq B$, and this set is easily seen not to equal any of the 6 listed sets. A similar analysis holds if $A \cap B = B$.

(3.19) A countable subset A of Ω is a countable union of sets each with a single element and hence A, as does A^c, belongs to $\mathcal{F}(\mathcal{A})$. It suffices to show that this collection is a σ-field. The complement of Ω is empty and hence countable. If A is countable, then A^c has countable complement; if A has countable complement then A^c is countable. If $A := \bigcup_{n=1}^{\infty} A_n$ and $A_{n_0}^c$ is countable, then $A^c \subset A_{n_0}^c$ is countable. Otherwise all A_n are countable and A is countable by Exercise 3.2(b). Hence it is a σ-field and as the smallest σ-field containing $\mathcal{A}$ equals $\mathcal{F}(\mathcal{A})$. If Ω is countable, then every subset of Ω is countable by Exercise 3.2(a) and $\mathcal{F}(\mathcal{A}) = 2^{\Omega}$.

(3.20) $x - x = 0 \in \mathbf{Q}$; if $x - y \in \mathbf{Q}$, then $y - x = -(x - y) \in \mathbf{Q}$; and if $x - y \in \mathbf{Q}$ and $y - z \in \mathbf{Q}$, then $x - z = (x - y) + (y - z) \in \mathbf{Q}$ and $\sim$ is an equivalence relationship. Show next $[x] = \{x + q : q \in \mathbf{Q}\}$. If $\sim$ gave a countable partition, then we would have a countable set of equivalence classes each containing a countable set of elements. This would imply, by Exercise 3.2(b), that $\mathbf{R}$ was countable. This contradicts Proposition 3.1.

(3.21) Since $x - x = 0$ is rational, $x \not\sim x$.

(3.23) Since $(n, m) \sim (p, q)$ if and only if $n/m = p/q$ it follows that $\sim$ is an equivalence relationship. Let $\phi(n, m) = n/m$. Now use Exercises 3.6 and the second part of (3.4).

(3.25) Use a diagonal process as in the proof of Proposition 3.1.

(3.26) Least upper bound of $(a_n)_{n=1}^{\infty} = -[\text{greatest lower bound of } (-a_n)_{n=1}^{\infty}]$.

(3.28) All $f : \Omega \longrightarrow \{0, 1\}$ have the form $\mathbf{1}_A$ where $A = f^{-1}(\{1\})$ is a subset of Ω.

(3.29) Let $a_n = b_n = -\frac{1}{n}$ for all n.

(3.30) If $A, B \in \mathcal{A}$, then $A \cup B = (A \cup B)^{cc} = (A^c \cap B^c)^c \in \mathcal{A}$. By induction the finite union of sets in $\mathcal{A}$ belongs to $\mathcal{A}$. If $(A_n)_{n=1}^{\infty} \subset \mathcal{A}$ and $B_n = \bigcup_{i=1}^{n} A_i$, then $B_n \in \mathcal{A}$ and $(B_n)_{n=1}^{\infty}$ is an increasing sequence in $\mathcal{A}$. Hence $\bigcup_{n=1}^{\infty} A_n = \bigcup_{n=1}^{\infty} B_n \in \mathcal{A}$.

(3.31) Since the series has all positive entries it suffices to show that the partial sums are bounded above. If $m > n > n_0 > x$, then $\sum_{n=0}^{m} x^n/n! \leq (\sum_{n=0}^{n_0} x^n/n!) + \frac{x^{n_0}}{n_0!} \sum_{n=n_0}^{m} (x/n_0)^{n-n_0} \leq (\sum_{n=0}^{n_0} x^n/n!) + \frac{x^{n_0}}{n_0!} \cdot \frac{1}{1-(x/n_0)}$.

(3.32) Suppose S is bounded above and that M is its least upper bound. Since $M - 1 < M$ there exists a positive integer n such that $n^2 > M - 1$. Then $(n+1)^2 = n^2 + 2n + 1 > M - 1 + 2n + 1 > M$. Since $(n+1)^2 \in S$ this is a contradiction and S is not bounded above.

(3.33) The composition of two strictly increasing mappings from $\mathbf{N}$ to $\mathbf{N}$ is also strictly increasing.

Chapter 4

(4.1) By Definition 4.1, $(-\infty, a) = \bigcup_{n=1}^{\infty}(a - n, a) \in \mathcal{B}(\mathbf{R})$; hence $\mathcal{A}_2 \subset \mathcal{A}_1 \subset \mathcal{B}(\mathbf{R})$ and $\mathcal{F}(\mathcal{A}_2) \subset \mathcal{F}(\mathcal{A}_1) \subset \mathcal{B}(\mathbf{R})$. Since $[p, q) = (-\infty, p)^c \cap (-\infty, q)$ for $p, q \in \mathbf{Q}, p < q$ and $(p, q) = \bigcup_{n=1}^{\infty}[p + \frac{1}{n}, q)$ we have $(p, q) \in \mathcal{F}(\mathcal{A}_2)$ for all rationals p and q. If a and b are real numbers, $a < b$, let $(p_n)_{n=1}^{\infty}$ denote a decreasing sequence of rationals converging to a and let $(q_n)_{n=1}^{\infty}$ denote an increasing sequence of rationals converging to b. Then $(a, b) = \bigcup_{n=1}^{\infty}(p_n, q_n)$, and $(a, b) \in \mathcal{F}(\mathcal{A}_2)$. By Proposition 3.9, $\mathcal{B}(\mathbf{R}) \subset \mathcal{F}(\mathcal{A}_2)$.

(4.2) Use the method in Proposition 4.9.

(4.3) $\Omega = \{-1, 1\}, \mathcal{F} = 2^{\Omega}, X(-1) = -1, X(1) = 1$.

(4.4) $X^2(\omega) = X(\omega)$ if and only if $X(\omega)(1 - X(\omega)) = 0$ and $X(\omega) = 0$ or 1, $X = \mathbf{1}_A$ where $A = f^{-1}(\{1\})$.

(4.5) If f and g are two continuous functions and $f(q) = g(q)$ for any rational q, then, as any real number can be approached by rationals, $f(x) = g(x)$ for any real number x and $f = g$. $\mathbf{1}_{\mathbf{Q}}$.

(4.6) $X^{-1}(B)$ is a subset of Ω.

(4.7) Let $X(\omega) = n$ for all $\omega \in A_n$, $X = \sum_{n=1}^{\infty} n \mathbf{1}_{A_n}$.

(4.8) $X = 2 \mathbf{1}_{[0,2)} - \mathbf{1}_{[2,3)} + 3 \mathbf{1}_{[3,4]} + \mathbf{1}_{(4,5]} + 4 \mathbf{1}_{(5,6]}$. The partition consists of $[0, 2), [2, 3), [3, 4], (4, 5], (5, 6]$ and the complement of their union.

(4.9) $X = 71_{\{1\}} + 1_{\{2\}} + 31_{\{3\}} + 41_{\{4,5,6\}} - 21_{\{8,10\}}$; $\mathcal{F}_X$ is generated by the partition $[\{1\}, \{2\}, \{3\}, \{4,5,6\}, \{8,10\}, \{1,2,3,4,5,6,8,10\}^c]$ of $\mathbf{N}$.

(4.10) $\mathcal{F}$ is generated by $\{\{1,2\}, \{3,4\}, \{5,6\}, \{7\}\}$; $\mathcal{F}_X$ by $\{\{1,2\}, \{3,4\}, \{5,6,7\}\}$. $Y = 1_{\{1,2,3,4\}} + 91_{\{5,6,7\}}$. X is $\mathcal{F}$ measurable, X is not $\mathcal{F}_Y$ measurable, Y is $\mathcal{F}_X$ measurable.

(4.11) (Use Lemma 4.17(c)) If $\epsilon > 0$ is arbitrary, then there exists a positive integer n_ϵ such that $|x_n - x| < \epsilon$ for all $n \geq n_\epsilon$. Since $n_j \geq j$ for all j, $|x_{n_j} - x| < \epsilon$ for all $j \geq n_\epsilon$.

(4.12) If x is rational, then $0 = f(x + \frac{\sqrt{2}}{n}) \not\to f(x) = 1$ as $n \longrightarrow \infty$. If x is irrational, choose a sequence of rational numbers $(q_n)_{n=1}^\infty$ which converges to x. Then $f(q_n) = 1$ all n and $f(x) = 0$.

(4.13) Let $f_n(x) = n(f(x + \frac{1}{n}) - f(x))$. By Proposition 4.9 and Corollary 4.20, f_n is Borel measurable. Since f' is the pointwise limit of the sequence $(f_n)_{n=1}^\infty$, Proposition 4.22 implies that f' is Borel measurable.

(4.14) Let $X = \sum_{q \in \mathbf{Q}} q 1_{\{q\}}$. Then $X^{-1}(B) = B \cap \mathbf{Q}$ if $0 \notin B$ and $X^{-1}(B) = (B \cap \mathbf{Q}) \cup \mathbf{Q}^c$ if $0 \in B$ for all B Borel. Since any subset of $\mathbf{Q}$ is countable, it is a Borel set, by Example 4.3, and hence $B \cap \mathbf{Q}$ and $\mathbf{Q}^c$ are also Borel sets and X is Borel measurable. Alternatively, if $\mathbf{Q} = (q_n)_{n=1}^\infty$, then $X_m := \sum_{n \leq m} q_n 1_{q_n}$ is easily seen to be Borel measurable and $X_m \longrightarrow X$ pointwise as $n \longrightarrow \infty$.

(4.15) Suppose $X_n \longrightarrow X$ pointwise as $n \longrightarrow \infty$. If $X(\omega) > 0$, then $X_n(\omega) > 0$ for all n large. Hence $X^+(\omega) = X(\omega)$ and $X_n^+(\omega) = X_n(\omega)$ for all n large and $X_n^+(\omega) \longrightarrow X^+(\omega)$ as $n \longrightarrow \infty$. If $X(\omega) < 0$, then $X_n(\omega) < 0$ for all n large. Hence $X^+(\omega) = 0$ and $X_n^+(\omega) = 0$ for all n large and $X_n^+(\omega) \longrightarrow X^+(\omega)$ as $n \longrightarrow \infty$. If $X(\omega) = 0$, then $X^+(\omega) = 0$ and for any $\epsilon > 0$, $-\epsilon < X_n(\omega) < \epsilon$ for all n large. Hence $0 \leq X_n^+(\omega) < \epsilon$ for all n large and $X_n^+(\omega) \longrightarrow X^+(\omega)$ as $n \longrightarrow \infty$. This shows $X_n^+ \longrightarrow X^+$ pointwise as $n \longrightarrow \infty$. Hence $X_n^- = X_n^+ - X_n \longrightarrow X^+ - X = X^-$ pointwise as $n \longrightarrow \infty$. If $X_n^+ \longrightarrow X^+$ and $X_n^- \longrightarrow X^-$ pointwise as $n \longrightarrow \infty$, then $X_n = X_n^+ - X_n^- \longrightarrow X^+ - X^- = X$ pointwise as $n \longrightarrow \infty$.

(4.16) $\{\omega \in \Omega : \lim_{n \to \infty} X_n(\omega) < \infty\} = \bigcup_{k=1}^\infty \{\omega \in \Omega : \lim_{n \to \infty} X_n(\omega) \leq k\} = \bigcup_{k=1}^\infty (\bigcap_{m=1}^\infty \{\omega \in \Omega : X_m(\omega) \leq k\})$.

(4.17) If $\lim_{n \to \infty} x_n = x$, then for any subsequence $\lim_{j \to \infty} x_{n_j} = x$ by Exercise 4.11. If $\lim_{n \to \infty} x_n \neq x$, then $\lim_{n \to \infty} |x_n - x| \neq 0$. Hence there exists $\epsilon > 0$ and an infinite set of integers $(n_j)_{j=1}^\infty$ such that $|x_{n_j} - x| \geq \epsilon$ for all j. No subsequence of $(x_{n_j})_{j=1}^\infty$ converges to x. See Lemma 10.1.

(4.18) $g(X)^+(\omega) = g(X)(\omega) = g(X(\omega)) \implies g(X(\omega)) \geq 0$; otherwise it is 0. $(g^+(X))(\omega) = g^+(X(\omega)) = g(X(\omega)) \implies g(X(\omega)) \geq 0$; otherwise it is 0.

(4.19) $f(X_n)(x) = f(X_n(x)) = 1_{(-\infty,0]}(X_n(x)) = 1$ if n is odd and equals 0 if n is even.

(4.20) $f = g \cdot 1_{[0,\infty)}$ where $g(x) = x$ for all $x \in \mathbf{R}$.

(4.21) (a) There exists an increasing sequence $(d_n)_{n=1}^\infty$ such that $d_n \leq a_n$ for all n and $\lim_{n \to \infty} d_n = d$ and $(e_n)_{n=1}^\infty$ decreasing such that $b_n \leq e_n$ for all n and $\lim_{n \to \infty} e_n = d$. Then $d_n \leq c_n \leq e_n$ for all n. By Definition 4.16,

$\lim_{n \to \infty} c_n = d$. (b). If $d \in (a, b)$, then there exists, by Lemma 4.17(b), a positive integer n_0 such that $a_n \in (a, b)$ for all $n \geq n_0$ and a positive integer n_1 such that $b_n \in (a, b)$ for all $n \geq n_1$. If $n \geq n_2 := n_0 + n_1$, then $a < a_n \leq c_n \leq b_n < b$ and $c_n \in (a, b)$ for all $n \geq n_2$. By Lemma 4.17(b), $\lim_{n \to \infty} c_n = d$.

(4.22) $|e^x - e^0| \leq \sum_{n=1}^{\infty} |x|^n/n! \leq \sum_{n=1}^{\infty} |x|^n = |x|/(1 - |x|) \longrightarrow 0$ as $|x| \longrightarrow 0$. This shows continuity at 0. $|e^x - e^y| = e^y|e^{x-y} - e^0|$ and continuity at 0 implies continuity at any point y. $|e^{\Delta x} - e^0 - \Delta x|/|\Delta x| \leq \sum_{n=2}^{\infty} |\Delta x|^{n-1}/n! \leq \sum_{n=2}^{\infty} |\Delta x|^{n-1} = |\Delta x|/(1 - |\Delta x|)$ shows that exp is differentiable at 0 and that $\frac{d}{dx} \exp(x) = \exp(x)$ when $x = 0$. $|e^{x+\Delta x} - e^x - e^x \Delta x|/|\Delta x| = e^x|e^{\Delta x} - e^0 - \Delta x|/|\Delta x|$ and differentiability at the origin implies differentiability at x.

(4.23) Let $\lim_{n \to \infty} x_n = \lim_{n \to \infty} y_n = c$, $\lim_{n \to \infty} f(x_n) = \alpha$ and $\lim_{n \to \infty} f(y_n) = \beta$. We need to show $\alpha = \beta$. Let $z_{2n} = x_n$ and $z_{2n-1} = y_n$ for $n \geq 1$. Then $\lim_{n \to \infty} z_n = c$. (By Lemma 4.18, there exists n_ϵ such that $|x_n - c| < \epsilon$ for all $n \geq \epsilon$ and there exists m_ϵ such that $|y_n - c| < \epsilon$ for all $m \geq m_\epsilon$; if $n > 2(n_\epsilon + m_\epsilon)$, then $|z_n - c| < \epsilon$.) By hypothesis $\lim_{n \to \infty} f(z_n)$ exists and equals some real number δ. Since $(f(x_n))_{n=1}^{\infty}$ and $(f(y_n))_{n=1}^{\infty}$ are subsequences of $(f(z_n))_{n=1}^{\infty}$, $\alpha = \beta = \delta$ by Exercise 4.11. By Definition 4.18, f is continuous if and only if $\alpha = f(c)$. The idea in this exercise appears in the remarks on Riemann sums after Definition 11.12.

(4.24) If f is continuous, then $\lim_{n \to \infty} f(x_n) = f(x)$ for any sequence $(x_n)_{n=1}^{\infty}$ which converges to x. Hence $f(x^+) = f(x) = f(x^-)$. Conversely, suppose $f(x^+) = f(x) = f(x^-)$. If f is not continuous, then there exists a sequence $(x_n)_{n=1}^{\infty}$ which converges to x and $\epsilon > 0$ such that $|f(x_n) - f(x)| \geq \epsilon$ for all n. Since $x_n \neq x$ for any n we can choose a subsequence of $(x_n)_{n=1}^{\infty}$, $(x_{n_j})_{j=1}^{\infty}$, such that either $x_{n_j} > x$ for all j or $x_{n_j} < x$ for all j. In the first case $f^+(x) \neq f(x)$ and in the second $f^-(x) \neq f(x)$. See Exercise 7.5.

Chapter 5

(5.1) Let $B_n = A_n^c$, $(B_n)_{n=1}^{\infty}$ is increasing and $(\bigcup_{n=1}^{\infty} B_n)^c = \bigcap_{n=1}^{\infty} A_n$. By the proof of Proposition 5.3, $\lim_{n \to \infty} P(A_n) = 1 - \lim_{n \to \infty} P(B_n) = 1 - P(\bigcup_{n=1}^{\infty} B_n) = P((\bigcup_{n=1}^{\infty} B_n)^c) = P(\bigcap_{n=1}^{\infty} A_n) = P(\lim_{n \to \infty} A_n)$.

(5.2) Let $B_1 = A_1$ and $B_n = A_n \backslash (A_1 \cup \cdots \cup A_{n-1})$ for $n > 1$. Then $(B_n)_{n=1}^{\infty}$ is a pairwise disjoint sequence of $\mathcal{F}$ measurable sets, $P(B_n) \leq P(A_n)$ since $B_n \subset A_n$, and $\bigcup_{n=1}^{\infty} B_n = \bigcup_{n=1}^{\infty} A_n$. Hence $P(\bigcup_{n=1}^{\infty} B_n) = \sum_{n=1}^{\infty} P(B_n) \leq \sum_{n=1}^{\infty} P(A_n)$. Let $A_1 = A_2 = \Omega$ and $A_n = \emptyset$ for $n > 2$.

(5.3) If $B := \{\omega_1, \ldots, \omega_m\} \subset A_n$, then $m/n \leq \sum_{i=1}^{m} P(\{\omega_i\}) = P(B) \leq 1$. Hence $m \leq n$. Since each A_n is countable and $A = \bigcup_{n=1}^{\infty} A_n$, Exercise 3.2(a) implies that A is countable.

(5.4) $\mathcal{F}$ is generated by the partition $\{\{1\}, \{2, 3\}, \{4\}, \{5, 6\}\}$, $\mathcal{F}_X$ by the partition $\{\{1\}, \{2\}, \{3, 4\}, \{5, 6\}\}$, and, since $X^2 = \mathbf{1}_{\{2,3,4\}} + 91_{\{5,6\}}$, $\mathcal{F}_{X^2}$ is generated by the partition $\{\{1\}, \{2, 3, 4\}, \{5, 6\}\}$. Since $\mathcal{F}_X \not\subset \mathcal{F}$, X is not measurable, and as $\mathcal{F}_{X^2} \subset \mathcal{F}$, X^2 is measurable. If $P(\{4\}) = a$, then $2a = 1 - (5/12)$ and $a = 7/24$. $P[X^4 \leq 2] = P(\{1, 2, 3, 4\}) = 1 - P(\{5, 6\}) = 17/24$.

(5.5) $P(\{\omega : X(\omega) = X(\omega)\}) = 1$ and $X \sim X$. $P(\{\omega : X(\omega) = Y(\omega)\}) = P(\{\omega : Y(\omega) = X(\omega)\})$. Hence $X \sim Y$ implies $Y \sim X$. If $A = \{\omega : X(\omega) = Y(\omega)\}$ and $B = \{\omega : Y(\omega) = Z(\omega)\}$ and $P(A) = P(B) = 1$, then $A \cap B \subset \{\omega : X(\omega) = Z(\omega)\}$ and $P(A \cap B) = P(A) + P(B) - P(A \cup B) \geq 2 - P(A \cup B) \geq 1$. Hence $X \sim Z$. If $A_n = \{\omega : X_n(\omega) = Y_n(\omega)\}$ and $P(A_n) = 1$, then $P(A := \bigcap_{n=1}^k A_n) = 1$ (the above shows that this is true for $k = 2$ and by induction this is true for all k). By Proposition 5.3, $P(A := \bigcap_{n=1}^\infty A_n) = 1$. If $B = \{\omega : X_n(\omega) \longrightarrow X(\omega)$ as $n \longrightarrow \infty\}$ and $C = \{\omega : Y_n(\omega) \longrightarrow X(\omega)$ as $n \longrightarrow \infty\}$, then $A \cap B = A \cap C$. Hence $P(B) = P(A \cap B) + P(A^c \cap B) = P(A \cap B)$ and $P(C) = P(A \cap C) + P(A^c \cap C) = P(A \cap C)$ and $P(B) = P(C)$.

(5.6) $P(\Omega) = 1$ and $\Omega \in \mathcal{G}$. If $A \in \mathcal{G}$, then $P(A) = 0$ or 1 and $P(A^c) = 1$ or 0 which implies $A^c \in \mathcal{G}$. Suppose $(A_n)_{n=1}^\infty \subset \mathcal{G}$ are pairwise disjoint. If $P(A_n) = 0$ for all n, then, by Exercise 5.2, $P(\bigcup_{n=1}^\infty A_n) \leq \sum_{n=1}^\infty P(A_n) = 0$ and $\bigcup_{n=1}^\infty A_n \in \mathcal{G}$. If $P(A_{n_0}) = 1$ for some n_0, then $1 \leq P(A_{n_0}) \leq P(\bigcup_{n=1}^\infty A_n) \leq 1$ and $P(\bigcup_{n=1}^\infty A_n) = 1$. Hence $\bigcup_{n=1}^\infty A_n \in \mathcal{G}$.

(5.7) .2703

(5.8) $(a) \implies (b) \implies (c)$ by Proposition 5.3. Suppose (c) hold. Let $(A_n)_{n=1}^\infty$ denote a disjoint sequence of measurable sets and let $B_n = A_1 \cup \cdots \cup A_n$ and $A = \bigcup_{n=1}^\infty A_n$. Then $P(B_n) = \sum_{j=1}^n P(A_j)$ and $(B_n)_{n=1}^\infty$ is an increasing sequence which converges to A and $(A \backslash B_n)_{n=1}^\infty$ is a decreasing sequence and $\lim_{n\to\infty}(A \backslash B_n) = \emptyset$. By (c) $\lim_{n\to\infty} P(A \backslash B_n) = 0$. Since $B_n \subset A$ we have $P(A \backslash B_n) + P(B_n) = P(A)$ and $P(A) = \lim_{n\to\infty} P(B_n) = \lim_{n\to\infty} \sum_{j=1}^n P(A_j) = \sum_{j=1}^\infty P(A_j)$. Hence $(c) \Longleftrightarrow (a)$. The statement (c) is an *if* (P) *then* (Q) statement for a decreasing sequence of sets, and rewriting this in the form *if not* (Q), *then not* (P) we obtain (d).

(5.9) Use $P[\omega \in \Omega] = \int_0^\infty \alpha \exp(-\lambda x)dx = 1$. $\int_0^n \alpha e^{-\lambda x}dx = \alpha \frac{e^{-\lambda x}}{-\lambda}\Big]_0^n = \frac{\alpha}{\lambda}(1 - e^{-\lambda n}) \to \frac{\alpha}{\lambda}$ as $n \to \infty$. Hence $\alpha = \lambda$.

(5.10) Since $\mathcal{F}_{\mathbf{1}_A} = \{\emptyset, A, A^c, \Omega\}$ and $\mathcal{F}_{\mathbf{1}_B} = \{\emptyset, B, B^c, \Omega\}$ the result follows from Lemma 5.11.

(5.11) If $a = P(\{5\})$, then $P(\{6\}) = (1/3) - a$, $P(\{1, 3, 4\}) = 7/12$, $P(\{1, 2, 3, 5\}) = (5/12) + a$, $P(\{1, 3\}) = 1/3$. By independence, $1/3 = (7/12)((5/12) + a)$ and $a = 13/84$. Hence $P(\{6\}) = 15/84$.

(5.12) If $a = P(\{5\})$, then $P(\{6\}) = (1/6) - a$. $P(A \cap B) = P(\{2\}) = 1/6$, $P(A) = (1/4) + a$ and $P(B) = (7/12) - a$. By independence $1/6 = ((1/4) + a)((7/12) - a)$ which implies $a^2 - (a/3) + (1/48) = 0$. Hence $a = 1/4$ or $1/12$. Since $0 \leq a \leq 1/6$, $a = 1/12$ and $P(\{6\}) = 1/12$.

(5.13) $i = 1$, $P[\max(X, Y)] = 1 - P[X = 0, Y = 0] = 1 - P[X = 0]P[Y = 0] = 1 - (1/n^2)$. $P[\max(X, Y)] = i] = P[\max(X, Y)] \leq i] - P[\max(X, Y)] \leq i - 1]$ and $P[\max(X, Y)] \leq i] = P[X \leq i, Y \leq i] = P[X \leq i]P[Y \leq i] = i^2/n^2$. $P[\max(X, Y)] = i] = \frac{i^2}{n^2} - \frac{(i-1)^2}{n^2} = \frac{2i-1}{n^2}$.

(5.14) $P[X = Y] = \sum_{n=1}^\infty P[X = Y = n] = \sum_{n=1}^\infty P[X = n]P[Y = n] = \sum_{n=1}^\infty p^2 q^{2n-2} = \frac{p^2}{q^2} \sum_{n=1}^\infty (q^2)^n = p^2/(1 - q^2) = p/(1 + q)$. $P[X \geq Y] = \sum_{n=1}^\infty P[Y = n, X \geq n] = \sum_{n=1}^\infty P[Y = n]P[X \geq n] = \sum_{n=1}^\infty pq^{n-1} \cdot$

$(\sum_{m \geq n} pq^{m-1}) = \sum_{n=1}^{\infty} pq^{n-1}(pq^{n-1}/(1-q)) = \sum_{n=1}^{\infty} pq^{2n-2} = 1/(1+q)$.
Alternatively, by symmetry $P[X \geq Y] = P[Y \geq X]$ and $P[X \geq Y] + P[Y \geq X] - P[X = Y] = 1$. From the first part $2P[X \geq Y] = 1 + (p/1+q) = 2/(1+q)$ and $P[X \geq Y] = 1/(1+q)$.

(5.15) Since $(x,y) \in \pi_1^{-1}(A)$ if and only if $\pi_1(x,y) = x$ and $\pi_1(x,z) = x$ for any $z \in \Omega_2$, we have $(x,z) \in \pi_1^{-1}(A)$ if and only if $(x,y) \in \pi_1^{-1}(A)$. If $\mathcal{F}_i \neq \mathcal{F}_\emptyset$ for $i = 1,2$, then there are $A_i \subset \Omega_i$ such that $\emptyset \neq A_i \neq \Omega_i$ for $i = 1,2$. Then $A_1 \times A_2 \not\subset \pi_1^{-1}(\mathcal{F}_1) \cap \pi_2^{-1}(\mathcal{F}_2)$ since every set in $\pi_1^{-1}(\mathcal{F}_1) \cap \pi_2^{-1}(\mathcal{F}_2)$ has either the form $A \times \Omega_2$, $A \in \mathcal{F}_1$ or $\Omega_1 \times B$, $B \in \mathcal{F}_2$.

(5.16) $X^2 = 16 \cdot \mathbf{1}_{\{1,3\}} + 4 \cdot \mathbf{1}_{\{2,4,6\}}$, $X \cdot Y = 12 \cdot \mathbf{1}_{\{3\}} - 6 \cdot \mathbf{1}_{\{2,6\}}$, $(X-3)^+ = \mathbf{1}_{\{1,3\}}$, $(Y-2)^+ = \mathbf{1}_{\{3,5\}}$. If $P(\{3\}) = a$ and $P(\{6\}) = b$, then $a + b = 1/3$. If $(X-3)^+$ and $(Y-3)^+$ are independent random variables, then $\{1,3\}$ and $\{3,5\}$ are independent events and $P(\{3\}) = P(\{1,3\}) \cdot P(\{3,5\})$, $(\frac{1}{6} + a)(a + \frac{1}{3} - a) = a$ and $a = 1/12$ and $b = 1/4$.

(5.17) Let $x = P(\{1\})$ and $y = P(\{4\})$. Then $3x + 2y = 11/12$. X and Y independent implies $\{1,2\}$ and $\{1,3,5\}$ are independent events. Hence $2x(2x+y) = x$, and as $x \neq 0$, $2x + y = 1/2$, $x = 1/12$, $y = 1/3$.

(5.18) Price of call option \$1.23, hedging portfolio (.5 shares, $-\$2.77$ bonds), (a) -\$.024, (b) $-\$.41$, (c) $-\$.43$, (d) \$1.54, (e)=(f) -\$.31.

(5.20) $k = 16$, \$2.02.

(5.21) If $e^{rT} > u$, then one could make more money without any risk by depositing money in the bank.

(5.23) Price of a put option for 1 share=\$1.738. Sell x shares and hold $500 - x$ shares. $1.738(500 - x) = 15x$ and $x = 52$. Loss on hedging, \$2,572; loss by not hedging, \$4,500.

(5.24) An option is more valuable than a contract. The potential profit at time T is $Su - k$ and discounting back gives the second estimate.

(5.25) Any rearrangement is obtained from a bijective mapping $\theta : \mathbf{N} \mapsto \mathbf{N}$. If $s_n = \sum_{i=1}^{n} a_i$ and $s = \sum_{n=1}^{\infty} a_n$, then $s_n^* := \sum_{i=1}^{n} a_{\theta(i)} \leq s_m$ for some m. Since s is the least upper bound of the sequence $(s_n)_{n=1}^{\infty}$ this implies s is an upper bound for the sequence $(s_n^*)_{n=1}^{\infty}$. Hence $\sum_{i=1}^{n} a_{\theta(i)}$ converges to $s^* \leq s$. Since $\sum_{n=1}^{\infty} a_n$ is a rearrangement of $\sum_{n=1}^{\infty} a_{\theta(n)}$ we also have $s \leq s^*$ and $s = s^*$.

(5.26) $\sum_{j=2^n+1}^{2^{n+1}} a_j \leq 2^n a_{2^n}$. Let $a_n = n^{-p}$. If $p \leq 0$, then $n^{-p} \not\to 0$. If $p > 0$ let $f(x) = x^{-p}$. Then $f'(x) = -px^{-p-1} < 0$ for $x > 0$ and $(a_n)_{n=1}^{\infty}$ is decreasing. Since $2^n a_{2^n} = (2^{1-p})^n$ the series converges if and only if $2^{1-p} < 1$, that is if and only if $p > 1$.

(5.27) By de Morgan's laws $[(A \backslash B) \cup C]^c = (A^c \backslash C) \cup (B \backslash C)$ and $\mathcal{G}$ is closed under complements. $\bigcup_{n=1}^{\infty}((A_n \backslash B_n) \cup C_n) = (\bigcup_{n=1}^{\infty}(A_n \backslash B_n)) \cup \bigcup_{n=1}^{\infty} C_n$. If $C_n \subset C_n^*$, $C_n^* \in \mathcal{F}$ and $P(C_n^*) = 0$, then $\bigcup_{n=1}^{\infty} C_n \subset \bigcup_{n=1}^{\infty} C_n^* =: C^*$, $C^* \in \mathcal{F}$ and $P(C^*) = P(\bigcup_{n=1}^{\infty} C_n^*) \leq \sum_{n=1}^{\infty} P(C_n^*) = 0$. If $B_n \subset B_n^*$ where $B_n^* \in \mathcal{F}$ and $P(B_n^*) = 0$, then $\bigcup_{n=1}^{\infty} B_n \subset B^* := \bigcup_{n=1}^{\infty} B_n^* \in \mathcal{F}$ and $P(B^*) = 0$. Hence $(\bigcup_{n=1}^{\infty} A_n) \backslash B^* \subset \bigcup_{n=1}^{\infty}(A_n \backslash B_n) \subset \bigcup_{n=1}^{\infty} A_n$ and $\bigcup_{n=1}^{\infty}((A_n \backslash B_n) \cup$

$C_n) = (\bigcup_{n=1}^{\infty} A_n \backslash D) \cup C^*$ where $D \subset B^*$ and $\mathcal{G}$ is closed under countable unions. Since $\Omega = (\Omega \backslash \emptyset) \cup \emptyset$, $\Omega \in \mathcal{G}$ and $\mathcal{G}$ is a σ-field. It is necessary to show that Q is well defined; that is if $(A_1 \backslash B_1) \cup C_1 = (A_2 \backslash B_2) \cup C_2$ where $B_i \subset B_i^*, C_i \subset C_i^*$ and $P(B_i^*) = P(C_i^*) = 0$, $A_i \in \mathcal{F}$, then $P(A_1) = P(A_2)$. $A_1 \subset (A_1 \backslash B_1^*) \cup B_1^* \subset A_2 \cup B_1^* \cup C_2^*$ implies $P(A_1) \leq P(A_2) + P(B_1^*) + P(C_2^*) \leq P(A_2)$. Similarly $P(A_2) \leq P(A_1)$ and $P(A_2) = P(A_1)$. Clearly $Q(\Omega) = 1$. If $((A_n \backslash B_n) \cup C_n)_{n=1}^{\infty}$ are sets in $\mathcal{G}$, then by the above $Q(\bigcup_{n=1}^{\infty}(A_n \backslash B_n) \cup C_n) = P(\bigcup_{n=1}^{\infty} A_n)$; and if the sets are pairwise disjoint, then so are $((A_n \backslash B_n^*))_{n=1}^{\infty}$ where $B_n \subset B_n^*$, $B_n^* \in \mathcal{F}$ and $P(B_n^*) = 0$ and $P(\bigcup_{n=1}^{\infty}(A_n \backslash B_n^*) = \sum_{n=1}^{\infty} P(A_n \backslash B_n^*) \leq P(\bigcup_{n=1}^{\infty} A_n)$. As

$$P(A_n) \leq P((A_n \backslash B_n^*) \cup B_n^*) = P(A_n \backslash B_n^*) + P(B_n^*) = P(A_n \backslash B_n^*) \leq P(A_n),$$

we have $P(A_n \backslash B_n^*) = P(A_n)$ and $P(\bigcup_{n=1}^{\infty} A_n) = \sum_{n=1}^{\infty} P(A_n)$, and Q is σ additive. Note that $\mathcal{G}$ is the σ-field generated by $\mathcal{F}$ and the subsets of $\mathcal{F}$ measurable sets of P measure 0. The σ-field $\mathcal{G}$ is called the completion of the σ-field $\mathcal{F}$. To develop further the theory of continuous stochastic processes, one needs the σ-field $\mathcal{G}$ in order to overcome a number of very subtle technical points about measurable functions. When $(\Omega, \mathcal{F}, P) = (\mathbf{R}, \mathcal{B}, \mathbf{m})$ the sets in $\mathcal{G}$ are called Lebesgue measurable sets.

Chapter 6

(6.1) Let $\Omega = \{-1, +1\}$, $\mathcal{F} = 2^{\Omega}$ and $P(\{-1\}) = P(\{+1\}) = 1/2$. If $X(\omega) = \omega$ for all $\omega \in \Omega$, then $\mathbb{E}[X] = 0$ and $\mathbb{E}[X^2] = 1$.

(6.2) $X_1 = \frac{1}{2}\mathbf{1}_{[1/\sqrt{2}, 1)}$, $X_2 = \frac{1}{4}\mathbf{1}_{[1/2, 1/\sqrt{2})} + \frac{1}{2}\mathbf{1}_{[1/\sqrt{2}, \sqrt{3}/2)} + \frac{3}{4}\mathbf{1}_{[\sqrt{3}/2, 1)}$.

(6.3) $a = 45/37$, $3269/444$, $35/222$, $291961/222$.

(6.4) Let $A_n = \{\omega : |X(\omega)| \geq 1/n\}$. $0 = \mathbb{E}[|X|] = \int_{\Omega} |X| dP \geq \int_{A_n} |X| dP \geq P(A_n)/n$. Hence $P(A_n) = 0$. If $A = \{\omega : |X(\omega)| > 0\}$, then $A = \bigcup_{n=1}^{\infty} A_n$ and $P(A) \leq \sum_{n=1}^{\infty} P(A_n) = 0$.

(6.6) Pointwise convergence always implies convergence almost surely. If $X_n \to X$ almost surely as $n \to \infty$ and if $X_n(\omega) \not\to X(\omega)$ for some $\omega \in \Omega$, then $P(\{\omega \in \Omega : X_n(\omega) \to X(\omega)\}) \leq P(\Omega \backslash \{\omega\}) = 1 - P(\{\omega\}) < 1$. This contradiction shows that $X_n(\omega) \to X(\omega)$ as $n \to \infty$ for all ω.

(6.7) Let $\Omega = \mathbf{N}$, $\mathcal{F} = 2^{\Omega}$, $P(\{n\}) = 1/2^n$. If $X(n) = r^n$, then $\mathbb{E}[X] = \sum_{n=1}^{\infty}(r/2)^n < \infty$ if $r < 2$. $\mathbb{E}[X^2] = \sum_{n=1}^{\infty}(r^2/2)^n = \infty$ if $r^2 > 2$. If $r = 3/2$, then $r < 2$ and $r^2 = 9/4 > 2$.

(6.8) $\sum_{n=1}^{\infty} 2^n \mathbf{1}_{A_n} \leq |X| \leq \sum_{n=1}^{\infty} 2^{n+1} \mathbf{1}_{A_n}$ and

$$\sum_{n=1}^{\infty} 2^n P(A_n) \leq \mathbb{E}[|X|] \leq 2 \sum_{n=1}^{\infty} 2^n P(A_n).$$

(6.9) Use geometric series, $a = 1, b = 2$. $P(\{n\}) = 2^{-n} = \frac{dP}{dQ}(n) \cdot Q(\{n\}) = \frac{dP}{dQ}(n) \cdot 2 \cdot 3^{-n}$. Hence $\frac{dP}{dQ}(n) = \frac{1}{2}(\frac{3}{2})^n$, $\frac{dQ}{dP}(n) = (\frac{dP}{dQ}(n))^{-1} = 2(2/3)^n$.

(6.10) $\alpha^2 + \alpha$, $e^{\alpha(e-1)}$.

(6.11) $0, 0$

(6.12) Let $\Omega = \mathbf{N}, \mathcal{F} = 2^{\mathbf{N}}, P(\{n\}) = b_n/M$ where $M = \sum_{n=1}^{\infty} b_n$. Then $(\Omega, \mathcal{F}, P)$ is a probability space. Let $X(n) = a_n$, $X_m(n) = a_{n,m}$ and $Y(n) = \lim_{m \to \infty} a_{n,m}$ for all n and m. Since $\sum_{n=1}^{\infty} a_n b_n < \infty$, X is integrable, and since $X_m \to Y$ pointwise as $n \to \infty$ and $|X_m| \le |X|$, we can apply the Dominated Convergence Theorem.

(6.13) Suppose $(a_n)_{n=1}^{\infty}$ satisfies the Cauchy Convergence Criterion. If $\epsilon > 0$, then there exists a positive integer n_0 such that $|a_n - a_m| < \epsilon$ for all $n, m > n_0$. If $(n_j)_{j=1}^{\infty}$ is a strictly increasing sequence of positive integers, then $n_j > n_0$ for all j sufficiently large and $|a_{n_{j+1}} - a_{n_j}| < \epsilon$. Hence $\lim_{j \to \infty}(a_{n_{j+1}} - a_{n_j}) = 0$. If $(a_n)_{n=1}^{\infty}$ does not satisfy the Cauchy Convergence Criterion, then there exists some $\epsilon > 0$ such that for any positive integer n_0 we do not have $|a_n - a_m| \le \epsilon$ for all $n, m > n_0$. Choose $n_2 > n_1$ such that $|a_{n_2} - a_{n_1}| > \epsilon$; then choose $n_4 > n_3 > n_2$ such that $|a_{n_4} - a_{n_3}| \ge \epsilon$, and by induction, choose $n_{2j+2} > n_{2j+1} > n_{2j}$ such that $|a_{n_{2j+2}} - a_{n_{2j+1}}| \ge \epsilon$. The sequence $(a_{n_{j+1}} - a_{n_j})_{j=1}^{\infty}$ does not converge to 0. See Lemma 11.1.

(6.14) $P(A) = \int_A dP = \int_A f(X)dP \le \int_{\Omega} f(X)dP = \mathbb{E}[f(X)] = \int_B f(X)dP + \int_{B^c} f(X)dP = \int_{B^c} f(X)dP \le \int_{B^c} dP = P(B^c) = 1 - P(B)$.

Chapter 7

(7.1) Use $|\sum_{i=n}^{m} a_i| \le \sum_{i=n}^{m} |a_n|$ and the Cauchy Convergence Criterion.

(7.2) Fix $x \in (a, b)$. For $k > 0$ let $A_k := \{\epsilon > 0 :$ there exists $\delta_\epsilon > 0$ such that $|f(x) - f(y)| < k\epsilon$ if $|x - y| < \delta_\epsilon\}$. Then $kA_k = A_1$ and f is continuous $\Leftrightarrow A_1 = \mathbf{R}^+ \Leftrightarrow A_k = \mathbf{R}^+$. This rather simple exercise is often used (see Exercise 7.6 for a typical application).

(7.3) If $|x - y| = \delta$, then $|(1/x) - (1/y)| = \delta/|x \cdot y| \nrightarrow 0$ as $x, y \to 0$ and $|x - y| \to 0$. $|x^2 - y^2| = \delta|x + y| \nrightarrow 0$ as $x, y \to \infty$ and $|x - y| \to 0$.

(7.4) If $f : [a, b] \mapsto \mathbf{R}$ is continuous, then by Proposition 7.7 it is uniformly continuous and the restriction to (a, b) is also uniformly continuous. Conversely suppose $f : (a, b) \mapsto \mathbf{R}$ is uniformly continuous. It suffices to show that $\lim_{x \to a, x > a} f(x)$ and $\lim_{x \to b, x < b} f(x)$ both exist. If, say, $\lim_{x \to a, x > a} f(x)$ does not exist, then there exist sequences $x_n \longrightarrow a$ and $y_n \longrightarrow a$, $x_n > a$ and $y_n > a$ and $\delta > 0$ such that $|f(x_n) - f(y_n)| > \delta$ for all n. Since $|x_n - y_n| \longrightarrow 0$ this contradicts uniform continuity.

(7.5) (See Exercise 4.24.) Let $\lim_{n \to \infty} x_n = x$. If $x_n < x$ all n, show that $\lim_{n \to \infty} f(x_n) = lub(\{f(x_n)\}_{n=1}^{\infty}) = f^-(x)$; and if $x_n > x$ all n, show that $\lim_{n \to \infty} f(x_n) = glb(\{f(x_n)\}_{n=1}^{\infty}) = f^+(x)$. If f is not continuous at x, then, by Exercise 4.24, we have $f(x + \epsilon) - f(x - \epsilon) \ge f^+(x) - f^-(x)$ for any $\epsilon > 0$. Let $m \in \mathbf{N}$ and suppose $a < x_1 < x_2 < \ldots < x_n < b$ and $f^+(x_i) - f^-(x_i) > (1/m)$ for all i. We can choose $(y_i)_{i=1}^{n+1}$ such that $a = y_1 < x_1 < y_2 < x_2 < \ldots < y_n < x_n < y_{n+1} = b$. Then $f(b) - f(a) = f(y_{n+1}) - f(y_1) = \sum_{i=1}^{n}(f(y_{i+1}) - f(y_i)) \ge \sum_{i=1}^{n}(f(x_i^+) - f(x_i^-)) \ge n/m$. Hence $n \le m(f(b) - f(a))$. Now apply Exercise 3.3.

(7.6) Let $\epsilon > 0$ be arbitrary. Choose n_0 such that $\|f_n - f\| \le \epsilon$ for all $n \ge n_0$. This implies $|f_n(x) - f(x)| < \epsilon$ for all $x \in [a, b]$ and all $n \ge n_0$. By Proposition 7.7, f_{n_0} is uniformly continuous and there exists $\delta > 0$ such that

$|f_{n_0}(x) - f_{n_0}(y)| < \epsilon$ if $|x - y| < \delta$. If $|x - y| < \delta$, then $|f(x) - f(y)| \leq |f(x) - f_{n_0}(x)| + |f_{n_0}(x) - f_{n_0}(y)| + |f_{n_0}(y) - f(y)| < 3\epsilon$. Now apply Exercise 7.2. Let $x \in [a, b]$. Then $|g_n(x) - g_m(x)| \leq \|g_n - g_m\| \longrightarrow 0$ as $n, m \longrightarrow \infty$ and $(g_n(x))_{n=1}^{\infty}$ is a Cauchy sequence of real numbers which converges to a real number that we denote by $g(x)$. Then $|g(x) - g_m(x)| = \lim_{n \to \infty} |g_n(x) - g_m(x)| \leq \lim_{n \to \infty} \|g_n - g_m\|$. Since the right-hand side does not depend on x this shows $\|g - g_m\| \leq \lim_{n \to \infty} \|g_n - g_m\|$. Let $\epsilon > 0$ be arbitrary. Choose n_0 such that $\|g_n - g_m\| \leq \epsilon$ for all $n, m \geq n_0$. Then $\|g - g_n\| \leq \epsilon$ for all $n \geq n_0$. An application of the first part of the exercise completes the proof.

(7.7) $\|h_m - h_n\| = \|T(h_{m-1}) - T(h_{n-1})\| \leq k\|h_{m-1} - h_{n-1}\| \leq k^2\|h_{m-2} - h_{n-2}\| \leq \cdots \leq k^{n-1}\|h_{m-n+1} - h_1\| = k^{n-1}\|T(h_{m-n}) - T(h)\| \leq k^n\|h_{m-n} - h\|$. Let $h = h_0$. Then $h_{m-n} - h = \sum_{i=0}^{m-n-1}(h_{i+1} - h_i)$ and $\|h_{i+1} - h_i\| \leq k\|h_i - h_{i-1}\| \leq \cdots \leq k^i\|h_1 - h_0\|$ imply $\|h_{m-n} - h\| \leq (\sum_{i=0}^{m-n-1} k^i)\|h_1 - h\| \leq (1 - k)^{-1}\|T(h) - h\|$. The sequence $(h_n)_{n=1}^{\infty}$ converges, by the previous exercise, to $f \in \mathcal{C}([a, b])$. Then $f = \lim_{n \to \infty} h_n = \lim_{n \to \infty} T(h_{n-1}) = T(\lim_{n \to \infty} h_{n-1}) = T(f)$. (We write $g = \lim_{n \to \infty} g_n$ if $\lim_{n \to \infty} \|g - g_n\| = 0$). Since $k < 1$ it is clear that T maps convergent sequences to convergent sequences.) If $T(g) = g$, then $\|f - g\| = \|T(f) - T(g)\| \leq k\|f - g\|$, and this implies $f = g$. The result in this exercise is the extremely useful *Banach Contraction Principle*.

(7.8) The Riemann sum is $\sum_{j=1}^{n-1}(\frac{j}{n})^2 \cdot \frac{1}{n} = \frac{1}{n^3} \cdot \frac{(n-1)n(2n-1)}{6}$. This tends to $1/3$ as $n \longrightarrow \infty$.

(7.9) $\exp(1/2), 1$ (see Lemma 9.14.), $e^{(-2)} - 2N(-2)$ where N is obtained from the normal tables or by using Exercise 1.7 (see Example 10.6).

(7.10) Let $\mu = \mathbb{E}[X]$. Then $\mathrm{Var}(X) = \mathbb{E}[(X - \mu)^2] = \mathbb{E}[X^2 - 2\mu\mathbb{E}[X] + \mathbb{E}[X]^2] = \mathbb{E}[X^2] - 2\mu^2 + \mu^2 = \mathbb{E}[X^2] - \mathbb{E}[X]^2$. $\mathbb{E}[aX + b] = a\mathbb{E}[X] + b$, $\mathrm{Var}(aX + b) = \mathbb{E}[(aX + b - \mathbb{E}[X] - b)^2] = \mathbb{E}[(aX - a\mathbb{E}[X])^2] = a^2\mathbb{E}[X - \mathbb{E}[X])^2] = a^2\mathrm{Var}(X)$. $\mathrm{Var}(X) = 0$ if and only if $X = \mathbb{E}[X] = c$ almost surely by Exercise 6.4.

(7.11) If X and Y are independent then clearly $F_{X,Y}(x, y) = F_X(x) \cdot F_Y(y)$. To prove the converse it suffices by Proposition 7.9 to show: $\mathbb{E}[f(X)g(Y)] = \mathbb{E}[f(X)] \cdot \mathbb{E}[g(Y)]$ for all bounded Borel measurable functions f and g (call this statement $(*)$ for convenience). By using $f = f^+ - f^-$ and $g = g^+ - g^-$ we can suppose that f and g are positive. By (6.10) and Lemma 6.10 there exist increasing sequences $(f_n)_{n=1}^{\infty}$ and $(g_n)_{n=1}^{\infty}$ such that $f_n \longrightarrow f$ and $g_n \longrightarrow g$ pointwise as $n \longrightarrow \infty$ where each f_n and g_n is a finite sum of functions, each of which has the form $c \cdot \mathbf{1}_{(a,b]}$ where $a, b, c \in \mathbf{R}$ and $a < b$ and there exists a positive number m such that $f_n(x) < m$ and $g_n(x) < m$ for all n and x. Since $f_n(X) \longrightarrow f(X)$ and $g_n(X) \longrightarrow g(X)$ as $n \longrightarrow \infty$ pointwise, the Monotone Convergence Theorem implies $\mathbb{E}[f(X)] = \lim_{n \to \infty} \mathbb{E}[f_n(X)]$, $\mathbb{E}[g(X)] = \lim_{n \to \infty} \mathbb{E}[g_m(X)]$ and $\mathbb{E}[f(X) \cdot g(X)] = \lim_{n \to \infty} \mathbb{E}[f_n(X) \cdot g_n(X)]$, and it suffices, by linearity to show $(*)$ when $f = \mathbf{1}_{[a,b)}$ and $g = \mathbf{1}_{[c,d)}$. If $f_a = \mathbf{1}_{(-\infty, a)}$, then for $a < b$, $f_b - f_a = \mathbf{1}_{[a,b)}$, and by linearity it suffices to prove $(*)$ for f_a and f_b. Now $f_a(X) = \mathbf{1}_{X^{-1}\{(-\infty, a)\}}$ (see Proposition 5.19) and $\mathbb{E}[\mathbf{1}_{X^{-1}\{(-\infty, a)\}}] = P\{\omega : X(\omega) < a\} = \lim_{n \to \infty} P\{\omega : X(\omega) \leq a - \frac{1}{n}\}$, $\mathbb{E}[\mathbf{1}_{Y^{-1}\{(-\infty, b)\}}] = \lim_{n \to \infty} P\{\omega : Y(\omega) \leq b - \frac{1}{n}\}$ and

$\mathbb{E}[\mathbf{1}_{X^{-1}\{(-\infty,a)\}}, \mathbf{1}_{Y^{-1}\{(-\infty,b)\}}] = \lim_{n\to\infty} P\{\omega : X(\omega) \le a - \frac{1}{n}, Y(\omega) \le a - \frac{1}{n}\}$. By our hypothesis this holds. The function $F_{X,Y}$ is called the joint distribution of X and Y. If $F_{X,Y}$ is twice continuously differentiable, then $F_{X,Y} = F_X \cdot F_Y$ if and only if X and Y have densities and $f_X(x) \cdot f_Y(y) = \partial^2 F_{X,Y}/\partial x \partial y := f_{X,Y}$ (the joint density of X and Y). A much shorter proof of this exercise using characteristic functions exists.

(7.12) $\phi_1 = \mathbf{1}_{[0,+\infty)} \cdot f$ and $\phi_2 = \mathbf{1}_{(-\infty,0]} \cdot f$ where $f(x) = x^2$ for all $x \in \mathbf{R}$.

(7.13) If $x_i \ge 0$, then $x_i = e^{y_i}$ where $y_i \in \mathbf{R}$. Let $\Omega = \{1, \ldots, n\}, \mathcal{F} = 2^n$ and $P(\{i\}) = 1/n$. $(\Omega, \mathcal{F}, P)$ is a probability space. Let $X(i) = y_i$ for $1 \le i \le n$. By Jensen's inequality (Proposition 7.29), $\exp(\mathbb{E}[X]) \le \mathbb{E}[e^X]$; that is $\exp((y_1 + \cdots + y_n)/n) = (\exp y_i \cdots \exp y_n)^{1/n} = (x_1 \cdots x_n)^{1/n} \le (e^{y_1} + \cdots + e^{y_n})/n = (x_1 + \cdots + x_n)/n$.

(7.16) $P[X + Y = n] = \sum_{i=0}^n P[X = r, Y = n-r] = \sum_{i=0}^n P[X = r]P[Y = n-r] = \sum_{i=0}^n \frac{e^{-\lambda}\lambda^r}{r!} \frac{e^{-\beta}\beta^{n-r}}{n-r!} = \frac{e^{-(\lambda+\beta)}}{n!} \sum_{i=0}^n \frac{n!}{r!(n-r)!} \lambda^r \beta^{n-r} = \frac{e^{-(\lambda+\beta)}}{n!}(\lambda + \beta)^n$.

(7.18) $P\{X \ge 0\} = P\{X - 1000 \ge -1000\} = P\{|X - 1000| \ge 1000\}/2 = P\{|X - 1000|/200 \ge 1000/200\}/2 \le .02$.

(7.19) The risk is the variance of the portfolio. If the total invested is M, then $20x + 15y = M$ where the portfolio consists of x shares in stock A and y shares in stock B. The expected return is $22x + 19y$ and the variance is $\mathbb{E}[(xX_A + yX_B - 22x - 19y)^2] = x^2\text{Var}(X_A) + y^2\text{Var}(X_B) + 2xy\mathbb{E}[(X_A - 22)(X_B - 19)] = x^2 + 16y^2 - 6xy$. By the method of Lagrange multipliers we obtain the equations $2x - 6y = 20\lambda$ and $32y - 6x = 15\lambda$. Hence $15x = 73y$; that is $x : y = 73 : 15$ and the portfolio should consist of 83% A shares and 17% B shares. If, for example, \$10,000 is used to set up the portfolio, then it would consist of 4332 A shares and 890 B shares.

(7.21) Fix $x, y \in (a, b)$ and $t, 0 < t < 1$. For $i = 1$ or $i = 2$, $\max(\phi_1, \phi_2)(tx + (1 - t)y) = \phi_i(tx + (1 - t)y) \le t\phi(x) + (1 - t)\phi(y) \le t\max(\phi_1, \phi_2)(x) + (1 - t)\max(\phi_1, \phi_2)(y)$.

(7.22) See the proof of Proposition 7.27.

Chapter 8

(8.1) $\sum_{i=1}^{10} i^2 = 385$, and $a = 1/385$. $X = \mathbf{1}_{\{1,2,3,4,5\}} + 61_{\{6\}} + 71_{\{7\}} + 81_{\{8\}} + 91_{\{9\}} + 101_{\{10\}}$. On taking out what is known, $\mathbb{E}[X|X] = X$. $\mathbb{E}[X|Y] = \mathbf{1}_{\{1,2,3\}} + \frac{257}{77}\mathbf{1}_{\{4,5,6\}} + \frac{2584}{294}\mathbf{1}_{\{7,8,9,10\}}$. $\mathbb{E}[Y|X] = \frac{151}{55}\mathbf{1}_{\{1,2,3,4,5\}} + 31_{\{6\}}$. Since $\mathcal{F}_Y = \mathcal{F}_{Y^2}$, $\mathbb{E}[X|Y^2] = \mathbb{E}[X|Y]$, $\mathbb{E}[X \cdot Y|\mathcal{F}_X] = X \cdot \mathbb{E}[Y|\mathcal{F}_X] = X \cdot \mathbb{E}[Y|X] = \frac{151}{55}\mathbf{1}_{\{1,2,3,4,5\}} + 181_{\{6\}}$. $\mathbb{E}[\mathbb{E}[X|\mathcal{F}_Y]|\mathcal{F}_X] = \frac{11615}{4235}\mathbf{1}_{\{1,2,3,4,5\}} + \frac{257}{77}\mathbf{1}_{\{6\}} + \frac{2584}{294}\mathbf{1}_{\{7,8,9,10\}}$.

(8.2) If $0 < P(B) < 1$, then, almost surely, $\mathbb{E}[\mathbf{1}_A|\mathbf{1}_B] = \frac{P(A\cap B)}{P(B)}\mathbf{1}_B + \frac{P(A\cap B^c)}{P(B^c)}\mathbf{1}_{B^c}$. If $P(B) = 0$ or 1, show that A and B and hence $\mathcal{F}_{\mathbf{1}_A}$ and $\mathcal{F}_{\mathbf{1}_B}$ are independent. As independence drops out, $\mathbb{E}[\mathbf{1}_A|\mathbf{1}_B] = \mathbb{E}[\mathbf{1}_A] = P(A)$ almost surely.

(8.3) If $\omega \in G_n$, then $\mathbb{E}[\mathbf{1}_A|\mathcal{F}](\omega) = \int_{G_n} \mathbf{1}_A dP/P(G_n) = \int_\Omega \mathbf{1}_A \cdot \mathbf{1}_{G_n} dP/P(G_n) = \int_\Omega \mathbf{1}_{A\cap G_n} dP/P(G_n) = P(A \cap G_n)/P(G_n)$.

(8.4) Let $A_n = \{\omega \in \Omega : \mathbb{E}[X|\mathcal{G}](\omega) \leq -1/n\}$. By Proposition 8.7, $0 \leq \int_{A_n} X dP = \int_{A_n} \mathbb{E}[X|\mathcal{G}]dP \leq -P(A_n)/n$ and this implies $P(A_n) = 0$. Hence $P(\{\omega \in \Omega : \mathbb{E}[X|\mathcal{G}](\omega) \leq 0\} = 0$ and $\mathbb{E}[X|\mathcal{G}] \geq 0$ almost surely. Since $|X| \pm X \geq 0$, $\mathbb{E}[|X| \pm X\||\mathcal{G}] = \mathbb{E}[|X| \,|\mathcal{G}] \pm \mathbb{E}[X|\mathcal{G}] \geq 0$ and $|\mathbb{E}[X|\mathcal{G}]| \leq \mathbb{E}[|X| \,|\mathcal{G}]$. Hence $\mathbb{E}[\,|\mathbb{E}[X|\mathcal{G}]|\,] \leq \mathbb{E}[\,\mathbb{E}[|X| \,|\mathcal{G}]\,] = \mathbb{E}[|X|]$.

(8.5) (a)(.37 shares and \$ -2.59 bonds) for the first month, and if price increases (.75 shares and \$ -6.01 bonds) for the second month; (b)(.64 shares and \$6.48 bonds) for the first month; if price increases ($-.25$ shares and \$3 bonds) for the second month; if the price decreases (-1 shares and \$9.02 bonds) for the second month. Value of call option in 1 month \$.74 if share price increases in first month and 0 otherwise. Value of put option in 1 month \$.74 if share price increases in first month and \$2.03 otherwise. A good estimate for all of these can be obtained by using a zero interest rate.

(8.6) Let N denote the number of accidents per month and let X_i denote the number injured in the ith accident. We find $\mathbb{E}[\sum_{i=0}^{N} X_i]$ by conditioning on N. We have $\mathbb{E}[\sum_{i=0}^{N} X_i] = \mathbb{E}[\mathbb{E}[\sum_{i=0}^{N} X_i|N]] = \sum_{n=0}^{\infty} \mathbb{E}[\sum_{i=0}^{n} X_i]P(N = n) = \sum_{n=0}^{\infty} n\mathbb{E}[X_1]P(N = n) = \mathbb{E}[X_1] \cdot \mathbb{E}[N]$.

(8.7) Taking out what is known ((a) implies (b)); letting $Y = \mathbf{1}_\Omega$ shows (b) implies (c). Since $\mathbb{E}[X|\mathcal{G}]$ is $\mathcal{G}$ measurable (c) implies that X is a $\mathcal{G}$ measurable random variable satisfying (8.20). Hence (c) implies (a).

(8.8) Let $A_n := \{\omega : X(\omega) - Y(\omega) \geq 1/n\}$. Since $0 = \int_{A_n}(X - Y)dP \geq \int_{A_n}(1/n)dP = P(A_n)/n$, we have $P(A_n) = 0$. Taking the union over n implies that $P(\{\omega : X(\omega) \geq Y(\omega)\}) = 0$. Similarly $P(\{\omega : X(\omega) \leq Y(\omega)\}) = 0$ and $P(\{\omega : X(\omega) \neq Y(\omega)\}) = 0$. Hence $P(\{\omega : X(\omega) = Y(\omega)\}) = 1$. For the second part apply the first part to X and $Y := \mathbb{E}[X|\mathcal{G}]$.

(8.9) $\mathbb{E}[X^2 - 2X\mathbb{E}[X|\mathcal{G}] + \mathbb{E}[X|\mathcal{G}]^2|\mathcal{G}] \geq 0$. $\mathbb{E}[X\mathbb{E}[X|\mathcal{G}]|\mathcal{G}] = \mathbb{E}[X|\mathcal{G}]\mathbb{E}[X|\mathcal{G}]$ on taking out what is known and $\mathbb{E}[\mathbb{E}[X|\mathcal{G}]^2|\mathcal{G}] = \mathbb{E}[X|\mathcal{G}]^2\mathbb{E}[\mathbf{1}_\Omega|\mathcal{G}] = \mathbb{E}[X|\mathcal{G}]^2$. This is a special case of Jensen's inequality for conditional expectations.

(8.10) $\mathbb{E}[XY|\mathcal{H}] = \mathbb{E}[\mathbb{E}[XY|\mathcal{G}]|\mathcal{H}]$ (by the Tower Law) $= \mathbb{E}[X\mathbb{E}[Y|\mathcal{G}]|\mathcal{H}]$ (on taking out what is known) $= \mathbb{E}[X\mathbb{E}[Y]|\mathcal{H}]$ (independence drops out) $= \mathbb{E}[Y]\mathbb{E}[X|\mathcal{H}]$.

Chapter 9

(9.1) For $0 \leq s \leq t \leq T$, $\mathbb{E}[X_t|\mathcal{F}_s] = \mathbb{E}[\mathbb{E}[X|\mathcal{F}_t]|\mathcal{F}_s] = \mathbb{E}[X|\mathcal{F}_s] = X_s$. For $0 \leq s \leq T \leq t$, $\mathbb{E}[X_t|\mathcal{F}_s] = \mathbb{E}[X_T|\mathcal{F}_s] = X_s$. Since X_T is $\mathcal{F}_T$ measurable we have for $0 \leq T \leq s \leq t$, $\mathbb{E}[X_t|\mathcal{F}_s] = \mathbb{E}[X_T|\mathcal{F}_T] = X_T = X_s$.

(9.2) $\mathbb{E}[W_t^3|\mathcal{F}_s] = \mathbb{E}[(W_t - W_s + W_s)^3|\mathcal{F}_s] = \mathbb{E}[(W_t - W_s)^3|\mathcal{F}_s] + 3\mathbb{E}[(W_t - W_s)^2 \cdot W_s|\mathcal{F}_s] + 3\mathbb{E}[(W_t - W_s)W_s^2|\mathcal{F}_s] + \mathbb{E}[W_s^3|\mathcal{F}]$. On taking out what is known $\mathbb{E}[W_t^3|\mathcal{F}_s] = \mathbb{E}[(W_t - W_s)^3|\mathcal{F}_s] + 3W_s\mathbb{E}[(W_t - W_s)^2|\mathcal{F}_s] + 3W_s^2\mathbb{E}[W_t - W_s|\mathcal{F}_s] + W_s^3$. As independence drops out $\mathbb{E}[W_t^3|\mathcal{F}_s] = \mathbb{E}[(W_t - W_s)^3] + 3W_s\mathbb{E}[(W_t - W_s)^2] + 3W_s^2\mathbb{E}[W_t - W_s] + W_s^3$. Since $W_t - W_s$ is $N(0, t-s)$, $\mathbb{E}[(W_t - W_s)^2] = t - s$, $\mathbb{E}[(W_t - W_s)^3] = 0$ and $\mathbb{E}[W_t - W_s] = 0$. Hence $\mathbb{E}[W_t^3|\mathcal{F}_s] = 3W_s(t-s) + W_s^3$ and $\mathbb{E}[W_t^3 - 3tW_t|\mathcal{F}_s] = 3W_s(t-s) + W_s^3 - 3t\mathbb{E}[W_t - W_s + W_s|\mathcal{F}_s] = 3W_s(t-s) + W_s^3 - 3tW_s = W_s^3 - 3sW_s$.

(9.3) By Exercise 8.9, $\mathbb{E}[X_n^2|\mathcal{F}_j] \geq \mathbb{E}[X_n|\mathcal{F}_j]^2 = X_j^2$.

(9.4) The $A'_j s$ are disjoint and $\sup_{i \leq n} |X_i(\omega)| > t \iff \omega \in \bigcup_{j=1}^{n} A_j$. By Exercise 8.4 and taking out what is known, $\mathbb{E}[\mathbf{1}_{A_j} |X_n|] = \mathbb{E}[\mathbb{E}[\mathbf{1}_{A_j} |X_n| |\mathcal{F}_j]] \geq \mathbb{E}[|\mathbb{E}[\mathbf{1}_{A_j} X_n |\mathcal{F}_j]|] = \mathbb{E}[|\mathbf{1}_{A_j} \mathbb{E}[X_n |\mathcal{F}_j]|] = \mathbb{E}[|\mathbf{1}_{A_j} X_j|] = \int_{A_j} |X_j| dP \geq tP(A_j)$. Hence $P(\sup_{i \leq n} |X_i| > t) = \sum_{j=1}^{n} P(A_j) \leq \frac{1}{t} \sum_{j=1}^{n} \mathbb{E}[\mathbf{1}_{A_j} |X_n|] = \frac{1}{t} \mathbb{E}[\mathbf{1}_{\bigcup_{j=1}^{n} A_j} |X_n|] \leq \frac{1}{t} \mathbb{E}[|X_n|]$.

(9.5) Proposition 8.9 and induction can be used to show that Y_n is integrable for all n. $\mathbb{E}[X_1 \cdots X_n \cdot X_{n+1} |\mathcal{F}_n] = X_1 \cdots X_n \mathbb{E}[X_{n+1} |\mathcal{F}_n]$ (on taking out what was known) $= X_1 \cdots X_n \mathbb{E}[X_{n+1}]$ (independence drops out) $= X_1 \cdots X_n$.

(9.6) $\mathbb{E}[\frac{e^{\theta Y_{n+1}}}{\phi(\theta)^{n+1}} |\mathcal{F}_n] = \mathbb{E}[\frac{e^{\theta Y_n} \cdot e^{\theta X_{n+1}}}{\phi(\theta)^n \phi(\theta)} |\mathcal{F}_n] = \frac{e^{\theta Y_n}}{\phi(\theta)^n} \mathbb{E}[\frac{e^{\theta X_{n+1}}}{\phi(\theta)} |\mathcal{F}_n] = \frac{e^{\theta Y_n}}{\phi(\theta)^n}$ (this exercise is a special case of the previous exercise).

(9.7) Since $\mathbb{E}[X|\mathcal{F}_n]$ is $\mathcal{F}_n$ measurable for any integrable random variable, $(Y_n)_{n=1}^{\infty}$ is previsible. It is easily seen that the sequence $(Z_n)_{n=1}^{\infty}$ consists of integrable random variables and that it is adapted to the filtration. $Y_1 = \mathbb{E}[X_1 - X_0|\mathcal{F}_0] = \mathbb{E}[X_1 - X_0|\mathcal{F}_\emptyset] = \mathbb{E}[X_1]$. When $n = 2$, $\mathbb{E}[Z_2|\mathcal{F}_1] = \mathbb{E}[X_2|\mathcal{F}_1] - \mathbb{E}[Y_2|\mathcal{F}_1] = \mathbb{E}[X_2|\mathcal{F}_1] - \mathbb{E}[Y_1 + \mathbb{E}[X_2 - X_1|\mathcal{F}_1]|\mathcal{F}_1] = \mathbb{E}[X_2|\mathcal{F}_1] - \mathbb{E}[Y_1|\mathcal{F}_1] - \mathbb{E}[X_2 - X_1|\mathcal{F}_1] = \mathbb{E}[X_2|\mathcal{F}_1] - Y_1 - \mathbb{E}[X_2|\mathcal{F}_1] + \mathbb{E}[X_1|\mathcal{F}_1] = X_1 - Y_1 = Z_1$. For $n \geq 2$, $\mathbb{E}[Z_{n+1}|\mathcal{F}_n] = \mathbb{E}[X_{n+1}|\mathcal{F}_n] - \mathbb{E}[Y_{n+1}|\mathcal{F}_n] = \mathbb{E}[X_{n+1}|\mathcal{F}_n] - \mathbb{E}[Y_n + \mathbb{E}[X_{n+1} - X_n|\mathcal{F}_n]|\mathcal{F}_n] = \mathbb{E}[X_{n+1}|\mathcal{F}_n] - \mathbb{E}[Y_n|\mathcal{F}_n] - \mathbb{E}[X_{n+1}|\mathcal{F}_n] + \mathbb{E}[X_n|\mathcal{F}_n] = X_n - \mathbb{E}[Y_n|\mathcal{F}_n] = X_n - Y_n = Z_n$. The result in this exercise is part of *Doob's Decomposition Theorem*.

Chapter 10

(10.1) By Lemma 7.31, $\mathcal{M}(\mathcal{G}) = \mathcal{F}(\mathcal{G}) = \mathcal{F}$. Now apply Proposition 5.3.

(10.2) For the first part it suffices to show that the process has Gaussian, independent and stationary increments. $P(\frac{|W_t|}{t} \leq 1, t \in [0,1]) = P(\frac{|cW_{t/c^2}|}{t} \leq 1, t \in [0,1])$. Let $u = t/c^2$. Then $cu = t/c$ and $P(\frac{|W_t|}{t} \leq 1, t \in [0,1]) = P(\frac{|W_u|}{cu} \leq 1, 0 \leq c^2 t \leq 1) = P(\frac{|W_u|}{u} \leq c, 0 \leq u \leq 1/c^2)$.

(10.3) If $s > t$, then $\mathbb{E}[(W_t - W_s)^2 \cdot W_t] = \mathbb{E}[(W_t - W_s)^2] \cdot \mathbb{E}[W_t] = (s - t) \cdot 0 = 0$. If $t > s$, then $\mathbb{E}[(W_t - W_s)^2 \cdot W_t] = \mathbb{E}[(W_t - W_s)^2 \cdot (W_t - W_s) + (W_t - W_s)^2 \cdot W_s] = \mathbb{E}[(W_t - W_s)^3] + \mathbb{E}[(W_t - W_s)^2] \cdot \mathbb{E}[W_s] = 0$ since $\mathbb{E}[(W_t - W_s)^2] = t - s$, $\mathbb{E}[W_s] = 0$ and $\mathbb{E}[X^3] = 0$ for any normal random variable with mean 0 (see Exercise 1.3).

(10.4) 50.5 cents, 53 cents.

(10.5) Consider the disjoint events $A := \{\text{some } \xi, 0 \leq \xi \leq T, W_\xi = a, W_T > a\}$, $B := \{\text{some } \xi, 0 \leq \xi \leq T, W_\xi = a, W_T < a\}$, $C := \{\text{some } \xi, 0 \leq \xi \leq T, W_\xi = a, W_T = a\}$, $D := \{W_t < a, 0 \leq t < T, W_T = a\}$. Then $\{\max_{0 \leq t \leq T} W_t \geq a\} = A \cup B \cup C \cup D$, $P(C) \leq P(W_T = a) = 0$, $P(D) \leq P(W_T = a) = 0$, and by symmetry, $P(A) = P(B) = P(W_T > a) = \frac{1}{\sqrt{2\pi T}} \int_a^\infty e^{-x^2/2T} dx$. Hence $P(\{\max_{0 \leq t \leq T} W_t \geq a\}) = \frac{2}{\sqrt{2\pi T}} \int_a^\infty e^{-x^2/2T} dx = 1 - N(a/\sqrt{T})$.

Chapter 11

(11.1) Let $(n_m)_{m=1}^{\infty}$ denote an increasing sequence of positive integers. Let $(X_{n,j})_{j=1}^{\infty}$ denote a subsequence of $(X_{n_m})_{m=1}^{\infty}$ which converges almost surely to X and let $(Y_{n,j,k})_{k=1}^{\infty}$ denote a subsequence of $(Y_{n,j})_{j=1}^{\infty}$ which converges almost surely to Y. $(aX_{n,j,k} + bY_{n,j,k})_{k=1}^{\infty}$ is a subsequence of $(aX_{n_m} + bY_{n_m})_{m=1}^{\infty}$ which converges almost surely to $aX + bY$.

(11.3) The first part is the same as Proposition 11.6. For the example let $\Omega = [0,1], \mathcal{F} = \mathcal{B}, P = \mathbf{m}$. For $0 \leq j \leq 2^n$ let $Y_{j,n} = n\mathbf{1}_{[\frac{j}{2^n}, \frac{j+1}{2^n}]}$. Then $\mathbb{E}[Y_{j,n}] = \frac{n}{2^n}$. The collection $(Y_{j,n})_{0 \leq j \leq 2^n, n=1,2,\ldots}$ is countable and can be written as a sequence $(X_n)_{n=1}^{\infty}$. Clearly, $\|X_n\|_1 \longrightarrow 0$ as $n \longrightarrow \infty$. For any t there exists $j_t, 0 \leq j_t \leq 2^n$ such that $Y_{j_t,n}(t) = n$. Hence $X_n(t) \not\longrightarrow 0$ as $n \longrightarrow \infty$.

(11.4) See the solution to Exercise 6.13.

(11.6) By Proposition 11.19 and Example 11.21(a), $W_T^3 = 3\int_0^T W_t^2 dW_t + 3\int_0^T W_t dt$, and by Proposition 11.20, $3TW_T = 3\int_0^T t dW_t + 3\int_0^T W_t dt$. Hence $W_T^3 - 3TW_T = 3\int_0^T (W_t^2 - t) dW_t$ and this is a martingale by Proposition 11.16.

(11.7) $\mathbb{E}[\sum t_i(W_{i+1} - W_i)] = 0$ implies $\mathbb{E}[\int_0^T t dW_t]) = 0$. $\text{Var}(\int_0^T t dW_t) = \int_0^T \mathbb{E}[t^2] dt = T^3/3$ by Proposition 11.15. $\mathbb{E}[W_{t_i}(t_{i+1} - t_i)] = 0$ implies $\mathbb{E}[\int_0^T W_t dt] = 0$. $\mathbb{E}[|\sum_{i=0}^{n-1} W_{iT/n}(T/n)|^2] = \frac{T^2}{n^2}\sum_{i,j=0}^{n-1} \mathbb{E}[W_{iT/n}W_{jT/n}] = \frac{T^3}{n^3}\frac{(n-1)\cdot n \cdot (2n-1)}{6} \to T^3/3$ (see Exercise 7.8). Since $d(tW_t) = W_t dt + t dW_t$, $TW_T = \int_0^T W_t dt + \int_0^T t dW_t$. Independence would imply $\text{Var}(TW_T) = T^2\text{Var}(W_T) = T^3 = \text{Var}(\int_0^T W_t dt) + \text{Var}(\int_0^T t dW_t) = (T^3/3) + (T^3/3)$, and this is not the case.

(11.9) Suppose $\|X_n - X\|_1 \longrightarrow 0$ as $n \longrightarrow \infty$. By Proposition 11.6, $X_n \longrightarrow X$ in measure as $n \longrightarrow \infty$. Let $\epsilon > 0$ be arbitrary. Using $\|X_n\|_1 \leq \|X_n - X\|_1 + \|X\|_1$ and Lemma 9.9(a) we can suppose $\|X_n\|_1 \longrightarrow 0$ as $n \longrightarrow \infty$. For $n > n_0$, $\int_{\{X_n > m\}} |X_n| dP \leq \|X_n\|_1 < \epsilon/2$ for any $m > 0$. For $n = 1, 2, \ldots, n_0$, Lemma 9.9(a) implies that for m sufficiently large we have $\int_{\{|X_n| > m\}} |X_n| dP < \epsilon/2$. This implies that $(X_n)_{n=1}^{\infty}$ is uniformly integrable. Conversely, suppose $(X_n)_{n=1}^{\infty}$ is uniformly integrable and $X_n \longrightarrow X$ in measure as $n \longrightarrow \infty$. Let $\epsilon > 0$ be arbitrary. Choose $m > 0$ such that $\int_{\{|X_n - X| > m\}} |X_n - X| dP < \epsilon/2$ for all n. By Proposition 11.2, there exists a positive integer n_0 such that $\int_{\Omega} |X_n - X|/(1 + |X_n - X|) dP < \epsilon/2(1 + m)$ for all $n \geq n_0$. Hence, if $A = \{|X_n - X| \leq m\}$, then

$$\int_A |X_n - X| dP \leq (1 + m)\int_A \frac{|X_n - X|}{(1 + |X_n - X|)} dP \leq \epsilon/2.$$

Combining these two estimates we obtain $\|X_n - X\|_1 \longrightarrow 0$ as $n \longrightarrow \infty$.

(11.10) Since the process is continuous it suffices to show that along any continuous path we can find a suitable 24-hour period. Let n be the number of days in the month and let ω denote a continuous path. Then $X_n(\omega) - X_0(\omega) = 0$. We require $t_0, 0 \leq t_0 \leq n - 1$ such that $X_{t_0+1}(\omega) - X_{t_0}(\omega) = 0$. We have $\sum_{i=0}^{n-1}(X_{i+1}(\omega) - X_i(\omega)) = X_n(\omega) - X_0(\omega) = 0$. If $X_{i+1}(\omega) - X_i(\omega) = 0$ for all i, take $t = i$ for any $i, 0 \leq i \leq n - 1$. Otherwise there exists an i and $j, 0 \leq i, j \leq n-1$ such that $X_{i+1}(\omega) - X_i(\omega) > 0$ and $X_{j+1}(\omega) - X_j(\omega) < 0$. Suppose $i < j$ (the other possibility is handled the same way). At the end points of the interval $[i, j]$ the function $g(t) := X_{t+1}(\omega) - X_t(\omega)$ takes positive and negative values. By the Intermediate Value Theorem (Proposition 7.3) it takes the value 0 at some point t_0 in the interval. Then $g(t_0) = X_{t_0+1}(\omega) - X_{t_0}(\omega) = 0$. (This is a case of Ampère's Horizontal Chord Theorem.)

(11.11) At $t = 0$, .337 shares and -\$4.89 bonds, and at 3 months .444 shares and -\$7.02 bonds.

Bibliography

In writing this book I looked at a number of books and should have consulted, and tried to read, many more. My choice was restricted to my own meager collection, to the limited ever-aging number available in our college library, and to the interesting books I borrowed from Shane Whelan. The set below, listed thematically, contains some I have had for many years and other more recent acquaintances. They form a biased, and uneven, guide to further reading.

(a) **General Interest**

1. P. Boyle, F. Boyle, *Derivatives*, Risk Books, 2001.

2. B. Bryson, *A Short History of Nearly Everything*, Doubleday, London-New York, 2003.

3. P. J. Davis, R. Hersh, *The Mathematical Experience*, Houghton Mifflin Company, Boston, 1982.

4. J. R. Newman, *The World of Mathematics*, Vol. 4, George Allen and Unwin, London, 1960.

5. N. Ya. Vilenkin, *In Search of Infinity*, Birkhäuser, Boston, 1995.

(b) **History of Mathematics**

1. N. Bourbaki, *Elements of the History of Mathematics*, Springer, Berlin, 1994.

2. H. Eves, *Great Moments in Mathematics (Before 1650)*, The Mathematical Association of America, 1980.

3. J. J. O'Connor, E. F. Robertson, *www-groups.dcs.st-and.ac.uk*

(c) **Mathematical Education**

1. H. Lebesgue, *Measure and the Integral*, Holden-Day, 1966.

(d) **Elementary Probability Theory**

1. E. O. Thorp, *Elementary Probability*, Robert E. Krieger Publishing Company, Malabar, FL, 1965, reprinted 1983.

(e) **Intermediate Probability Theory**

1. W. Feller, *An Introduction to Probability Theory and Its Applications, Vol. 1*, 2nd ed., 1957, John Wiley & Sons Inc., New York, London.

2. G. R. Grimmett, D. R. Stirzaker, *Probability and Random Processes*, Oxford Science Publications, Second Edition, 1992.

3. D. Williams, *Probability with Martingales*, Cambridge Mathematical Textbooks, 1991.

(f) **Advanced Probability Theory**

1. R. Durrett, *Stochastic Calculus*, CRC Press, Boca Raton, FL, 1996.

2. M. Loève, *Probability Theory*, Van Nostrand, Princeton, NJ, Third Edition, 1963.

(g) **Very Advanced Probability Theory**

1. P. Malliavin, *Stochastic Analysis*, Springer, Grundlehren der Math. Wissenschaften, 1997.

(h) **Measure Theory**

1. R. Bartle, *The Elements of Integration*, Wiley, New York, 1966.

2. J. L. Doob, *Measure Theory*, Springer-Verlag Graduate Texts in Mathematics, New York, 1994.

3. P. R. Halmos, *Measure Theory*, Van Nostrand, The University Series in Undergraduate Mathematics, Princeton, NJ, 1950.

4. H. Lebesgue, *Leçons sur L'Intégration et la Recherche des Fonctions Primitives*, Gauthier-Villars, Paris, 1904.

(i) **Advanced Measure Theory**

1. L. Schwartz, *Radon Measures on Topological Spaces and Cylindrical Measures*, Published for the Tata Institute of Fundamental Research by Oxford University Press, 1973.

(j) **Finance-Technical but non-rigorous**

1. M. Baxter, A. Rennie, *Financial Calculus, An Introduction to Derivative Pricing*, Cambridge University Press, 1996.

2. P. P Boyle, *Options and the Management of Financial Risk*, Society of Actuaries, Illinois, 1992.

3. D. Luenberger, *Investment Science*, Oxford University Press, 1998.

4. T. Mikosch, *Elementary Stochastic Calculus with Finance in View*, World Scientific, Singapore, 1998.

(k) **Finance-Advanced Technical**

1. D. Brigo, F. Mercurio, *Interest Rate Models-Theory and Practice*, Springer Finance, Berlin, 2001.

2. D. Sornette, *Why Stock Markets Crash*, Princeton University Press, NJ, 2003.

Index

Titles in This Series

TITLES IN THIS SERIES